Developmental Essentials

- The Foundation of Youth Conditioning -

First Edition

Brian J. Grasso
Lee Taft
Tony Reynolds
Dr. Cynthia LaBella
Dr. Kwame Brown
Dr. John Berardi
Dr. Evan Osar
Craig Ballantyne
Scott Colby
Bill Hartman

Official Textbook of the IYCA Development Essentials Coaching System™

Editing
Sarah Franczyk
Sara Beth Nylander

Acknowledgements

The IYCA was created as a concept in October of 2003. It has taken two long years and the assistance of countless people to turn this concept into a physical reality. I will humbly attempt to acknowledge those people here.

Sara, you are the most beautiful and inspirational women in the world. It's your day-to-day encouragements and never ending desire to keep me in a positive mindset that have made all the difference with regards to this project. Thank you sometimes isn't enough.

Lee and Tony, you guys have become my best friends and two of the most amazing cornerstones a business could have. To say that I feel safe and supported with you two around would be a tremendous understatement. We have become a small extended family and I think that is one of the greatest things that have come out of this venture thus far.

BR – don't think for an instance that I didn't recognize how difficult it was for you to ignore your wife and sons for an hour every night while we tried to make sense of a business plan. Thank you for your hard work and guidance.

The IYCA really began to take shape with the help of two people – Kwame and Chris. Chris, for a long time you were the ONLY one helping me out and keeping me sane. I won't forget that. Kwame, you came along at just the right time. Right when I started having critics, in walks Kwame with all his credentials and outspoken personality! It was perfect timing for me and I thank you so much for that.

Bill, you have been a constant source of motivation for me ever since we become friends over three years ago. You could easily own this industry with your knowledge, and I am both humbled and overjoyed that you decided to stay with the IYCA and author what has become arguably the best chapter we have.

Alwyn, you are simply my hero. Professionally, your association with us offers the IYCA more credibility than anyone ever could. Personally, I think you are the most amazing human being I have ever met and I am proud to call you a friend. The reality is that I could write a full-page acknowledgement to you alone.

Jeff, your insistent passion is what attracted me to find a position for you within the IYCA. Keep the passion going and shine on.

Evan, our road has been such an odd one. From a student of yours suggesting that we meet to you becoming one of my most trusted colleagues. Thank you so much for your support and help with everything.

John, you were the last addition to the IYCA contributors list, but certainly one of the most distinguished. In you, we have the leading expert in the world on nutritional science and I am so proud of that.

Cynthia, you have added a great deal of credibility to our organization. You and Mike have both been so supportive in your guidance and help with the IYCA. Here's to many years of work together.

Scott, I know that you considered yourself the 'dark horse' in terms of our contributors, but I always viewed your work as some of our most important. Thank you for accepting the position with the IYCA and thank you also for your understated confidence in what we are doing.

Erin, you are my oldest friend in the industry. In fact, you started treating me when I was still in high school! You can't develop chemistry and trust in someone that easily – our relationship spans over ten years and two businesses, but chemistry and trust is what we have. Thank you for continuing to be a part of this.

Stephen, you add a sense of maturity and class to this organization unlike anyone else in our industry could. Thank you sincerely for deciding to get involved with the IYCA.

Craig, you are one of the quietest yet most respected professionals in our industry today. It is a pleasure to have you on board.

Lastly, to Ryan Lee. You gave me the tools and the belief system to go after this. You are a true friend and great leader for our industry.

Preface

My editor told me to keep this preface short and to the point. No easy challenge for a guy who is known to be long-winded and possesses the deft skills of being able to expand a short story into a long, arduous tale!

Having said that, I thought it was important for you to hear the story behind why the IYCA was created.

The following shortened version of a long story is one that still saddens me to this day and marks one of the very toughest times of my life...

On August 17, 1993, I walked home from a chiropractic clinic. The clinic was just around the corner from my childhood home, but the walk that day seemed to take forever.

"Your football playing days are over, that's for sure".

Those words were still ringing in my ears—he was almost cavalier when he said it. I don't think he realized at all the impact those words would have on my life.

I was a football player. That's what I did. Football is what defined me as a person. It couldn't be over.

Granted, the pain in my back was unbearable and the amount of medication I was consuming prior to practices, which was roughly five to ten times the recommended dosage, was starting to become both expensive and ineffective. Still, I was a young and healthy man in the prime of my life—how is it that my football playing days are over?

It took me two full years to recover emotionally and mentally from that day. I had started to experience back pain on a very regular basis at the age of sixteen, but like most teenagers, opted to ignore it assuming it was nothing more than a little tightness. The pain got worse and worse, to the point that pain inhibitors became my best friend. I would pop pills before practice to shield the pain and then pop more after practice to try and dull the aches. A seventeen-year-old kid addicted to pain medication; I needed them to function.

Where and how did this all start?

Since I was twelve years old, I was fascinated by weights and weight training. I bought my first set of dumbbells when I was thirteen and went down to the basement every day after school in order to perform the exercises depicted on the sheets that came with the dumbbell set.

Over the years, my fascination grew and I joined a local gym in my neighborhood. Now fifteen and maturing quickly, I loved the feel of lifting heavy weights and the looks of admiration you often got from other folks who caught your set in the mirror. I was big and strong. At fifteen I weighted 220 lbs. and could squat over 315 lbs. I was easily the biggest and strongest kid on my football team and that fact gave me both incredible satisfaction and a motivation to widen the gap even more.

Over the next couple of years, my squat and bench press poundage's increased steadily, 325 lbs., 345 lbs., 365 lbs., 385 lbs., 405 lbs. However, I should take a moment here to outline the fact that my form on these lifts was atrocious. I know it now and I knew it then. I would watch older guys squat in the gym and recognize I was doing things incorrectly. It didn't matter as far as I was concerned. I was hoisting up 400+ lbs. on a regular basis.

There was no particular missed lift. There was no incident I can recall. I just started to hurt everywhere. My back, knees and shoulders were an absolute mess, and I could barely lift a bar on some days because of the aches.

That was the beginning of the end. The story goes on longer and gets more twisted in terms of the things I did to myself in a desperate attempt by a young man who at seventeen years of age, was watching the prime of his athletic life dissolve into a muddle of tears, pain, sorrow and confusion.

My athletic career over, I decided to pursue education and hopefully a profession in sport science. I didn't know it at the time, but my primary motivation was to help ensure that no other kid had to endure what I did.

Thus, the IYCA.

We did not create an industry; we are just hoping to help regulate one that is in desperate need of leadership.

Leadership and direction is something I lacked as a young, budding athlete. That is not an indictment on my coaches in anyway. They simply weren't qualified to set me straight when it came to exercise selection, programming or nutrition. I was, like so many other teenagers remain today, lost in the process of how, yet absorbed and obsessed with the desire to become bigger, stronger, faster and better.

Herein lies the problem; while many young athletes are directionless, many coaches, trainers, therapists and physicians are just as guilty of providing poor direction. The majority of young athletes in today's sporting world are not developed and nurtured – they are trained intensively and beyond many of their capabilities. Injuries, emotional burnout, parental and coach politicking, exhaustive playing and training schedules, hazing and win-at-all-costs mentalities – these are the traits and characteristics that dominate the youth sporting world.

If you are enlightened enough to open this book, then perhaps you are willing to take things one step further and attempt to make a lasting change for the young athletes in your part of the world.

Some Men See Things As They Are And Say 'Why'?
Others Dream Things That Never Were And Say 'Why Not'?

- George Bernard Shaw

The IYCA is my dream.

Enjoy and God Bless.

Brian.

Table of Contents

1. Talent Identification & Development on an International Basis ... 1

2. Positive Coaching Strategies & Pedagogy ... 25

3. Motor Skill Development ... 67

4. Speed Training & Movement Economy ... 103

5. Practical Application of Strength & Power Development ... 145

6. The Science and Application of Developmental Flexibility ... 203

7. Bioenergetics & Energy System Development ... 283

8. Postural Development & Implications on Sport Participation and Training ... 307

9. Endocrine Development & Implications ... 361

10. Young Athletes & Nutrition ... 381

11. References ... 435

12. Author Biographies ... 475

1

Talent Identification and Development on an International Basis

Brian Grasso

The youth sporting industry in North America is largely fragmented and lacking particular direction or system of development. In other parts of the world, there exists a unified, structured and systematic approach to identifying and developing gifted youngsters within the context of sport.

There are three specific categories within this process: talent identification, talent selection and talent development.

Talent Identification

The initial stage of a systematic development program is to identify potentially talented youngsters via basic and rudimentary measurements of health and broad aspects of physical development. This stage is considered the primary phase of talent identification" and includes health screenings in order to uncover any structural or physiological malfunctions. The primary phase transpires most typically between the ages of three and ten. Only basic information regarding relative health is gleaned from this phase. Assuming definitive or authoritative stances on future development would be incongruous and hasty since growth and assessing future potential is largely unpredictable.

The secondary phase of talent identification occurs typically during or slightly after puberty, but younger for athletes involved in sports that traditionally have more youthful ages of elite competition—

for instance, figure skating and gymnastics. The assessments in this phase are implemented on young athletes who have already encountered organized training; the secondary phase in fact, is considered to be the most crucial phase in talent identification. Basic biometric measurements are taken including, bi-acromial diameter (shoulder width), which correlates to overall body strength, as well as length of the foot and arch, which can impact running and jumping abilities[1]. Psychological profiling is also an important requirement during the second phase of talent identification. Broad psychological testing, administered by qualified psychologists, will disclose the degree of psychological ability or connection a young athlete has with respect to a particular sport. These assessments further showcase the need for any future psychological training that the young athlete may need to incur.

The third phase of talent identification is more directed towards the elite athletes within a development system. The main focus of this phase is to scrutinize the athlete's innate abilities within the context of a specific sport. Specifically, "the athlete's health, his/her physiological adaptation to training and competing, his/her ability to cope with stress and most importantly, his/her potential for further performance improvements"[2]. Statistics from all of these assessments are complied and cross referenced against the data collected in the first two phases of talent identification, this is done in order to typify the growth and development each athlete incurred during their athletic careers. An individual athlete's test information is contrasted against an "optimal mode"[3] and only the finest entrants will be deemed worthy for elite level status.

In terms of methods of talent identification, there are two possibilities:

1. _Natural Selection_[4] – the typical North American style of identifying talented young athletes is via survival of the fittest.

Young athletes register to play a particular sport and if they show promise or proficiency, will be encouraged to pursue higher levels of competition. This style of development lacks any sort of scientific or developmental strategy, and instead focuses on youngsters 'winning' or 'succeeding' at a young age. This method also tends to instigate the contemporary concerns of burnout, insidious onset injuries (due to one dimensional means of training) and sport specialization in young athletes.

2. *Scientific Selection*[5] – This method allows for coaches and sport officials to identify and select youngsters who demonstrate proficiency or promise in a particular sport, and advance them through the subsequent phases of talent identification.

Criteria Used for Identifying Talent

In the truest and most traditional sense of talent identification, biological and physiological limitations—uncovered in the initial phase— would serve to preclude a young athlete from ascending into the highest ranks of nation-wide sport development. It was often concluded that these limitations, or lack of necessary sporting ability, couldn't be overcome by any degree of directed training[6]. Non-selected individuals were not however, cast aside and excluded from sporting activities or physical fitness. In fact, they were encouraged to participate in more recreational forms of training and competition.

Several factors or criteria were used to determine future potential:

1. *Health*[7]: Innately healthy children were selected or recommended for participation in a given sport development program. Comprehensive medical examinations were conducted to ensure health and guard against physical shortcomings.

2. _Biometric Qualities_[8]: Anthropometrical measurements are key factors with respect to assessing future potential. Height, weight, length of limbs and bi-acromial diameter are all factors, which may play a significant role within the context of a certain sport. In the teenage years, x-rays can be used to determine if growth is complete.

3. _Heredity_[9]: Although not always the case, children often acquire their parents' capacities—both from a physical ability and mental aptitude perspective. However, certain elements of instruction, training and social habituation can change this.

Coaching plays a significant role within the realm of talent identification. In fact, it has been suggested that key issues within the talent identification stage include having "many highly qualified and well-educated coaches,"[10] and a "guarantee that these highly qualified and well-educated coaches work with beginners and not only high-level athletes."[11] This latter point is an objectionable issue, certainly within North American sports. Many resources have pointed to the fact that within talent identification, the keen eye of a qualified coach (observing young athletes during both training as well as competition) is the true initial phase of identification and that subsequent testing and medical assessment serves as little more than a reinforcement of the facts. The issue resides in the fact that the base level of sport (beginning youth), is lacking many truly qualified and well-educated coaches. The best coaches in North America (and that includes strength and conditioning professionals) often clamor to work exclusively with the more elite athletes within a system; the young athletes are therefore left with inadequately trained coaches or volunteers. The results in the talent pool of a given country can be disastrous—

- Political posturing for the best young athletes in order to "win" rather than creating a development process that equally benefits and directs all youngsters.

- Overuse and acute injury due to early sport specialization and inadequate conditioning means (in lieu of properly designed, developmentally-based training stimulus).

- Emotional burnout due to increased pressure and mandates to "win."

- An alienation of the less talented young athletes can lead to a cessation of physical training altogether, and therefore dangerous ramifications in the lifelong health of those youngsters

A visual picture of the athlete talent pool within North America might look like this:

ELITE ATHLETES: National Team, Olympic, Professional

ADVANCED ATHLETES: College, Semi-Pro

ADOLESCENT ATHLETES: High School

YOUTH ATHLETES: Rec. Sports, House Leagues

Again, the issue lies in the fact that we have our best coaches working, often exclusively, with the top caliber athletes within this paradigm. The phase or stage with the largest talent pool and most sensitive needs is left to volunteer coaches and parents with little, to no education in the appropriate sport sciences.

Talent Selection & Development

Talent selection is the second stage "in the process of nurturing potential high performers in sport,"[12] while talent development represents the third stage. Typically, competition is the primary means of "selection" with respect to young athlete advancement. However, a critical point here is the issue of early selection. Those who mature and grow at a slower rate are often at a distinct disadvantage with respect to selection via competition. It is commonly only those young individuals who excel in competition at a young age who are offered, or seek, additional abet in the form of adjunct training and other forms of sport science services (therapeutic care, nutritional support or psychological development for example). Without a distinct nation-wide development system, such as in North America, it is often only those with financial resources that are able to seek such services. It would appear to be more beneficial to have a systematic and structured means of development in which the coaches and handlers of young athletes are supremely qualified and athletic advancement is open and available to all young people within the nation.

National Systems

The following is a general overview of the approach various country's take with respect to talent identification, selection and development, as described in "talent identification and selection & development," from the Institute of Youth Sports.

Australia
The three distinct phases of sporting development are evident within the Australian system through their **Talent Search Program:**

Phase One:

Adolescents aged fourteen to sixteen are screened within their school setting via a series of eight physical and physiological assessments, the results of which are correlated against a national database. If the youngsters' scores show a favorable correlation versus the national standards, then they are progress on to *Phase Two*. *Phase One*, therefore, serves as the identification stage of development.

Phase Two:

The testing or screening process continues in this phase, but becomes more sport specific in nature. The specific testing protocol serves to hone the results found in *Phase One*. If increased potential for a specific sport is indicated, then more advanced laboratory assessments will likely be conducted; this would be considered the "selection" phase.

Phase Three:

Young athletes who have been identified as talented and selected towards a particular sport via testing, will be invited to participate in a talented athlete program, which would be considered the "development" phase of this system.

The Australian Talent Search Programme was developed in the late 1980s and fully implemented by 1994. Guided by the Australian Sports Commission, plans and programs were created for particular sports, such as:

- Athletics (track & field)
- Canoeing
- Rowing
- Swimming
- Triathlon
- Water polo
- Weightlifting

It was determined that sufficient talent development was viable in these sports, over the six-year interval leading up to the 2000 Sydney Olympic Games.

The Australian Institute of Sport (AIS), which opened in 1981, is involved intimately with the talent development process nation-wide. The AIS strives to "enhance the sporting performances of Australia's elite and potential elite athletes and teams"[13]. Specifically, the AIS provides training facilities and lodging for high-performance and future elite athletes. The AIS also provides access to the following amenities:

- Elite Coaches
- Strength & Conditioning Coaches/Programs
- Nutritional Guidance
- Career & Educational Support

adapted from 'Talent identification, selection & development' p. 11

The AIS offers roughly 600 scholarships annually. The scholarship athletes must enlist in a technical or academic course, or they may wish to seek employment. School aged scholarship athletes are enrolled in a local school where they are monitored and required to maintain a certain level of academic progress.

Canada

Within the most populous and athletically competitive areas of Canada, young athletes are often identified via school or club team competitions by recruits or scouts. In addition to this style of identification, Canada also has established various sport schools throughout the country. These sports schools serve to "facilitate optimal development of talented 14 – 18 year olds"[14]. The mandate of the sport schools is to direct the respective student-athletes towards success in both the sporting and academic establishments.

Gaining acceptance into a sport school is determined by a provincial athlete selection criterion – athletes must be classified as "elite" and endorsed for acceptance by the respective provincial sport association. Additionally, each prospective student-athlete must meet academic standards, specifically in the subject areas of English, French and math.

The primary benefit of the Canadian sport schools is in the flexibility they offer with respect to schedules and curriculum delivery. For instance, within the same high school setting, the "sport school students" and the "regular students" will take the same classes, incur the same academic requirements and partake in the same examinations. However, "special classes" or tutorial sessions are offered to the sport school students due to their condensed schedules. Very often, the sport school students will take academic classes in the morning, and then be released to sport training sessions or practices in the afternoon, followed by a tutorial session.

There are three fundamental factors to the Canadian sports schools:

- Academic program that is adapted to training and competition demands
- Sufficient time for quality training
- Sport science support services

adapted from 'Talent identification, selection & development' p. 12

China

The Chinese talent identification program is a nation-wide effort that is associated directly with its school athletic programs. Their identification system incorporates a research-based approach intended to forecast future athletic potential via six different criteria:

- General growth pattern
- Maximum growth duration
- Physique, motor abilities, coordination and temperament
- Rate of development of physique, motor abilities, coordination & record of performance
- Health & heredity factors
- Assessment of regulatory of training progress

* adapted from 'Talent identification, selection & development' p. 13

Talent identification and selection are considered long-term processes, which are linked to issues such as maturity and continued performance improvements. Determining conclusively a child's potential via a single evaluation process is therefore deemed impossible. The Chinese system is based around three separate phases of talent identification and selection:

- Assessing what event or sport is most suitable for an individual
- Re-evaluation of their potential as their performance improves
- Selection of middle to high-level athletes

* adapted from 'Talent identification, selection & development' p. 13

In many sports, selected athletes will undergo further testing to determine sport specific potential, for instance with high jump, there are "18 test indices related to the high jump that result in the calculation of an index of potential"[15]. These assessments are sport specific in nature and substantially more complex and comprehensive than the original six criteria used in the preliminary phases of talent identification.

Germany

Within the former German Democratic Republic, identifying talent involved both general and sport specific stages. In the generalized initial phase, anthropometric figures were amassed and results relating to performance within physical education assessments were gathered. A six-month testing and training timeframe comprised the second, more sport specific stage during which information such as an athlete's attitude towards training was determined.

Subsequently, young athletes were inserted into a specialized development program via intensive and highly structured club sporting system.

Former Soviet Union

Talent identification occurred initially via regional sport competitions; the best and most successful individuals and teams eventually advanced to the national level-final competitions. At these final events, National Team, Olympic, and world-class Soviet athletes adjudicated over the competitions and identified the most talented youngsters. These "identified" athletes were then "recruited into specialist sport schools"[16].

The Soviet sport schools were developmentally based and included:

- *Children's & Young People's Sport Schools*—the initial foundation of the Soviet system for developing elite athletes.
- *Specialist Children's & Young People's Sport Schools of Olympic Reserves*—these institutions were more specific in which athletes specialized in only one sport.
- *School of Higher Sports Mastery*—these elite schools served the leading athletes of the former Soviet Union.

* adapted from 'Talent identification, selection & development' p. 13

Talent Identification Methods

By definition, talent identification "involves the prediction of performance over various periods of time by measuring number of attributes and abilities alone or in combination"[17]. Not unlike creating a functionally effective training protocol for an athlete. However, accurately predicting potential performance is, in reality, based on several factors and therefore not necessarily an infallible practice. In fact, when determining potential performance, it is naïve to assume that "prerequisite factors for a specific performance exist"[18]. Several principal factors must be considered:

- Cultural characteristics
- Socioeconomic levels
- Nutritional status
- Family and peer influences

* adapted from 'Talent identification, selection & development' p. 15

Factors such as these ones "make the creation of a universal model for talent identification relevant to all sports complex"[19].

There are however, several means of establishing certain prerequisite characteristics for a specific performance:

- Univariate studies
- Single discipline-multivariate studies
- Multidisciplinary-multivariate studies

Univariate Studies

"Univariate studies set out to compare one single variable between elite athletes and non-athletes"[20]. Essentially, this infers that any variable can be regarded as being a performance indicator in a particular sport if a considerable difference is shown during the assessment of two groups. Furthermore, any variable showing the greatest division from the general population average is considered to be the most significant determinant. The easiest example of this would be "maximal oxygen uptake in marathon runners"[21].

Within elite athletics however, it is likely that all competitors of a particular event or sport will posses similar decisive-performance determinants. Having said that, the next important variables now become crucial with respect to sporting success. These secondary factors are referred to as *relevant variables*. Referring back to the marathon runner's example above, "all elite long distance runners would be expected to possess a high VO2 max. However, their anaerobic power and speed become relevant variables that could influence the final outcome of a race"[22].

It has been concluded however, that using single variable studies related to performance potential or indication seem to lack a certain comprehensive perspective with respect to uncovering crucial factors of sporting success.

Single Discipline Multivariate Studies

"Single discipline multivariate studies investigate the influence of a number of variables on performance in one discipline, for example, physiology or psychology, while taking into account the relationship between the variables in that particular discipline"[23]. Studies for example, have been conducted on certain physical parameters (such as the varying combinations of flexibility and strength) in order to distinguish potential talented participants in gymnastics. Other studies have concentrated on psychological aspects of performance having ascertained that "self-concept, locus of control and trait anxiety"[24] were primarily accountable for performance success in female gymnastics.

Studies involving variables from a single discipline have been determined to be insufficient at measuring true potential or performance, however.   A broader look at several disciplines and therefore a variety of performance variances is required.

Multidisciplinary-Multivariate Studies

"Multidisciplinary-multivariate studies incorporate a number of disciplines using multiple variables in their design and are a promising means of identifying talent"[25].   Multidisciplinary-multivariate studies work to bridge a gap between scientific, clinical testing and functional ability.   For example, clinical testing cannot be isolated as a reliable indicator of potential performance for several reasons:

- Assessments may or may not be directly transferable to one's ability on the field of play.
- Many coaches lack the necessary scientific background to either interpret or apply the results accrued from clinical testing.
- Coaches or scientists who do possess appropriate scientific background may not have adequate practical experience to create relevant developmental programs to progress a young athlete's abilities.
- Unless clinical evaluations are accessible and conducted at regular intervals, they may be meaningless and lack the capacity to truly monitor an athlete's progress.

Field or functional evaluations are also not appropriate in identifying potential if they are isolated as the only predictor. Poor technical instruction, game pressure or stress, and minor orthopedic/structural restrictions could all negatively impact the functional ability of an athlete. In North America, field or functional assessment is typically the only measurement used to evaluate future potential (i.e. how well the young athlete excels in a given sport). The limitations of this practice are many and were touched on above:

- Many coaches and trainers lack the ability to teach and progress a young athlete's capacity for movement and speed.
- Young athletes are seldom progressed through a developmental training protocol aimed at increasing systemic strength (which would have a positive correlation on both movement performance and injury avoidance).
- Rarely are healthy young athletes evaluated from a structural or orthopedic perspective. Consequently, minor orthopedic restrictions or dysfunctions may limit functional performance.

In the absence of a sound developmental training program (intended to systematically improve all bio-motor abilities) and appropriate instruction on movement aptitude, using field or functional assessment as the only relevant predictor of future potential is ineffective. In this case, only the naturally gifted youngsters receive attention from a talent identification and development standpoint.

Systematic Approach to Identification, Selection and Development

According to "Talent Identification, Selection & Development," from the Institute of Youth Sports, there are seven key issues to implementing a successful nation-wide athletic development system:

1. Ethical Issues:

Although the initial phases of a research-based testing system are founded on matching a young athlete with his or her most suitable sport, the child's preferences must be taken into consideration. In fact, the best interest of the young athlete should be deemed more important than the interests of a given sport or national governing body.

It is also crucial to ensure that young athletes who do not "advance beyond the talent identification and selection phases are not discarded but rather encouraged to maintain their involvement in sport at an appropriate level"[26]. Talent identification and selection systems should not be considered appropriate only for the most gifted youngsters. In fact, diverging systems should be created that allow less talented young athletes to enjoy recreational-sport participation and athletic-development stimulus while more advanced athletes are progressed through a specialized and directed sporting path. This balanced system would aid in eliminating the incidents of childhood obesity and other health issues, which tend to emanate from lack of activity.

2. Maturational & Chronological Age:

When identifying future potential via biological means (i.e. body weight, height etc.), maturation must also be considered—given that biological variables are "more maturational-age dependent than chronological-age dependent"[27]. Maturation assessment is important when identifying young talent in physical capacities such as agility and speed develop earlier than anaerobic lactic power and strength. Simply stated, a pre-adolescent athlete may possess tremendous-biological variables, but lack strength because that particular capacity has yet to develop optimally.

3. Age Grading In Competition:

Although most youth sporting activities are based on success of competition, it must be understood that lack of achievement by a given young athlete is not an isolated determinant for future potential. For example, lack of success or proficiency in one sport cannot justly predict the future potential of a young athlete in other sports. Although competition or field evaluation is considered valuable in identifying future potential, the risks or concerns of formal competition with young athletes are many:

- Early specialization forced by over zealous parents and coaches
- Intensive training and adult-based prescription
- Parental over-enthusiasm
- High attrition rates and burn-out

adapted from 'Talent identification, selection & development' p. 20

4. **School Involvement:**

As noted previously in this chapter, some nations use the elementary school system as a main crux for their talent identification process. Physical education instruction in the early school years should involve the development of basic sporting and movement skills and establish a base of introduction to a wide variety of sports and activities. This is a pragmatic practice in that the school system is the one foundation through which you can reach all of the youngsters within a given society or country.   Unfortunately in North America, physical education classes are being cut in lieu of an ever-expanding academic curriculum and many students receive only a base number of physical education hours per week.   More over, the classes themselves are often not based on developmentally sound principals of athletic development.

5. **Coach Involvement**:

Coaches involved in private club activities should be educated to the highest extend with regards to both talent identification parameters, as well as vital aspects of athletic development. While many youth sporting coaches claim proficiency at identifying talent within their respective sports, very few coaches are qualified to create training programs that serve to optimally develop young athletes based on chronological and maturational age-related-exercise stimulus.   Far too often, adult-based exercise prescription is used when training young athletes and form and function of a particular exercise or routine is compromised in lieu of providing physically challenging training programs.

6. **Genetic and Environmental Factors**:

Every child possesses certain physical and psychological qualities, which are genetically based. Generally speaking, these inherited qualities will allow a young athlete to achieve various degrees of success in particular sports. It can be concluded that "there are, within reason, no untalented children, only children that take part in unsuitable events"[28]. It has also been suggested that success in certain sports is more conditional on genetic factors (i.e. sports requiring higher physical and psychological strains) while success in other sports may be based more on environmental factors (i.e. sports considered to be precision skill-based). The relationship between the genetic factors and the environmental stimulus (i.e. suitable training) will inevitably influence potential success.

7. **Sport Specific Differences**:

The age at which respective sports begin to identify and select talent may be quite different. In varying nations, certain sports enjoy a high level of participation at the youth level (hockey in Canada for instance) while other sports do not possess as much of a base-pool (and summarily less potential talent). These "major" sports do not need to recruit participants from outside of their respective sport while the "minor" sports would be advised to do so.

Physical & Cognitive Development

While physical education and basic activity are becoming less of a priority for many youths and school systems throughout North America, it must be understood that there exists a positive correlation between quality physical education stimulus and academic performance. In fact, a definitive association between movement education and cognitive processes has been shown.

Physical education has been recognized as a vital feature of a given school's curriculum, in that organized movement stimulus has a considerable impact on the development of thinking skills and that cognitive improvements are linked to school children's exposure to movement aptitude programs. Researchers have shown that well conducted physical activity programs with pre-school children serve to advance the cognitive progresses of young children[29]. Other researches have concluded that quality physical education advances the development of both motor skills and intellectual skills[30].

According to Gardner (Harvard University, 1994), there are seven intelligences termed "multiple intelligences":

1. bodily/kinesthetic
2. verbal/linguistic
3. mathematical/logical
4. visual/spatial
5. musical
6. interpersonal
7. intrapersonal

adapted from 'Physical education cognitive development and academic performance' p.8

Quite obviously, only physical education has an impact on bodily/kinesthetic intelligence. School-aged children whose physical education stimulus is either negated or minimized due to improper or unguided-movement-aptitude exposure, run the risk of developing poor lifestyle habits and quite simply never become well-rounded adults. Clearly, the physical education offered in North American schools is in need of reform.

Of important note from an athletic development standpoint, is the reality that even the most elite of athletes gain their foundational athletic ability from introduction to general motor stimulus during the pre-adolescent ages. In fact, as noted in the Talent Identification portion of this chapter, many nations throughout the world utilize the elementary school system as their primary initiation stage of the entire sport talent identification process. Having said that, whether the goal is to create a world-class athlete or to develop sound-lifestyle habits that will serve to maintain a long healthy life, the beginning process is essentially the same.

While many schools continue to maintain a heightened academic focus, often at the expense of suitable physical stimulus, some studies have shown that this approach to education may not be the most appropriate even from a scholastic perspective. In the Vanves study (Fourestier, 1996; Hervet, 1952) students at a chosen school experienced a revision to their standard class timetable, which included an additional 9.5 hours of school-time per week and the supplement of two siestas each day. Academic lessons were truncated by 26% and offered only during the morning hours. Afternoons were devoted to the exposure to a vast array of physical education; including gymnastics, swimming, team sports and general outdoor activities. When contrasted to other, more traditionally scheduled schools of comparable students, the academic results showed to be analogous. More over, the students attending the modified school were described as "more calm, attentive and exhibited less disciplinary problems than the control (traditionally scheduled) classes"[31].

Other studies of parallel note have shown similar findings. The Australian study (Dwyer *et al.*, 1979) included 519 fifth grade students from seven different schools. During the study, fourteen-week physical-education classes were arbitrarily assigned to the students, with each class lasting seventy-five minutes in length. This resulted in a 14% cutback of total academic instruction. Notwithstanding this reduction, there were no considerable differences in the arithmetic performance or reading skills of the students during the fourteen-week trial. In fact, a two-year follow up study showed that the students had "developed an advantage in both arithmetic and reading scores, with a continuing advantage in teacher ratings of classroom behavior"[32].

References

[1] Bompa, T. (1994)

[2] Bompa, T. (1994)

[3] Bompa, T. (1994)

[4] Bompa, T. (1994)

[5] Bompa, T. (1994)

[6] Bompa, T. (1994)

[7] Bompa, T. (1994)

[8] Bompa, T. (1994)

[9] Bompa, T. (1994)

[10] MacPhail, A., Kirk, D., &Tan, B. (2001)

[11] MacPhail, A., Kirk, D., &Tan, B. (2001)

[12] MacPhail, A., Kirk, D., &Tan, B. (2001)

[13] MacPhail, A., Kirk, D., &Tan, B. (2001)

[14] MacPhail, A., Kirk, D., &Tan, B. (2001)

[15] MacPhail, A., Kirk, D., &Tan, B. (2001)

[16] MacPhail, A., Kirk, D., &Tan, B. (2001)

[17] MacPhail, A., Kirk, D., &Tan, B. (2001)

[18] MacPhail, A., Kirk, D., &Tan, B. (2001)

[19] MacPhail, A., Kirk, D., &Tan, B. (2001)

[20] MacPhail, A., Kirk, D., &Tan, B. (2001)

[21] MacPhail, A., Kirk, D., &Tan, B. (2001)

[22] MacPhail, A., Kirk, D., &Tan, B. (2001)

[23] MacPhail, A., Kirk, D., &Tan, B. (2001)

[24] MacPhail, A., Kirk, D., &Tan, B. (2001)

[25] MacPhail, A., Kirk, D., &Tan, B. (2001)

[26] MacPhail, A., Kirk, D., &Tan, B. (2001)

[27] MacPhail, A., Kirk, D., &Tan, B. (2001)

[28] MacPhail, A., Kirk, D., &Tan, B. (2001)

[29] Tan, B., & MacPhail, A. (2001)

[30] Tan, B., & MacPhail, A. (2001)

[31] Tan, B., & MacPhail, A. (2001)

[32] Tan, B., & MacPhail, A. (2001)

2

Positive Coaching Strategies and Pedagogy

Craig Ballantyne, Brian Grasso and Lee Taft

Youth sports are becoming bigger and more organized than ever before. It wasn't that long ago when youth sports participation primarily consisted of calling local friends and meeting at the park to play sandlot. Today the parks are being overrun by leagues and coaches who organize every little aspect of the sporting experience. Such games as youth basketball, soccer, football, and baseball are refereed by paid officials and coached by parents. This is not always a bad thing, but the people who are coaching and organizing the young athletes need to keep in perspective what developing a young athlete is about.

The explosion in youth sports can be looked upon from two different views: One, parents and coaches see the potential to have the next superstar division one or professional athletes; two, adults see the need to keep children active and give them a healthy alternative to computer games and television programs. The hope is that the second view is the ultimate motive. Regardless of the reasons, proper coaching of young athletes needs to be employed.

Our goal as sport coaches is to provide athletes with a positive psychological experience and a positive learning experience. We can have a lifelong positive impact on young athletes, helping them to be winners in sport and society. During a young athlete's formative years, athletes might spend as much time each day with their coaches as they do with their parents. It is clear coaches play a significant role in preparing children for the rest of their lives. Given the enormous responsibility on coaches, it is important that we take the right approach when working with children.

The goal of this chapter is to explore and educate the reader on what it takes to be a good coach of young athletes, and how to go about preparing to work with children. This chapter will explore many different styles and methods of coaching. It is important for the reader to realize there is not one particular method or strategy that will prove effective all the time and with every athlete. Being a good coach means understanding children have different needs and learning styles.

Coaching young children is rewarding, and it can be easy for a coach to get caught up in the sport. It is important to keep in mind sports may not be the only thing in the child's life, and allowing the child to grow socially, emotionally, and physically can create a positive experience that proves to keep the child involved. "Remember that as a coach you are first and foremost an educator whose primary mission is to help each of your athletes become all that he or she can become not only in sport but in life."[1]

Guidelines for Coaching Young Athletes

Young athletes need to be treated as such. They are not little adults; they are not grouped into one mass of young athletes. Each athlete has his/her own identity with his/her own special needs. These needs are greatly determined by the chronological and developmental age, and gender of the athlete. The other component need is the sensitive periods in which a particular ability is most apt to be trainable. These and other guidelines will be discussed in this section.

The program structure for young athletes needs to follow certain considerations and guidelines in order to establish optimal development and well being. As with any program, a particular method of training will be chosen. As an example of establishing guidelines for young athletes, the following *six guidelines for choosing methods for physical fitness* are modified from Josef Drabik:

1. Age: The components of program design need to be considered when designing a program for young athletes. The physiological, neurological, muscular, and mental qualities change according to the chronological and developmental stage of the athlete.

2. Sensitive periods: "The effect of intensive training of a particular motor ability is greater if this training takes place during the so-called sensitive period in development of this ability." The sensitive period is a period of development of the human organs and other systems that determine ability and are developing.

3. Demands of a sport: What demands will be placed on the athlete while participating in a particular sport. The athlete will need to prepare for these demands to be successful and safe.

4. Optimizing the level of fitness: It is important to develop a level of a fitness component so it is advantageous to success. If too much time is spent on any one component of fitness at the expense of others that will help performance, the performance will suffer.

5. Structuring the workout: It is important to organize exercises in the order of importance and development. Do not put small auxiliary exercises before explosive exercises if power training is the goal.

6. Gender: Realize boys and girls develop at a different rate when designing programs.[2]

Guidelines need to be established for every sporting or fitness situation. A basketball developmental program needs to establish guidelines for their organization just as the physical education programs need to establish guidelines for the different levels.

One of the main concerns with training programs for children is the adoption of training programs that have been designed for adults. Many coaches feel if they water it down, it will be compatible with the child's development. Another common problem is when programs designed for elite athletes are used with children. "Far too often, the sports programs of children imitate programs of well- known elite athletes—those who, through their national or international achievements, have captivated the imaginations of young athletes and their coaches[3]". The following guidelines are modified from Tudor Bompa's book "Total Training for Young Champions[4]":

1. Develop a long term program: During the early stages of development the program should focus on multilateral development with the later years of development turning more to specialization

2. Adding variety: It is important for athletes to participate in a variety of activities and sports for overall motor skill development. The variety within a particular sport is important as well.

3. Allow for individual characteristics: Things such as chronological age, developmental age, and athletic training age are important to understand when establishing guidelines for training.

4. Suitable training load increases: All the components that go into designing a training program need to be carefully monitored with respect to increasing intensity.

Appropriate guidelines help in assuring young athletes will have fitting program design to meet their individual needs.

In the 1980's, Dr. Vern Seefeldt and Dr. Rainier Martens developed what is named the "Bill of Rights for Young Athletes[5]". Dr. Seefeldt is a professor at the Institute for the Study of Youth Sports. They developed this in response to the concerns regarding the abuse of young athletes. Many organizations have adopted the "Bill of Rights for Young Athletes" as a guideline for coaches and parents. The "Bill of Rights for Young Athletes" is listed below in its exact wording:

1. Right to participate in sports
2. Right to participate at a level commensurate with each child's maturity and ability
3. Right to have qualified adult leadership.
4. Right to play as a child and not as an adult
5. Right of children to share in the leadership and decision-making of their sport participation
6. Right to participate in safe and healthy environments
7. Right to proper preparation for participation in sports. Right to an equal opportunity to strive for success
8. Right to be treated with dignity
9. Right to have fun in sports

Developed by Dr. Vern Seefeldt, professor emeritus at the Institute for the Study of Youth Sports, and Dr. Rainer Martens.

It should be evident that the concern for proper programs for young athletes is an issue due to the establishment of such guidelines mentioned above. The Kentucky Youth Soccer Association[6] has established coaches' guidelines in their coaches' handbook. Basically, the guidelines cover the role of a coach as a facilitator of young people, being a positive role model, and being one that understands working with young athletes[7].

A Coach's Responsibilities to the Athletes

Aside from teaching proper sports and athletic skills, a coach must be aware of several things when coaching young athletes. Simply focusing on the sport or activity the athlete is presently involved in would be a disservice. "Apart from teaching sport skills, as an educator you have an obligation to your athletes not only as athletes, but as youngsters who have many other potential abilities, talents, and interests that should be allowed to develop[8]".

Specialization

A concern coaches must take seriously is avoiding specialization at an early age. Although early success makes it tempting to isolate the child from other sports, research has shown specialization at a young age leads to undesirable results later.

A study done by Harre in 1982 in the former East Germany—as sited in Tudor Bompa's book, "Total Training for Young Champions"—studies a group of young athletes ranging from nine to twelve years old who specialized and a group who followed a multilateral program. The results of the study are listed below[9].

Early Specialization Group:
- Quick performance improvement
- Best performance achieved at fifteen to sixteen years because of quick adaptation
- Inconsistency of performance in competition
- By age eighteen many athletes were burned out and quit the sport.
- Prone to injuries because of forced adaptation

Multilateral Program Group
- Slower performance improvement
- Best performance at eighteen and older, the age of physiological and psychological maturation.
- Consistency of performance in competitions
- Longer athletic life
- Few injuries

This study was included to show the magnitude of a coach's responsibility to his or her young athletes and the parents.

Why Kids are not Playing Sports

It is obvious youth sports are growing just by looking in recreation parks and schools on a spring, summer, or fall weekend. There are kids as far as the eyes can see playing little league baseball, youth soccer, and Pop Warner football. The positive side of this vision is the activity level and involvement of youths in sport. The negative side is extremely detrimental to the youth sporting and fitness movement and is what needs to be curtailed.

It all starts with an overzealous youth coach, maybe a parent or just a coach who has an insatiable urge to win or produce winners, one who doesn't truly understand the mission of youth sports and fitness. The coach may have established an agenda of his/her own and mowing down the hearts of a few kids unfortunate to not have great athleticism at a young age doesn't really matter to them. Win, and win at all costs!

This pressure to win at all costs and to create young athlete superstars is misplaced. The purpose of youth sports is not to act as a feeder system to professional sports, but instead to prepare our youth to contribute positively to society and simply to have fun and promote good health. After all, according to Dr. Richard Lapchick, director for the

Center for the Study of Sports in Society, the chance of a high-school athlete becoming a professional in any sport is 1/12000[10].

There is an issue of athletes being eliminated from youth sports at an early age. The elimination may occur indirectly by the child being pushed to the side until he/she finally has enough and quits, or directly by the coach having a cutting policy. "It is absurd that on the one hand we feel sports are good for kids and on the other hand we set up a system which eliminates poorer performers, girls, late-maturing boys, kids who are not aggressive enough, and so on". Terry Orlick, Sport Psychology professor at the University of Ottawa, and Cal Botterill, instructor at the University of Alberta and former YMCS director states, "Elimination is a critical problem, perhaps the most critical problem which exists in children's sport."[11]

Ultimately, the coaches need to try and reach out and create situations that encourage young athletes to always have an active role in sports and activities. "We should field as many teams as there are interested kids to fill them."[12] This obviously takes commitment by organizations to find qualified coaches for these athletes.

Many readers of this section may feel they would never intentionally cut or discourage young athletes from participation in sports. The problem lies with the foundation of sports in the United States. It is about winning and being the best, even at the most infant stages of youth sports. Let's face it, kids follow the direction and behaviors of those leading them. If coaches and parents emphasis winning, so will the kids.

Coaches must focus on the benefits of sport to the young athlete. This includes the athletes on opposition teams as well. It is not acceptable to intimidate or mock an opposing-young athlete in order to improve the chances of success for your team. A good coaching philosophy must incorporate the Golden Rule: treat others as you would wish to be treated. Aim to improve the sporting experience for all athletes, as well as the physical health and performance of each individual young athlete.

Winning obviously becomes a major component in the sporting industry once the athletes have reached a more advanced stage. Competition is a good thing at the proper time. The problem lies with young kids simply wanting to belong and have FUN, yet parents and coaches get caught up in the winning philosophy. The point is, even when youth coaches and parents intentions are good and are focused on the joy of participation, the minute the competitive juices and the pressures of losing creep in the equation, unconsciously coaches will begin to segregate the athletes according to talent—leaving out the less talented kids. This instantly shapes behaviors. Kids know when they do not measure up to the expectations of the coach when winning and performance is the gauge.

Taking the Emphasis off Winning

Kids today have a wide variety of options competing for their attention and leisure time. If we don't offer them a positive environment in sports, they'll find another activity that does. Coaches can create optimal environments for positive sports experiences, ones that will allow us to build character in kids, while more importantly providing them with lifelong friends and memories. Friendship and fun should transcend winning and negative pressure in sports.

The "win at all cost" mentality of many parents and coaches creates a stressful environment for kids and ultimately turns them away from sports. But that is one of the worst things that we can do – drive children from sport. Children participating in organized school sports have the potential to build character and other attributes, lead healthier lives, and reduce school dropout.[13]

As a coach of young athletes, you must eliminate the "win at all costs" attitude. At the worst end of the spectrum there are reports such as this one from a medical journal describing a 5 year old boy who was pressured by parents to lose weight in order to wrestle at a lower weight class.[14]

Performance pressure can have serious physical consequences. According to a recent newspaper article,[15] "Doctors in pediatric sports medicine say it is as if they have happened upon a new childhood disease, and the cause is the overaggressive culture of organized youth sports." One factor was repeatedly cited as the prime cause for the outbreak in overuse injuries among young athletes. Irresponsible training schedules imposed by parents on children of young ages, all in the name of winning can lead to disability throughout the athlete's adult life.

As it has been stated several times throughout this book, young athletes need time throughout the year to take breaks from their sport and to recover physically and mentally. The breaks are the right of the young athlete to be a child. According to Smith and Smoll, it is the right of the athlete to expect a positive sporting environment and to play as a child, not as an adult.[16]

Young athletes who play as many games per season as a professional athlete are the norm. This is creating all sorts of physical injury and mental stress. A staggering rate of youth by the time they reach their teens has burned out on playing games. Most of these cases are the result of participating to early, overwhelming game schedules and travel, an overemphasis on winning, youth specializing in one sport, bad sport experiences, and adults losing sight that they are youth.

Coaches should deemphasize winning and increase their emphasis on the athlete giving a full effort to help increase the young athlete's enjoyment of sport. Even Vince Lombardi, known for his quotes on winning, emphasized the process of effort over the act of winning. The only thing that athletes can control in the game is their own effort. Have the athlete focus on effort and you will help them develop mental toughness and the ability to bounce back from adversity. Success can be better defined as continually putting forth their best effort in the quest for victory.

Focusing on the scoreboard numbers can lead to failure. When your team loses, the PCA recommends acknowledging the positives immediately after the game and dealing with mistakes at practice when you can learn from them (teaching opportunity). For the unfortunate teams that lose often, you can set other performance goals to be met in games besides winning, such as increase in teamwork or on another game statistic such as improving the number of rebounds you get each week.

Avoid the win-at-all-costs attitude and need for perfection. You must prepare players to respond to mistakes (bad calls, team mate's mistakes, accidents, etc.). In each loss, there are bound to be many mistakes made by both the coach and player. You should teach the athletes to accept mistakes. Mistakes are what teach us and help us become better by helping us learn and how to respond better in the future. If you can teach the athlete to deal with mistakes and overcome adversity, you will be increasing the mental toughness of the athlete. The advanced sports psychology section covers some coping strategies.

Orlick and Botterill say "Children's first sports experiences are vitally important. If their experiences are positive and enjoyable they may become hooked for life. On the other hand, it these experiences are negative and unknowable, they can be turned off for a long time[17]". The most important thing a youth coach can do to encourage lifelong participation in sport and physical activity is to put enjoyment and fun above everything else.

If a youth coach feels his/her role is to organize games and practices and he/she does not have much impact on the learned behaviors of children first starting sport, he/she is mistaken, as seen by the above information.

It would be easy to go on with endless accounts and reasons for children dropping out of sports due to negative association. The purpose of this chapter is to aid in the teaching processes of young athletes. It should be evident that the issues raised in this section constitute time well spent mentioning the importance of a coaches role in youth sports.

A positive coaching approach will provide athletes the greatest opportunity to build positive character attributes. While sport is constantly referred to as a character builder, today's news demonstrates professional sport participation is not always synonymous with good character. Each week we hear stories of misconduct in professional sports. One of the reasons sports fail to build character consistently is that society puts too much emphasis on winning. While everyone loves a winner, the problem is society does not necessarily care how the win is achieved.

Most kids are already exposed to an overwhelming amount of negative messages each day. Teachers, parents, other authority figures, and peers are constantly sending destructive messages.

Imagine how all of those negative messages can impact their self-esteem and self-efficacy. Now imagine how they will feel at practice when you deliver positive messages for an hour: "Hey, good pass, nice effort, I like what you did there." This will increase their self-efficacy and effort in practice. Positive reinforcement will also help young athletes improve technical skills, behavior, and character because it encourages them to focus on what they are doing correctly.

Consistent delivery of positive messages and group acceptance are two reasons why gang culture is so successful. Gangs give positive feedback and acceptance to young adults that are otherwise blanketed by negative messages from authority figures[18]. Yet as coaches, we do not recognize the success of the positive approach nearly as often as we should. By providing positive feedback, you can help the young athletes remain in sport and develop physical and mental skills that will help them for life, no matter how bad life is for this child outside of your team's environment.

The positive approach fosters a better learning environment and it's easy to see why. Common sense tells us that constantly yelling at a child is bound to create a negative and defensive reaction over time. Yet many coaches continue to use the negative approach when times get tough. Yelling and punishment may work in the short term, but ultimately will undermine the success of your program. In contrast, the positive coaching approach helps:

- Decrease performance **anxiety**
- Decrease athlete dropout
- Increase positive athletic experience
- Increase self-esteem

Self-efficacy is another characteristic that can be improved with positive coaching. Self-efficacy is defined as individual's estimate or personal judgment of his or her own ability to succeed in reaching a specific goal. As an athlete increases self-efficacy, he or she will try harder in games and training[19]. According to Thompson, enjoyment leads to more practice and more production[20]. When the athlete's self-confidence increases, the athlete will choose to work longer and harder[21].

Positive Role Model

A coach is seen through the eyes of his/her athletes as a role model. It is an important role that must be taken seriously by the coach. Every action is being observed by the kids under his/her watch, even the bad ones.

A forgotten job of the coach is that of a role model. While we can protest our role model status just as Charles Barkley did when he said, "I am not a role model" in the famous Nike commercial, the fact is we really have no choice in the matter. It is the young athlete that chooses the role model, not the adults. We don't have a choice. So if we want our athletes to perform within the rules of the game, then we too must act within the rules of the game.

The Kentucky Youth Soccer Association has established a coach's handbook with guidelines for coaches within it. They established that a coach needs to demonstrate respect for the team members, opponents, officials, parents, spectators, and opposing coaches. They also list that the coaches need to show respect for the game itself.[22]

A final mention of the "role of a coach" comes from the outstanding example set by the Positive Coaching Alliance established at Stanford University in 1998. "PCA believes that winning is a goal in youth sports but that there is a second, more important goal of using sports to teach life lessons through positive coaching."[23]

The Positive Coaching Alliance has developed the "Positive Coach Mental Model". This model gets coaches to take his/her focus of the "win at all cost" thought and shift it into the "Double Goal Coach[20]" approach. "A Positive Coach is a "Double-Goal Coach" who wants to win, and has a second goal: to help players develop positive character traits, so they can be successful in life. Winning is important, but the second goal, helping players learn life lessons, is more important. A Positive Coach puts players first".

There are basically three elements to the Positive Coach Mental Model. Below is a modified description of the model.

1. Redefines what it means to be a winner: The definition for young athletes of what a winner is, changes from the score board to the effort and mastery of skills.
2. Fills the Player's "Emotional Tanks: Coaches give positive feedback through compliments and positive reinforcements rather than intimidation and fear.
3. "Honors the Game": The coach will honor the sport and the elements of it.

If a coach is serious about the athletes, he/she coaches he will take the role of coaching and all the aspects of coaching.[24]

Being Prepared

If a coach truly wants to provide the optimal learning situations for his/her team, planning must be an active part of the coaching process. Planning is more than just documenting a practice plan each day. It is doing the appropriate research of the sport and skills to be taught as well as learning about the athletes capabilities due to age, experience, and stages of development. Planning is about being organized with a road map to success. Planning is also about taking care of the little details that can grow to become big problems if left unattended.

A coach's plan can be unique to him/her and to his/her present situation. It is about understanding what needs to be accomplished, organizing the information and physical elements, and implementing the plan. Planning may consist of many years or it may consist of one day's session. As an example of a process of planning a practice let us look at an established guideline for planning a practice. In the "USA Track and Field Level 1 Curriculum Manual" an outline of a practice design is as follows:

1. Plan a practice in advance.
2. Consider biomotor abilities that need to be developed while designing the workout
3. Design workouts based on what the individual athletes need
4. Perform a proper warm up before the workout
5. Technical skills should be done early in the workout
6. Fitness and conditioning should be done later in the workout
7. Cool down when practice is over
8. Evaluate the training session once completed
9. Make the practices fun

This outline can be made more detailed for the finer points of the practice, but it gives the coaches a consistent plan to follow and design practices from.

Another well established organization that understands the short and long term results from planning is the USA Weightlifting organization. They are able to achieve phenomenal results due to the fine detail in their planning process. USA Weightlifting states, "To ensure continued improvement in weightlifting encompassing technique, skill, strength, power, speed, mobility and conditioning enhancements, a training plan is essential."[25]

An approach that is important for coaches of all levels to consider when designing a plan for the season is to start at the end and work back. USA Track and Field uses this approach when preparing for competitions[26]. The idea is to know the end result and plan accordingly to reach that goal.

Planning a Session

There is no set way to design a practice or session, yet there are important elements that make up an effective plan. Once you have established what your athlete(s) need from a stand point of skill development, it is time to organize your instructional method.

"Knowing how to teach is just as important as knowing what to teach[27]. A good coach will take the time to establish teaching methods that will set the athletes up for success. For example, if a coach decides to only talk about a new skill and explain it verbally, although he/she may have done an outstanding job explaining the skill, many athletes may not learn or comprehend through auditory learning. If the coach had done his/her work he/she would have planned to describe the skill, demonstrate the skill, and allow for practice time, and feedback. In a later section, teaching methods will be discussed in greater detail.

An outline of a basic plan for a session, as listed below, should include the following elements:

1. Date of the training session and
2. Phase the athletes are in (if applicable)
3. Length of the session
4. Goals or objectives of the session
5. Equipment (if applicable)
6. Time allotment of each ability being taught (warm up, review time, new skill, practice time, cool down...)
7. Closing comments coaches notes...

Creating a template that can be easily filled in on day to day bases makes the practice planning process much quicker. The other important thing to remember is it gives the coach a history of workouts that he/she can look back on. Having a documented outline of any given practice or training session can cover a coach if legal issues should arise, as well.

The depth that a coach wishes to go in terms of the planning process is virtually endless. It is the goal of the IYCA to instill the virtues of planning as a whole. A little-league baseball coach may establish a plan for each day and outline the basics that need to be covered in that plan. On the other end of the spectrum, an Olympic level coach may plan four or more years in advance with every aspect of the athletes' life under analysis. The bottom line is that planning is preparation for success of your athletes.

In summary, being organized by planning will give the athletes the best chance for success and will allow the coach to be prepared for situations that may arise. Remember, "Failing to plan is planning to fail".

The Learning Process is a Science

It truly is amazing how learning takes place. Learning a skill can not actually be seen; it is an invisible process. Learning is observed when the athlete's performance consistently shows improvement. Learning actually takes place in the athlete's central nervous system.

The confusing aspect of learning skills, especially with regard to young athletes, is that performance can not always demonstrate whether learning has taken place. For example, if a new skill was taught to a young athlete and within a couple of days the performance seemed to worsen or not improved, the inference may be to conclude that learning has not taking place, but what wasn't known is that the athlete had an injury that was affecting the performance of the skill. The point is to look at not only the performance but the variables that caused a poor performance[28].

Basically in the early stages of learning with young athletes it is more difficult to see the actual learning taking place due to other variables. In the case of a more advanced athlete, poor performance usually can be justified by intrinsic or extrinsic variables and not whether learning has taken place.

The Rate of Learning

There are many factors that influence the rate at which a young athletes learns a skill or technique and how they apply it. This rate varies from athlete to athlete as well. Josef Drabik says the learning process depends of factors such as age, emotional state, motivation, talents, intelligence, temperament, knowledge, and skills. Drabik goes on to mention the personality of the coach as well as the coach's teaching methods, knowledge of the technique and ability to analyze it, the communication skills, and the conditions where learning is taking place[29].

Sensory-Motor Habits and Learning

Learning a skill has to do with the sensory-motor habits that become developed in the process of learning the skill. Learning skill has to do with perfecting the sensory-motor

habits and practicing them until the action becomes automatic. The stages that occur in developing a sensory-motor habit in the learning process of a new skill are modified from Drabik (Children and Sports training):

1. Athletes in the initial stage tend to focus on the general movement and become overly tense and make overcompensations within the movement pattern.
2. The movements are more relaxed and economical and the focus is now in details of the technique.
3. In the final stage the technique and movement patterns become automatic and the need for conscious control is eliminated.

Becoming competent in any given technique or skill, to the point of it being automatic, is a critical component of skill development. The true success comes when this newly acquired skill can be expressed in live competition and tactical situations. "Success in competition depends not so much on the number of techniques known to an athletes buy on the ability to apply known techniques in tactical situations." A good coach will realize the new skills need to be taught in situation so the athlete learns to apply the skill to enhance performance.[30]

The Effect of Plasticity on Learning

Plasticity is important to briefly mention due to its effect on learning. Plasticity basically, is the brain's ability to adjust to changing situations. This is important when speaking of the learning of skills in young children. Children can learn new and different movement patterns due to the greater brain plasticity.

In an article from "Neuroscience for Kids-Brain Plasticity", learning is defined as "The ability to acquire new knowledge or skills through instruction or experience (Tortora and Grabowski (1996))". The article goes on to say "The capacity of the brain to change with learning is plasticity". The question that arises is how does the brain actually change through the learning process? Durabach, as quoted in the "Neuroscience for Kids" article, states there are two modifications that occur in the brain[31]:

1. "A change in the internal structure of the neurons, the most notable being in the area of synapses."
2. "An increase in the number of synapses between neurons."

With respect to brain plasticity, it is important to recognize the role of "critical periods", often referred to as sensitive periods, and the development of learning new skills throughout life. It is known that learning takes place throughout life, yet it becomes more difficult to acquire an entirely new skill. These critical periods are times at which the brain requires certain input from the environment in order for it to develop normally. In an article written by Bruce Murray, "Understanding Brain Development and Early Learning", he quotes (Eliot) who states "At a circuitry level, we know there truly are critical periods—stages of development—in the brain needs certain types of experience, or the circuits don't get put together properly."[32]

In the learning process of children it is plain to see, as mentioned earlier, the coach must be willing to expose young athletes to a variety of movement patterns and skills in order for them to develop greater abilities later in life. It is critical to understand how specialization inhibits the brain from developing many movement patterns.

Stages of Learning

When a new skill is being taught, the athlete must be taken through the proper progressions of learning this skill. It should be obvious that having a young athlete learn a new skill in its most advanced stage would be ridiculous, yet it happens all the time.

There are three basic stages of learning:

1. Beginning Stage: The athlete is figuring out in his/her mind what to do to perform this new skill. It is important as a coach to be patient and not give to much information. It is an overwhelming process for young athletes[33]. The beginning stage is finished when the athlete can perform the skill, even if the skill is completely correct.

   There are three things that an athlete must do in the beginning stage of learning a new skill. The following are modified from "A Coaches Guide to Teaching Sport Skills":

   - Recognized the previously learned movement patterns from a skill or group of skills that will be of help in learning the new skill.
   - Physically learn the new movement patterns that make up the new skill.
   - Integrate the previously learned skills and the new skills into a totally new movement pattern[34].

2. Intermediate Stage: The athlete now must concentrate on refining the skill through quality practice. The feedback and motivation need to be high[35]. In this stage the athletes need to concentrate on perfect practice. Practice alone will be insufficient for learning a skill correctly. In order for practice to be effective the athlete must me motivated to learn, need to pay attention to

relevant cuing from the coach, have to receive instructional feedback on correct and incorrect practice, must receive positive reinforcement in the way of performance or verbal from coaches or teammates[36].

3. Advanced Stage: The athlete now can perform the skill automatically. The athlete doesn't need to put as much thought into performing the skill. This allows the athlete to concentrate on applying the skill in the sport[37].

As the athlete goes through the different stages of learning a new skill it is important for the coach to become more direct and somewhat critical in his/her instruction. The athlete will need to hear cues that are more technical based in order to understand the intricacies of the skill in a more complex state.

Learning Styles

Many times coaches, unfamiliar with learning styles, will not understand why his/her athletes do not comprehend or are not learning what is being taught. Not everyone learns the same way. There are basically four styles of learning that young athletes will fall under:

1. Visual learners: The young athlete will need to see things demonstrated or written to learn it best.
2. Auditory learners: This athlete is going to learn best by sound. He/she will respond to the coach giving verbal instruction. He/she also tends to want to express himself/herself verbally.
3. Kinesthetic learners: Obviously this athlete will want to perform what is being taught to understand it best. He/she needs to get his/her hand on it, so to speak.
4. Combination learners: This athlete learns best with a combination of learning styles[38].

Once the coach understands how the athlete's process information it is the coaches job to give every athlete the best opportunity for learning.

Coaching Styles

There are many styles that coaches and teachers can use, but there are two main styles that will be discussed in this chapter. The coach must understand the style he/she is most comfortable with still must provide optimal learning for the athletes; if this isn't the case, it is the responsibility of the coach to change his/her style. The two styles are:

1. Telling style; The coach will decide everything with no input from students. The coach decides what, when, where, and how it is to be done.
2. Sharing style: The coach will outline the basic plan yet allow input and suggestions. The coach will make the final decision on what occurs.[39]

There may be times when the one or the other style will work best. For example; if the skill or situation is completely new to the athletes and having them give input will be detrimental to the learning process, or if there is a time frame to complete a task, sometimes the coach must dictate. On the other hand, if there is an abundance of time and the learning process can be directed in many ways, it would be fine to have the athletes share in the process.

Methods of Teaching

One of the most complex tasks a coach will face is teaching a new complex skill. What separates good coaches from the rest is the ability to find methods of instruction that allows learning difficult skills. As mentioned earlier in this chapter, learning a new skill creates a high amount of mental energy being focused on the task. This can cause a less fluid action by the athlete. Also, if too much information is given at once, the athlete gets confused and is not able to digest the information, causing poor technique and transfer to learning.

There are many teaching methods that can be used. Depending on how difficult the skill is and if the skill has close resemblance to a preciously learned skill, the method of instruction will vary from that of a completely new skill. In this section we will briefly describe several methods. All methods are modified from the book "Coaches Guide to Teaching Sport Skills":

1. Part-Whole Method: The athletes will be taught the individual parts of a skill before learning the whole skill.
2. Progressive-Part Method: Teach one part then the next part; when the two parts are mastered, then the third part is learned; it will be taught with the first two learned parts and so on, until the whole skill is learned.
3. Whole-Part-Whole-Method: Teach and practice the whole skill, then break the skill down and teach the individual parts until they are learned. Finally, teach the entire skill as a whole again.
4. Whole Method: Teach the entire skill as a whole until it is learned.

When a coach is trying to select which method is best to use he/she should ask the following questions:

1. "Can I teach the skill as a whole, or is it too complicated?"
2. "What is the best way to break down the skill into its parts and then help the athletes learn the parts well enough to be joined together and learned as a whole?"

It may be best if the whole skill can be taught to your athletes correctly from the start. If it can't be taught in full from the start, then as soon as the parts are learned the athlete needs to be taught the whole. Also, when the part instruction is being used, it is important the athlete see the whole skill demonstrated so they understand the final product. This helps them mesh the parts into the whole skill[40].

Progression Teaching

Regardless of the teaching method used by the coach, the progression of skill introduction needs to be easy to difficult. Josef Drabik states that the skills don't want to be too easy to cause boredom and loss of interest, and not too difficult because of frustration. Drabik says coaches want to progress from known skills that are basic for a given sport, and gradually add more advanced information and new skills[41].

In teaching a new skill, it is best to start with simple skills. Simple skills are easier for athletes to mimic just by seeing the demonstration. "It is generally considered that 80% of learning takes place through what is seen"[42]. Basically, the athletes will learn simple skills by demonstration and imitation of what they have seen.

In terms of complex skills, the coach must be more creative to teach the athlete the intricacies of the skill. The first thing a coach must do is break down the complex skill into smaller tasks to assist athletes in learning the skill. An example of this method would be the part or part-whole method discussed earlier. Once the athlete understands and has learned the parts then the whole skill can be taught and mastered.

It is important to remember this approach can not be done generically to every athlete in terms of a particular skill; one skill may be simple for some and difficult for others.

Introducing a New Skill

There is a basic outline to how a skill should be introduced. This is not to say that if the skill is extremely simple the steps can not be skipped; although, for the sake of consistency, in your teaching of new skills it is wise to stay with the formula.

The basic formula for introducing a new skill is to **verbally introduce** the skill: Give the name and description of the skill. Also, give the application to the sport situation the skill would be used, if possible. The next thing is to **demonstrate** the skill to the athletes: During this time the coach makes sure the demonstration is accurate so the mental image of the athlete is correct. The coach will want to give relevant cues during this time.

The next stage is to allow for **practice time:** athletes should be given ample time to practice the skill with a partner or individually. During the practice time the coach or partners should be giving verbal cues and physical assistance if possible. Finally, the coach needs to give **Feedback** as to how the athletes performed the skill.

Organization of Athletes during Instruction

It will be important that the coach puts thought into how he/she will arrange the athletes during the introduction of a new skill. If the coach is dealing with a small group, it is not as big of a deal. If the coach is dealing with a large team or group of athletes, it will be important all athletes can see the coach in order to hear the introduction clearly, as well as see the demonstration.

The coach must also put thought into the space available for adequate practice of the skill. In small spaces, the coach will need to be creative with organizing athletes in a group setting.

The coach must be a good organizer if he/she wishes to have a smooth learning process take place.

Goal Setting

Goal setting is a well-known technique that is used commonly in and out of the sporting environment. Coaches should help athletes set goals for training (action goals that increase effort) and competition (outcome goals). Performance will increase with systematic goal-setting. Coaches and athletes should know that the goals can be modified and altered up or down at any time.

Goal setting helps an athlete focus their activities toward goal and increases effort in working towards a goal. We have all heard of the SMART acronym for goal setting. This states that goals should be specific, measurable, attainable, realistic, and timed.

Athletes should set a limited number of specific goals. Three short and long term goals can be set with the short-term goals being used to guide the long-term goals. The focus should be on positive goal setting (i.e. performing well, not avoiding mistakes). Over time, athletes should reflect on their written goals with regular feedback. Coaches should help athletes find a social support network that will help them towards their goals.

Block or Distributed Practice

Now that the skills have been taught and the appropriate methods have been used to teach the skill, the coach must practice these skills in a practice session. "The traditional way to schedule skill drills within a team-sport practice is to repeat the skill a number of times with no interruption by other activities"[43]. An example might be practicing the forehand groundstroke in tennis for ten to fifteen minutes without moving to another skill or segment of the practice. This is called **block practice**.

Block Practice

Block practice allows the athlete to concentrate on the skill with no interruptions. This seems to be the fastest way for the nervous system to develop a pattern for that skill. It is easy to see why using the block practice will allow athletes to show faster progress due to repeated efforts at the same skill.

It is easy to get caught up in the development of a particular skill and forget the skill is only effective if it can be used in a competition setting. This is why motor skill studies have shown that **distributed practice** prove to be more effective with getting results in competition, even though block practice has produced better results during practice[44].

Distributed Practice

With the distributed practice method, the skill would be practiced once the athlete moves onto something else. The athlete may perform the same skill in a different location or with another variable added to it, or an entirely new skill will be practiced.

Reasons for Effectiveness of Distributed Practice:

1. Better reactions to varying situation: In a game situation the athlete must be able to react and call upon his/her "bank" of skills to meet the demand. Distributed practices will better prepare the athlete for this.

2. A better learning situation: When athletes perform different skills in a sequence, they are able to compare the techniques and use this information to remember the skill longer. It is better for performance as well.

3. Athletes have better attention: Due to the changing of skills, the athlete must concentrate harder, thus improving the learning process. The same skill practiced over and over gets boring for athletes.

4. Applying the skill: As soon as the athletes are able to perform the skill, they can use the distributed practice to assimilate situation within a game. The coach can change the speed, distance, direction, sequence, or opposition that might occur in the game setting.[45]

The setting deceivers whether distributed or block practice will work best. In competitions that are ever changing, the distributed practice would seem to be most effective. In a situation that calls for control and organization at all times, the block practice may serve as the best method. Also, when a skill is first being taught, the block practice will allow for fewer distractions when the athlete is already somewhat overwhelmed by the new skill.

Communication

Many coaches feel communication may be the most important aspect of coaching athletes. If communication is effective, the athletes and coach can establish a mutual respect knowing the lines of communication are open, and the process by which the coach communicates skills to the athletes is meaningful.

Before communicating with his or her athletes the coach should ask the following questions: the information below is modified from; Sports Coach site -Effective Communication.

- Why does the coach want to communicate- reasons...
- Who is the audience they will communicate with
- What would be the best time and place to communicate
- What exactly is to be communicated

- How is the information going to be communicated[46]

Just like every other aspect of coaching the communication should be planned out in order to be effective.

Penny Werthner, in the "Canadian Journal for Women in Coaching", states in reagards to the importance of communication, "Why is it crucial for you, as a coach, to be able to communicate well? Simply stated, skilful communication is crucial because so much of what you do involves providing information to your athletes, your head coach or assistant coaches, your club, and your provincial or national sport federation, as well as exchanging information with a variety of individuals or groups such as sport scientists"[47].

Penny goes on to list what she feels is important in having effective communication skills. The following list is borrowed from the "Canadian Journal for Women in Coaching":

Effective Communication Skills

- Being assertive
- Communicating non-verbally
- Knowing how to listen well
- Speaking clearly and concisely
- Giving constructive feedback
- Being able to receive criticism
- Choosing the right words
- Resolving conflict effectively

Being Assertive

Being assertive with your athletes means you clearly state what it is you expect. There may be disagreement, however you maintain a positive attitude and remain firm in your declaration.

Non Verbal Communication

It is important athletes see you smile when they arrive at a practice or there is some sort of recognition by nodding. It is important to have an upbeat approach to your actions. Avoid rolling your eyes when an athlete says or does something you are unhappy with.

Listen Well

If a coach wants to earn the respect of his/her athletes he/she must be willing to listen. This lets the athlete know what he/she is saying is being heard. Listening will also give the coach valuable information about an athlete.

Speaking Clearly and Concisely

The coach needs to speak clearly to the athletes to avoid confusing statements. Say what needs to be said. Also, if the coach needs to speak with an athlete about something that may be unsettling to the athlete or possible cause conflict, the coach needs to state clearly what it is he/she is feeling. The coach doesn't want to express his/her displeasure with the athlete in ways that cause a defensive mode by the athlete. The coach needs to clearly and concisely elaborate to the athlete what needs to be discussed and why.

Constructive Feedback

The coach can make huge advances in the athlete's performance if feedback is given properly. Limit the comments that are non instructional. The athlete needs to know why he/she didn't do it right, or what will help him/her to do it right. The timing of the feedback is important as well. Sometimes feedback needs to wait until practice or a game is over, other times it is critical to give feedback immediately, especially when learning a new skill.

Accepting Criticism

The coach must be willing to accept constructive criticism from the athletes and coaches around him/her. This will give clues into how others feel about the coaching job. The coach must be willing to step back and evaluate what is being said. Many times coaches don't realize he/she is not doing a good job due to the fact he/she gets no feedback. The coach should ask the athletes to clearly state any positive or negative feedback. This will open the doors to communication and effective learning.

Choosing the Correct Words

Choosing the correct words or listening to the words your athletes are using will help in the communication process. Words such as "I" can be used to take ownership; it can also be construed as selfish and a non-team player. The words "always and never" should be used with extreme caution because things don't always occur or never occur. The word "you" must be used carefully so not to have an accusatory tone. The word "they" is used many times to describe how a few people are feeling or are acting, yet the word "they" does not clarifying who it really is. A coach should ask who. Both the coach and the athlete need to be careful using the word "but". It many times means a decision was already made or the person was not listening. Finally, the words "should and ought" can be construed as finger pointing if used incorrectly. The athlete will feel as though he/she is not doing things correctly if the coach is always saying you should or ought to do it this way instead. The coach needs to offer a suggestion by saying "maybe you can try it this way to see if it is more effective".

It is not easy to do, however the choice of words used with and around athletes needs to be selected carefully. It can set the tone in a positive or negative way. Many times the coach does not mean to be negative, but the choice of words made the suggestion come across that way. Also, coaches should educate their athletes on proper word selection if they want positive statements from the coach. This will help athletes in other areas of life as well.

Resolving Conflict

There is no doubt every coach will most likely encounter a conflict on the team. It may be between athlete(s) and athlete(s) or athlete(s) and coach (es). The first and foremost action needs to be on recognizing the issue and confronting it. The goal is to resolve the conflict without it becoming a big distraction. Many times the conflict will bring about issues that need to be resolved and may never have been noticed unless a conflict arose. The important thing a coach must avoid is allowing the conflict to become negative to the point where too much focus is given to it and the practice, or in some cases, the season is jeopardized because of it.

In order to resolve the conflict the coach and athletes must get to the core of the problem and discuss the issues. There may not be a total resolution to the problem, but it must be understood the conflict cannot disrupt the team or atmosphere around the team. The coach must help the individuals involved understand people will have conflict and can still coexist and remain friendly.

Communication is an on going process that must be nurtured to bring about the best in all parties. Athletes cannot be expected to be simple bystanders and not be allowed to express how they feel. The dictator method of coaching has been used for years and has proven to be successful in many programs. The issue lies with what did the athletes learn form this style. A coach must be willing to teach his/her athletes how communication will help athletes in all aspects of life, not just in practice.

Sport Learning – Coaching Styles & Methods

Developing a young athlete is not based solely on a given conditioning-coach's understanding of scientifically valid measures of motor stimulus, strength training or flexibility exercises. In fact, it could be argued, given all of the critical information contained in this textbook on exercise selection, methodology and sensitive period development, that successful coaches will be the ones who can teach and relay information to young athletes well, more so than the coach who merely reads and digests the scientific information offered via clinical research. The **science** of developing an athlete is centered in the particular technical information associated with pediatric-exercise science, whereas the **art** of developing a young athlete is based on a coach's ability to teach.

There are several styles of coaching that do not adequately serve to aid in a young athlete developing skill, yet are none-the-less common amongst North American coaches and trainers. An example of this would be the "command coach". Command coaches presume the young athlete is a submissive receiver of instruction. The instructions given and information offered moves in one direction only, from the coach to the athlete. Coaches who display this habit believe coaching success is based on how well the athlete can reproduce the skills as taught or demonstrated by the coach.

There are also various misappropriations relating to how young athletes actually learn:

1. **Mirrors:** Many coaches believe young athletes will learn by merely reflecting the actions and nature of their coach. In this example, the coach or trainer is the most important figure in the relationship in that the athlete is a reflection of him or her.

2. **Empty Buckets**: Many coaches make the mistake of assuming young athletes are akin to an empty bucket in that their heads will fill up with the information the coach or trainer offers.

3. **Sponges**: Much like the "empty bucket" notion, very often a coach or trainer will make the assumption that as he/she delivers the information, a given young athlete will soak it up unreservedly.

Unfortunately, optimal learning does not occur in any of these ways. These aforementioned theories fail on several levels:

- Individual differences among athletes' learning styles are not addressed.
- Varying levels of physical maturity and prior athletic experiences are not considered.
- Does not account for the needs or interests of each individual athlete.
- Fails to recognize "cognitive processes are important in learning physical skills."[48]

Recently, researchers have underscored the significance of both perception and decision-making as it relates to information processing and skill development. The focus has been on "how individuals learn to interpret information in the environment and use this to make effective decisions about movement execution"[49]. There appears to be three chronological phases in performance or execution: (a) perceiving (b) deciding (c) acting.

The Perceiving Phase

During this phase, an athlete is attempting to establish what is happening and distinguish what information is applicable or valid.

For example, a basketball player just received the ball and must now decipher a series of factors including the position of both teammates and opponents on the court, the players own position as it relates to the rest of the players, as well as the basket and the stage of the game in relation to the score. Proficient players are able to sort through the key information quickly and separate it from other stimulus.

The Deciding Phase

This phase involves the athlete deducing the most appropriate path of action to take. In the case of our basketball player, it would include the decision to pass, dribble or shoot and which pass, dribble or shooting action would be the most suitable given the situation. Clearly, proficient athletes are more effective and decisive decision-makers.

The Acting Phase

Neural signals are sent to enlist muscles to carry out the desired task with suitable timing and adroitness. Although this execution phase is clearly important to sporting success, it must be understood that it alone is not responsible for on field accomplishment. The two preceding phases serve essentially to set up this final stage—a fact that is often ignored by coaches and trainers who maintain misappropriated beliefs regarding how athletes learn.

These three phases are co-dependent and take place in a rapid sequential manner.

Teaching Tactics

A great deal of teaching and coaching within youth sports currently focuses on developing techniques and skills within practice time or structured lessons. This custom very often leaves little time to actually play the game—during which the application of technical lessons becomes a vehicle through which young athletes will most optimally learn. A solution to this was developed from the research of Rod Thorpe and David Bunker at Loughborough University, which sought to create "an alternative approach to games teaching and coaching that assisted players to learn the tactics and strategies of game play in tandem with technique development"[50]. The crux of their system is based on incorporating modified games into the practice times of young athletes. Within their approach, "games are modified to suit the developmental level of the player. Modifications are made to rules, playing area and equipment"[51]. These modifications are based on items such as physical maturity, cognitive capacity and experience. As a young athletes gains proficiency, this "game form" of instruction changes in order to challenge the players' tactical awareness, decision-making ability and technique implementation capacity. Essentially, technical skills are taught and eventually perfected within the margins of modified sport play rather than via drills and lessons. This methodology allows the young athlete to learn appropriate sporting skills while incorporating the critical *perceiving* and *deciding* phases of functional learning as outlined above.

Individual sports can be broken down into sub-groups and categorized by their key characteristics. Many sports for example, share common qualities even though they seem to have no relation:

Football, Soccer, Hockey, Basketball:

- Tactical trait of entering the oppositions territory
- Contained defensive tactics that serve to limit offensive movement
- The use of a goal or object on which to score

Tennis, Volleyball, Badminton:

- The notion of offering the ball so that their opponents cannot return it effectively
- Similar technical skills including ball (item) positioning and trajectory
- A commonality amongst all the players on the floor from a technical perspective (i.e. they all must serve and receive the ball)

Baseball, Softball, Cricket:

- Ability to make contact with the ball and drive it into open areas
- Fielders lining up tactically in order to prevent scoring

Coaches could create and employ modified alternatives to their respective sports with the main characteristics associated with the technical and tactical aspects of the game kept in mind. This is a much different methodology than merely progressing athletes through various drills during practice time, but has been shown to be more effective at developing the cognitive and physical relationship that exists in developing sporting proficiency.

Chapter Summary

Hopefully this chapter was able to enlighten the coach and help them realize coaching is not about blowing the whistle and schooling offense and defense. It is about establishing a learning environment based on the art and science of coaching. It is about being prepared so athletes have the best possible chance to succeed.

Being a coach necessitates understanding the population with whom the coaching will be done with. Coaching requires employing the proper teaching methods and styles, understanding what the needs are of the athletes according to the developmental stages, communicating with athletes effectively to induce greater learning, and about taking the role of developing athletes in other areas of life seriously.

Being a coach is a rewarding job. It is a job that will bring coaches heartache and elation. Coaching is teaching! It should be the wish of every coach to have his/sher athletes say "I learned a lot from my coach, and I am a better athlete and person because of him or her".

The IYCA encourages every coach to educate themselves so the decisions being made are in the best interest of the athletes. Remember, sport and fitness should be fun for all athletes but especially, young athletes!

References

[1] Robert, C. & Corcos, D. (1988)

[2] Drabik, J. (1996)

[3] Bompa, T. (2000)

[4] Bompa, T. (2000)

[5] Martens, R. & Seefeldt, V. (1979)

[6] Kentucky Youth Soccer Association (2005)

[7] Kentucky Youth Soccer Association (2005)

[8] Robert, C. & Corcos, D. (1988)

[9] Bompa, T. (2000)

[10] Smith, R. & Small, F. (1996)

[11] Orlick, T. & Botterill, C. (1975)

[12] Orlick, T. & Botterill, C. (1975)

[13] Yin, Z. & Moore, J. (2004)

[14] Sansone, R. & Sawyer, A. (2005)

[15] Pennington, B. (2005)

[16] Smith, R. & Small, F. (1996)

[17] Orlick, T. & Botterill, C. (1975)

[18] Dishion. T., et al. (2005)

[19] Thompson, J. (1995)

[20] Thompson, J. (2003)

[21] Thompson, J. (2003)

[22] Kentucky Youth Soccer Association (2005)

[23] Positive Coaching Alliance (2005)

[24] Positive Coaching Alliance (2005)

[25] Kilgore, L. et al. (2001)

[26] Rogers, J. (2000)

[27] Robert, C. & Corcos, D. (1988)

[28] Robert, C. & Corcos, D. (1988)

[29] Drabik, J. (1996)

[30] Drabik, J. (1996)

[31] Hoiland, E. (2004)

[32] Murray, B. (2005)

[33] Special Olympics Coaching Guide (2003)

[34] Robert, C. & Corcos, D. (1988)

[35] Special Olympics Coaching Guide (2003)

[36] Robert, C. & Corcos, D. (1988)

[37] Special Olympics Coaching Guide (2003)

[38] Reading Master Learning Systems

[39] Mackenzie, B. (2005)

[40] Robert, C. & Corcos, D. (1988)

[41] Drabik, J. (1996)

[42] Special Olympics Coaching Guide (2003)

[43] Physical Education Digest (1995)

[44] Physical Education Digest (1995)

[45] Physical Education Digest (1995)

[46] Physical Education Digest (1995)

[47] Werthner, P. (2001)

[48] Kirk, D. & MacPhail, A. (2000)

[49] Kirk, D. & MacPhail, A. (2000)

[50] Kirk, D. & MacPhail, A. (2000)

[51] Kirk, D. & MacPhail, A. (2000)

3

Motor Skill Development

Dr. Kwame Brown and Scott Colby

Athletic movement is often associated with sports. However this type of movement has a deeply conserved evolutionary purpose (these movement patterns were originally used to hunt, escape prey, and perform manual labor. For the young, these movements are often developed through environmental exploration. In developed countries, the impetus to explore the environment is often dampened due to the fact that the focus is luxury and convenience. This creates a situation in which children often enter into competitive sports (or recreational play, for that matter) with immature movement patterns, thus immediately creating a disconnection between ability and expectation. This can discourage further participation and there may be dire consequences for the child's self esteem. Additionally, little time is devoted to physical education in public schools. Many educators, not realizing that there is a very intimate connection betweeen motor skill and cognitive skill, erroneously concentrate solely on academic training for children. The results of this error, the IYCA and many developmental experts predict, will be disastrous for our society, precipitating billions of dollars in injury treatment, pain management, and lowered productivity in the very areas that have been designated as priority (technological advances, intellectual development). Additionally, where it was once thought that the brain and spinal cord were fully developed by the end of early childhood, we will present evidence here that athletically relevant skills like balance, agility and coordination that are controlled by the relationship between the CNS and the biomechanical constraints of each individual continue to develop through adolescence.

There are those who say that the development of motor skills cannot be helped; only hindered. While the general skill of running will appear naturally in the course of development, the maturity of the skill and the robustness of the skill certainly benefit from training. Without any instruction at all, there will be an extremely wide range of adaptations and maladaptations to both environment and individual physical characteristics. There are many children who certainly benefit from extra instruction. In fact, a study was conducted in Australia called the "Move it, Groove It" intervention[1]. This study showed that compared to schools which did not receive the intervention, which included instructional resources for teachers, and funds to purchase equipment, the children in schools receiving the intervention showed markedly greater improvement in 8 functional movements. These movements included running, jumping, kicking, throwing, hopping, catching, balancing, and side galloping. This result, coupled with many other studies outlined later in this chapter that show that instruction and most importantly type of instruction influence development of skills, warrants a discussion of the basic concepts behind and the normal progression of motor development

Additionally, the reader, whether he/she is a coach, teacher, therapist, physician, parent or trainer, must recognize the difference between talent and developmental course. Some children that appear to have less ability than others may simply be lagging behind in development. The practitioner also must realize that the ages given in any developmental course are median or mean ages and are meant to be considered with the error inherent in such measurements. We will discuss in this chapter the development of movement skills from the earliest attempts at environmental exploration through the development of the various forms of locomotion and followed by a discussion of more complicated motor patterns and sophisticated athletic movements.

Early Motor Development

Newborns

Newborn movements can be classified into two general categories: random or spontaneous movements and infantile reflexes[2]. Reflexes are thought to be the means through which the nervous system develops via a phenomenon called activity-dependent plasticity. Even before the infant can consciously explore his or her environment, these reflexes are a means by which the CNS can gather information.

Spontaneous Movements

An infant's first movement that occurs without any obvious stimulation is considered a spontaneous movement. Some examples are squirming, thrusting legs or arms, and stretching fingers or toes[3].

If an infant is laid on his back in a supine position, he will usually thrust his legs in a spontaneous fashion. Interestingly, though, researchers showed that this kicking is indeed not random. The kicking is actually performed in a rhythmical and coordinated fashion. The hips, knees and ankles actually move in cooperation with each other[4].

There are four phases to these kicks: a flexion phase, a pause, a forward extension phase, and a between-kick interval. The kicks resemble the positioning and timing of an adult step. The infants kick so that the joints move in unison and the flexors and extensors co-contract. By the end of their first year, the infants tend to move the hip, knee and ankle sequentially, rather than in unison, much like an adult step[4].

An infant's arm movements are well-coordinated extensions of the elbow, wrist and finger joints, however these movements are not as rhythmical as the leg kicking. These coordinated patterns resemble patterns that are observed in late voluntary movements[5, 6].

Infantile Reflexes

Reflexive movements are involuntary and occur in response to specific stimuli. There are three main categories of infantile reflexes, and they can be classified as primitive, postural and locomotor[4].

Primitive reflexes are present from birth until about month four. Primitive reflexes differ from spontaneous movements in three ways. 1) Primitive reflexes occur in response to specific stimuli[4]. 2) They are specific and localized[4]. 3) The same stimuli will yield the same reflex repeatedly[7].

Postural reactions, also known as gravity reflexes, help the infant to automatically maintain posture in a changing environment[8]. An example: keeping the infant's head upright to help keep the breathing passages open and helping the infant roll over to eventually attain an upright position. Most postural reactions occur after two months of age[4].

Locomotor reflexes, also known as moving in place, appear much earlier than the corresponding voluntary motor behavior. The three locomotor reflexes are swimming, crawling and stepping[3].

In typically developing infants, the infantile reflexes gradually show less of a specific response with time. Eventually you will not be able to stimulate these reflexes[2]. Sometimes, the pattern of appearance and disappearance of a reflex is used to study the development of an infant. Deviation from the typical pattern may signal a developmental problem. There are two ways that a deviation may show: 1) A reflex may be exhibited when the infant should not, or 2) the infant may not exhibit a reflex when they should[3].

Some causes of persistent infantile reflexes are[9]:

- Cerebral palsy
- Increased intracranial pressure
- Neurodegenerative disorders
- Central nervous system injury
- Spinal cord injury
- Anoxic injury
- Congenital central nervous system infection

Some causes of absent or delayed postural responses are[10]:

- Benign hypotonia
- Spinal Muscular atrophy
- Spina bifida
- Congenital neuropathy Brachial plexus injury
- Congenital Muscle disorders

However, remember that reflexive responses are extremely sensitive to environmental conditions, so some infants may be ahead or behind the typical appearance or disappearance of a reflex.

Motor Milestones

A motor milestone is a fundamental motor skill whose attainment is associated with the acquisition of later voluntary movements. For example, to walk, you must be able to stand; to stand, you must be able to hold your trunk upright; to hold your trunk upright, you must be able to hold your head erect. Each skill has a preceding milestone associated with it[4].

Here are some major motor milestones and the age at which they are normally attained[10]:

Motor Milestones	Average Age of Attainment
Head control	2 months
Rolls to spine	4 months
Maintains sitting	6-7 months
Rolls to prone	7 months
Creeps on all fours	10 months
Stands momentarily	10 months
Cruises (walks without support)	10 months
Walks independently	12-14 months
Begins to run	2 years
Walks up and down stairs	2 years
Runs well	3 years
Walks up stairs, alternating feet	3 years
Walks down stairs, alternating feet	4 years
Hops on one foot	4 years
Skips	5 years
Walks with mature adult gait	7 years

Because of the sequential nature of motor milestones, they may provide clues for trained professionals to evaluate an infant and child's neurological health. The association of persistent infantile reflexes and delayed ambulation in infants and children with cerebral palsy has been documented[10].

Studies have shown that the milestone sequence is fairly predictable in typically developing infants. And although there is some variation in the acquisition of milestones, if an infant is substantially delayed in several milestones, this may indicate some developmental problems[4].

Development of Human Locomotion

Locomotion is the act of moving from place to place, as defined by the American Heritage Dictionary. During childhood years, height, leg length and weight change as a child grows into adolescence. These variables may influence the rate of development of locomotion from individual to individual.

Locomotion on two feet is an upright, bipedal movement. Humans have a number of locomotor options: walking, running, skipping, hopping, galloping, marching, or jumping, to name a few. The term "gait" is used to describe a particular pattern of locomotion. Different situations may affect one's gait pattern, including an injury, such as a sprained ankle or pulled muscle, walking on an icy sidewalk, or walking up a hill[4].

The first voluntary locomotion that an infant experiences is creeping and crawling. Creeping is defined as moving from place to place while on your hands and knees, and crawling is moving from place to place on your hands, knees, chest and stomach[3].

Walking

Children typically begin to walk between ten and eighteen months. When they first begin to walk, they exhibit a wide base of support, with flat feet. There is normally some bowing of the legs, which are a little externally rotated for stability. There is the presence of a lumbar lordosis (arched back). The same gait characteristics are seen in boys and girls[11].

Normal gait is cyclic and can be divided into two phases—stance phase and swing phase—and these phases are divided into sub-phases. A gait cycle is defined as the foot-strike of one limb and the subsequent foot-strike of that same limb.

The duration of stance phase is about 60% of the gait cycle. It consists of heel strike (when the heel of the reference foot strikes the ground, midstance (when the foot is flat on the ground and the weight of the body is directly over the supporting limb), and toe-off (when only the big toe of the reference limb is in contact with the ground)[10].

The duration of swing phase is about 40% of the gait cycle. It consists of acceleration (when the foot is no longer in contact with the ground and the swinging limb catches up and passes the torso) and deceleration (when the movement of the limb slows down and the foot is positioned for heel strike[10].

Early Walking

Less than half of one year old children exhibit heel strike when they first learn to walk. These children land with a flat foot. They do not exhibit reciprocal arm swing (leg and opposite arm moving forward at the same time) and the arms are held in the "high guard" position for balance. Children at age one keep their hip joint externally rotated throughout the gait cycle, and the knees remain flexed. These children have a diminished single leg support time (the amount of time one leg is in contact with the ground). One year old children have a high cadence (180 steps/min), a slow walking speed and a short step length. These variables are directly related to the child's age and leg length. At twelve months, 95% of children can squat down to play on the floor without the aid of any support. The development of this squat is present from the beginning of walking[12].

By eighteen months, heel strike is seen in the majority of children, as they exhibit a heel strike to toe-off gait pattern (due to increase range of motion at the ankle); 70% have reciprocal arm swing. The base of support narrows somewhat but remains wider than in a mature gait pattern[12].

Development of Mature Gait in Childhood

By age two, children have a reduced anterior pelvic tilt, as well as a reduced abduction and external rotation of the hips. Almost 80% of two year old walkers exhibit reciprocal arm swing. Compared to older walkers, they have increased knee flexion in stance. The length of time that one limb supports body weight (single limb support) while the other limb swings forward increases, but is under 34%. Ninety percent of two year olds can walk on their toes[12].

About 90% of three year old walkers have reciprocal arm swing, and the duration of single limb stance is about 35%. The base of support is relatively similar to adults. Children still have increase knee flexion during stance, and slightly increased pelvic rotation, hip joint rotation and hip abduction. However, the pattern of joint angles throughout the gait cycle is the same as an adult's[11].

For children age seven, their cadence has decreased and step length and velocity has increased. However, these variables are still different from an adult's until adequate growth occurs. Duration of single limb stance is about 38%[12].

Changes in gait between early childhood and adult occur on an individual basis due to different variables (such as the rate of growth), so it is difficult to generalize specific development trends.

Assessment of Gait

A proper assessment of a child's gait should include the following[12]:

- The child's history: The age of the child, their past and present medical history, and the age that motor skills were achieved.
- The family history: Have the parents or siblings had any trouble walking? Has anyone in the immediate family been treated for any problems with their legs or the way they walk? Did anyone in the family wear leg braces, corrective footwear or orthotics, or have surgery as a child.

- An observation of the child's gait noting whether:

- Heel strike is present or whether the child is walking flat-footed or up on their toes.

- Reciprocal arm swing is present

- The child can squat to play

- The child has excessive knee flexion during stance

- The walk is symmetrical, meaning the child moves his left and right sides equally.

- The child falls, and if so, are the falls occurring more or less frequently.

Common Developmental Orthopedic Concerns in Walking

There are some common pathologies that cause concern for parents and can alter a child's gait pattern[12].

"Toe walking": Some children learn to walk with a toe-walking pattern instead of with a flat foot. About 30% have a family history of toe-walking. Toe walking can be caused by cerebral palsy. Idiopathic (having no known specific cause) toe walking usually resolves sometime during childhood.

"Flat feet": This is a condition where the arch or instep of the foot collapses and comes in contact with the ground. Persistent flat feet after age six will not improve with exercise or with special orthotics or shoes.

"Knock Knees": This is an outward angulation of the lower legs; such when the knees are touching, the ankles are separated. This posture usually corrects by the age of seven or eight years (with knees together, ankles should just touch), although the knock-kneed posture continues into adulthood for some people.

In-Toed Gait can be caused by an anatomical variation at one of three levels: the hips, legs or feet. In toeing can be caused by femoral anteversion; internal tibial torsion; and problems of the foot including metatarsus adductus, clubfoot and dynamic in toeing.

If postures such as in-toed gait, knock knees and flat feet persist beyond the normal range and are painful, then the child should be referred to the appropriate clinician for a more comprehensive assessment[13].

General Motor Skills (Early Childhood through Adolescence)

Proprioception / Kinesthetic Awareness

Proprioception is an often misunderstood phenomenon, so we will define it here. Proprioception is not only the sense of where the limbs are in space, but also includes the regulation of the amount and velocity of the force applied to a movement. As one might imagine, there are many different systems involved in proprioception. Joint receptors, muscle spindles, and Golgi Tendon Organs are all peripheral receptors that act as sensors in the joints, muscles and tendons and provide information about muscle force and tension, as well as direction. Additionally, the vestibular (orientation) and visual systems also function in proprioception in different ways depending on what task is being performed. Finally, different parts of the brain and spinal cord are responsible for processing this type of information, specifically the cerebellum, the basal ganglia, the spinal cord, and parts of the motor cortex. Instead of exploring the process of proprioception fully, which is beyond the scope of this text, we will instead discuss here two of the major "tasks" of the proprioceptive system and how development affects these tasks. These two tasks are what we commonly refer to as "balance", and visuomotor coordination (the ability to process and use visual information in planning and executing movements). These characteristics have been directly observed and measured during development, and inferences about proprioception can be made from this information. The development of proprioception will also certainly influence the ability of the child to acquire and assimilate the movement patterns discussed above.

Balance

As balance is essential to virtually all athletic activities, it is imperative that we have some idea of how balance develops and the systems involved in balancing in order to develop proper training methods. We must also take care to introduce these training methods during the sensitive periods in development, or simply put, introduce them at a time when the child is able to take advantage of them. Static balance is defined (in a simple view) as maintaining the center of gravity in a stable position. Dynamic balance, then, consists of maintaining stability and body control between segments when the center of gravity (COG) is shifting. One must adjust the position of body segments and the tone of muscles very quickly in order to maintain the COG within the base of support. Many factors influence the ability to balance, including biomechanical constraints (proportionality, musculotendinous strength), the peripheral and central nervous system, the cognitive abilities of the individuals, and anthropometric characteristics (size, body composition). There are 2 general types of balance static (standing still) and dynamic (maintaining control during movement). Not only are the tasks different, but so are the mechanisms used by the CNS to affect each. For static balance, we tend to use a "closed loop" system, which denotes the involvement of ascending integrated sensory information from the visual, vestibular and proprioceptive systems. In this kind of system, constant adjustments are made using the information flow from sensory systems. The CNS acts on this information. However, due to the nature of this communication in both directions, this is slower compared to the "open-loop" system used in dynamic balance. In an open-loop system, a predetermined motor program is elicited in response to an internal decision. Corrective movements are largely ballistic in nature. If one considers this, it makes sense. During dynamic movement, actions must be executed very quickly. If the information flow is largely in one direction instead of having to go through sensory loops, actions can be executed more quickly. In support of this theory, Hatzitaki et al. found that during a dynamic balance task, the amplitude of the adjustment was smaller (more successful) with shorter reaction times[13]. Dynamic and static balance both improve from early childhood through adolescence[14, 15].

Dynamic

The ability to balance while the body is in motion improves throughout development. This improvement likely coincides with the development of the nervous system and the resulting "strategy" that the child's neuromechanical systems (a term used to describe the relationship between the nervous system and the structures of the body) will employ to achieve that balance. In other words, a toddler will not achieve balance in the same way that an older child or an adolescent will. The role of the CNS during a movement is to determine the degrees of freedom (which joints are to be released to rotate in certain directions and which are to be "tied together"). This is especially important with respect to postural stability. Dynamic balance has been described as the need to strike a compromise between the propulsion of the body (destabilization), and the need to maintain stability with respect to the center of mass[16].

In a recent study, both age and task difficulty influenced the level of balance control, measured by amplitude of excursion of the center of pressure (COP) on a force plate when performing reaching tasks. Younger children (4-6 year olds) were not able to reach as far in relation to their body size, and also exhibited quite a bit of variability in the way that they moved. Simply put, this can be interpreted as a period during which the neuromechanical systems are undergoing a great deal of change. Children, in their exploration of the environment, tend to use trial and error at first to select the most efficient strategy for movements. This is not something that they necessarily do consciously, but this phenomenon is observed in all primates. Older kids (aged 10-11) performed similar to adults on less difficult tasks, but performed more like younger children (4-6) on more difficult tasks[17]. This has implications not only for development, showing that older children are still developing, but also for testing procedures. If the task is not difficult enough, the child may look like a mature adult and one may mistakenly assume that the system in question is fully developed.

Balance during locomotion with respect to control by the CNS was reviewed recently by Assaiante et. al.[18]. An important result of this review was an overall picture of how the developing individual progresses with respect to the control of degrees of freedom by ascending and descending input. Assaiante outlined four periods in the developmental course of posturokinetic organization. The first, at infancy, is a descending (feedforward) strategy, denoting a preset program, in which babies develop postural responses "along a cephalocaudal gradient". This means that postural control is first developed proximally in the neck muscles, followed by the trunk and the distal muscles in the legs and arms. This makes sense given that in animals during development, it is well known that the descending pathways from the brain descend through the spinal cord early in development and then continue to refine their connections in the spinal cord in a cephalocaudal manner[19,20]. This also stands to reason from an evolutionary standpoint given the obvious importance of protecting the brain and internal organs as compared to the limbs. Head stabilization is performed very early in development in real time by activating the neck muscles first, followed by the axial muscles and the limbs. This is referred to as an "articulated" operation. Later in early childhood (second stage), coincident with the achievement of upright stance, the body begins to operate "en bloc" in large units, possibly in an effort to reduce the degrees of freedom as the interactions with the environment become more complex and the balance tasks become more dynamic in nature[36]. The observer may see the child move as if the head is "strapped down" to the trunk; they may move largely as a single unit. This strategy may also be due to the disproportionate size of the head in toddlers. At this stage, pelvic stability develops before the ability to control the head and shoulders. This denotes a reversal in the direction of development to cephalocaudal. The sensory information from the feet and the contact with the ground now becomes an important way to gather information about the environment. Also, the pelvis functions to limit lateral instability, again in an attempt to limit degrees of freedom. These efforts to limit degrees of freedom may also have much to do with muscular strength. Blocking the joints may compensate for this lack of strength. At around 7 years of age through adolescence, we return to a strategy involving separate articulation of the head and trunk, and descending control (feedforward) becomes more important. During young adolescence and adulthood, there is further refinement of the articulation of the neck. This is likely what gives adult athletes the ability to perform actions like looking around for the ball while running a pass pattern. Younger players tend to turn the whole body, or perform the neck turn inefficiently.

Static

Static balance, like dynamic balance, continues to develop through adolescence. Largo et al. found that timed performance on a static balance task where the subjects were required to choose one leg and stand on it as long as possible continued to improve from 5 years old to 18 years old[21]. Young children at around 4-6 years of age begin to switch from a ballistic method of control to one of sensory guidance[22]. The child tends to use more proprioceptive information (information concerning orientation of the limb in space, velocity and direction of movement) gained from the peripheral nervous system to create movement strategies. This trend reaches its peak at around 8 years, as children become better at integrating sensory information from the visual, vestibular and proprioceptive pathways for postural control in static balancing tasks. This probably coincides with maturation in the connections of the motor control centers such as the basal ganglia and cerebellum and motor cortex with the spinal cord. At this age, the velocity of postural sway has largely decreased to adult levels during standing. However, with a more complex task such as the Romberg stance (standing one foot in front of the other heel to toe with the eyes closed), 8 year olds still have trouble maintaining static posture[23]. The velocity of postural sway goes back up as the sensory integration is still not complete. So, while the major transitional period for basic static postural control appears to be between ages four and eight, more complex balance tasks show that this use of sensory information to control postural sway is still being refined into late childhood and adolescence.

Visuomotor ability

Visuomotor ability is the ability of the child to integrate visual information and the perception of that information into the planning and execution of movements. Visual representation is not as well developed in prepubertal children. Children develop between the ages of six and eleven the ability to use bidirectional representations of the outside world, replacing the unidirectional representations of early childhood[23]. Additionally, during a visuomotor coordination learning task where a path was to be followed with a pen, children had more irregular paths than adults. The largest directional bias in movement was observed at around eight years of age, followed by a decrease in this bias by eleven. This, in agreement with the aforementioned study, signifies that children at eight years old are beginning to make a transition toward the integration of proprioceptive information and visual information, and that young children not as capable as adults in integrating proprioception with visual information. However, young children (under eleven) are trainable with continuous visual feedback about mistakes. Children at six years old did not improve direction of movement, but did decrease error of movement (increased regularity)[24]. Thus, mirrors and video feedback can be very effective tools in teaching children movements. As the internal representation of the motor system will not yet be fully developed in young children, especially before the age of eight, patience will be required on the part of the practitioner. Young children may be less able to form complex representations of the outside world. This may in turn influence the level of kinesthetic awareness. This is yet another reason that in tasks and practice for most young children, we should avoid undue complexities in environment. This may be especially true with regard to the construct within which the child is working. For example, young children on the tennis court may be able to learn proper volley technique, but certainly the approach shot with the transition to net, where the player must maintain a sense of where the possible return may go, and where the other player is may be a bit complicated to introduce at this age. Younger children (usually before the age of eight) have with certain skills such as trouble catching balls traveling with a severe arc, as well. Obviously, children at this age should be taught proper catching techniques by having balls thrown with a straight or slightly curved trajectory. Thus, although these kinds of skills are trainable, it is important not to introduce complex tasks too early, as the systems involved in the desired integrative task may not be developed fully enough to benefit from the practice.

Development of Athletic Movements

Influencing Factors

Gallahue, in his textbook Understanding Motor Development, names maturation, physical development, heredity, environmental experience (stimulation, deprivation) as the major influencers in the acquiring of the fundamental movement skills. Butterfield and Loovis also found that performance of the mature pattern was significantly related to gender. They postulated that, since sports participation appeared to be equal, factors such as expectations from coaches, training, and opportunities to practice would influence the development of general athletic skills. One other possible factor is the importance of sports in the lives of young girls vs. boys. Girls appear to "catch up" by grade 8 in many ballistic skills with respect to the maturity of pattern. We will outline just a few of the basic athletic movements that children must develop to become competent athletes in order to introduce the reader to issues involved in the development of movement patterns in children, and especially the major influences on this development. More detail on the subject will be found in David Gallahue's text, Understanding Motor Development[16], Haywood and Getchell's text[4] as well as Payne and Isaacs' text on human motor development[25].

Running

Unlike walking, running has no double support phase (where both feet are in contact with the ground simultaneously). In fact, in running the double support phase is replaced by a flight phase, where no feet are in contact with the ground. Children usually begin to run about six to nine months after they begin to walk[26]. When a child first learns to run, he may adopt a wide base of support (for balance), a flat footed landing, knee extension at mid support, and a high arm guard position, also for balance. The arms may also swing out to the side. The child may try to make the movement simpler by eliminating arm swing. As they become more experienced and have better balance, they will take on the more natural running pattern.

Characteristics of Running at an Early Age

Initial Stage:

The beginning runner has limited range of motion at the knee. As the child pushes his foot off the ground, the knee does not fully extend. As the swinging leg comes forward, the thigh moves with enough acceleration so that the knee bends, but not enough to allow the thigh to reach a level parallel to the ground. Therefore, the range of motion at the knee is limited and the stride length is short in early runners[4,16,26].

The arms of an early runner extend at the elbow, which is a wasteful position. They also swing across the body rather than driving forward and back. This is probably to assist in balance, given the immaturity of trunk control at this stage, but is an inefficient running pattern. One must understand that this running pattern likely results not only from the immaturity of the nervous system, but also from the biomechanical constraints of the young child[4].

Influences in Early Running:

Lower limb strength is a variable that influences early running because of the flight phase – the toddler must have enough strength in each leg to lift themselves off the ground[27].

As children grow, their height, weight and leg length increases, as will strength, balance and coordination. This will usually result in an increase in stride length, running speed, and the amount of time in flight phase[4].

Proficient Running:

Proficient running requires an optimal and efficient use of movement patterns. The following are some developmental changes needed for beginning runners to increase performance[4].

- An increase in stride length which seems to indicate that the runner is applying greater force and the knee of the trailing limb is fully extended at push off. The heel is tucked close to the glutes, and the thigh swings through with greater acceleration, becoming parallel to the ground.

- Any lateral leg movement is eliminated and forces are kept in the forward-backward plane of motion. This makes the running pattern more efficient.

- The foot strikes the ground heel first, and then forefoot or it strikes the ground in a flatfoot position.

- Out-toeing is eliminated, and the base of support narrows.

- Support leg knee flexion is apparent as the body weight shifts over the leg.

- The trunk leans slightly anteriorly, and trunk rotatory strength increases which allows for an increase in stride length and a more efficient arm-leg opposition.

- The arms swing forward and backwards and move in opposition to the legs while the elbows remain at nearly 90 degrees.

Vertical and Horizontal Jumping

Initial Stage:

Jumping in young children is marked by inconsistent preparation and positioning, as well as difficulty in taking off from both feet at once. Also, children at this stage exhibit poor integrated body extension, the head tends to stay down. This characteristic of early jumping is possibly due to an inability to use peripheral visual cues, and lack of coordination of arms with the movement. Speculatively, the child may tend to look down in an effort to gain information about the body parts involved in jumping since they have trouble referencing the environment around them.   Alternatively, the head is larger in proportion to the body at this age and this may make it difficult to control the head when moving quickly. Young children will also have trouble exploding off the ground due to lack of muscular strength and extension.

By age three, children can change the angle of their trunk at takeoff to make either a horizontal or vertical jump[28], but young jumpers still usually keep the trunk too erect during the horizontal jump. This is in opposition to the tendency of the young child to pitch forward too far on the vertical jump. What is going on here? In very young children, the head is disproportionately large compared to the rest of the body. Therefore, there may be a need for the head to oppose the desired movement so as to maintain equilibrium. This, in combination with the lack of muscular strength in the trunk and limbs, causes children to functionally "strap" the head and neck to the trunk.

Intermediate Stage:

As the child continues to develop, the practitioner will observe knee flexion past 90 degrees, and an exaggerated forward lean on the vertical jump. The child is beginning to understand how to produce power but does so inefficiently. Now, one can observe the take off from both feet. Yet, the entire body still does not extend fully. While the arms attempt to aid in explosion from the ground, this pattern is disorganized as well. There is significant horizontal displacement during the vertical jump, possibly due to excess body lean and lack of extension.

Mature Jumping:

A mature jumping pattern will usually be observed in boys at approximately nine to ten years of age, and in girls at age ten to eleven[26]. This mature pattern will depend, as always, on the strength to body mass ratio, active range of motion, developmental stage, and experience / exposure to athletic activity.

A proficient jumper has the following characteristics:

- They stand in a preparatory crouch to stretch muscles and allow the legs to apply maximal force as they use a forceful "triple" extension (hip-knee-ankle) to take off.
- They take off for a horizontal jump with their heels coming off the ground, and both feet leaving the ground at the same time.
- They extend their arms backward and initiate take-off with a forward arm swing to a position overhead.

A proficient **vertical jumper** has the following characteristics:

- They direct force downward and extend their body throughout the flight of the jump. If they are reaching or striking an object overhead, the dominant arm reaches up and the opposite arm swings down.
- They tilt the shoulders laterally to increase the height of the jump.
- They keep the trunk mainly upright throughout the duration of the jump.
- They flex the hip, knees and ankles upon landing to absorb force.
- They have an upward head tilt with eyes on target, suggesting an increased ability to integrate proprioceptive information into the movement

A proficient **horizontal (broad) jumper** has the following characteristics:

- They direct force downward and back. They begin takeoff with their heels leaving the ground before their knees extend. The trunk may slightly lean forward.
- They flex the knees during the flight phase of the jump and bring the thighs forward until they are parallel to the ground.
- They swing the lower legs forward in preparation for a two footed symmetrical landing.
- Their trunk comes forward.
- They flex the knees and ankles upon landing to absorb force.

Throwing

Initial Stage:

Initially, the child will throw from the elbow, and the arm stays in front of elbow (pushing throw). The fingers will be spread at release and the follow-through is down and forward. The trunk stays perpendicular to target (little to no rotation) and the body weight is on the rear leg. The feet remain stationary (no steps), but an associated shuffling movement may occur.

Intermediate Stage:

As the child continues to grow and increase coordination skills, the practitioner will observe a neutral elbow flexion with the object held behind the head. The arm is swung forward over the shoulder. The trunk and shoulders rotate toward throwing side with the trunk flexing forward and a forward shift of weight with the throw. The child at this intermediate stage steps forward with ipsilateral leg.

Mature Throwing:

A mature throwing pattern will often be seen in boys by age six and a half to eight. In girls, this skill is usually mature by about age eight or nine. This skill in particular is greatly influenced by the amount of experience and proper instruction. Boys and girls who play baseball early in life, for example, will usually be proficient throwers at around the same age.

- The arm will swing backward during preparation, with the nondominant elbow raised for balance, and the weight is on the rear foot.
- The throwing elbow will move forward as it extends. Also, the forearm will pronate during the throw.
- Also, there is a definitive rotation toward throwing side, through hips, legs, spine, and shoulders
- As the throw is executed, there will be a deliberate step with the contralateral foot.

Influences in the maturation of throwing skill

There are several factors influencing the development of a mature throwing pattern and proficient skill, including instruction, types of instructional cues received, ball size used in training. Factors influencing performance with respect to distance include not only technical proficiency, but also body mass, forearm length (lever arm), and shoulder to hip ratio (torque production).

Especially important in achieving a mature throwing pattern is not only whether the child receives instruction[29,30], but what kind of instruction they receive. Hilda Fronske and Connie Blakemore, in 1997, showed that 3 specific verbal cues when giving instruction to 3rd-5th grade students over the course of a week improved not only the throwing pattern, but also the product (in this case distance). The three instructional cues (after further revision to improve effectiveness) were:

1) Take a long step toward the target with the opposite foot of your throwing arm;

2) Take your arm straight down, then stretch it way back to makes an "L" with the arm (keep the ball away from your head)

3) Watch the target and release the ball when you see your fingers[31].

When given these cues over the course of a week, children given instruction improved their throwing distance an average of 6 feet, compared with 4 inches improvement for the control group over the same period. It is important to note that this result was obtained over a short time, as it has also been shown that declarative (conscious verbal) knowledge of throwing technique is strong indicator of throwing ability (Payne and Isaacs). Additionally important, as with all object manipulation activities such as the jump shot, ball catching, and passing, the ability to achieve a mature ball-throwing pattern will be influenced by the size of the ball. This has been shown through research studies (Burton, Greer), and should be quite obvious, since a ball that is to large for the hand will not allow the child the ability to grip the ball correctly or produce the right motion. Additionally, a ball that is too heavy could be injurious to a young child when attempting to learn. Gender differences are also noted when considering throwing performance; girls tend to achieve a mature pattern later than boys and tend not to throw the ball as great a distance. However, the likely reasons for this should be noted. Certainly, throwing distance will be heavily influenced by leg and arm mass, as well as by other anthropometric features. However, the expression of a mature throwing pattern is likely affected greatly by sports participation. Unfortunately, young girls are still not encouraged as much as boys to pursue sports. This has been found to be a major factor in throwing performance, especially with respect to the father directing the young girl away from sports. Surely, this phenomenon has improved in the last few years, but still exists.

Catching

Initial Stage:

Initially, when children are attempting to catch, there are features of the immature pattern that stem not only from lack of muscular strength and coordination, but also lack of fine motor control and presence of fear. Avoidance reactions may have been learned at this point, maybe not; the specialist should concentrate on building confidence in this case. The arms are extended and held in front of body in preparation with the forearm supinated (palms up). Body movement is limited until after contact. The body is used to trap the object instead of using the hands to catch, and the fingers are extended (little use of hands).

Intermediate stage

Further development of catching will show that the avoidance response may have dissolved into just eyes closing at contact. The elbows are held at the sides and flexed to 90 degrees. The child may attempt to catch with the hands, but with a low success rate may revert back to body trapping. The hands are now held in opposition to each other (neutral thumbs up). At contact the hands will try to squeeze, but this is poorly timed.

Mature Catching:

- There is no avoidance response. The eyes track the object into the hands.

- The arms are relaxed at the sides, and the forearms held in front in preparation.

- Now, the arms give on contact, while the hands and fingers grasp the object (well timed and simultaneous). This is what coaches refer to when they say "soft hands".

Influences in the maturation of catching skill

There is quite a bit to say concerning the environmental factors which influence ball-catching ability. Among them are size and weight of the object being caught, prior experience, skill of the thrower (an obvious but often overlooked fact), developmental stage, and visual acuity.

Skipping

Initial Stage:

Early in life, when children begin to skip, one can see a one-footed; deliberate step-hop. Sometimes, the practitioner will also see double hopping or stepping. The stepping is usually exaggerated. There is no use of the arms, and the action is not smooth, but segmented, or "jerky"[16,26].

Intermediate Stage:

As the child continues to develop the ability to react to the ground and properly execute motor patterns, the step and hop will become more coordinated. There is now a rhythmical (maybe reciprocal) use of arms. However, there is often and exaggerated vertical lift on hop, and a flat-footed landing.

Mature skipping:

- The young athlete now executes a rhythmical, smooth weight transfer
- The rhythmical arm swing is now used mainly to aid in explosion.
- Now the exaggerated hop is a more controlled, efficient low vertical lift.
- The mature youth now lands on ball of foot first, using the stretch-shortening cycle to effect the ballistic movement.

Sliding (or shuffling)

Initial Stage:

A child during the toddler stage will usually exhibit an arrhythmical pattern when sliding. At this age, the feet will often cross due to and inability of the child to push off forcefully. There is also flexion of the trailing leg during the flight phase. Foot contact is heel to toe, and the arms are not used in any meaningful way (for balance or to create momentum)[16,26].

Intermediate Stage:

During early to middle childhood, the child will exhibit features of improved coordination. They will increase the tempo, and while the trailing leg may lead during flight, it lands adjacent to the lead leg. The arms will begin to function in aiding balance. However, one can observe an exaggerated vertical lift (as in skipping), and the pattern will appear choppy and stiff.

Mature sliding:

- There now exists a smooth action with a moderate pace.
- The trailing leg lands adjacent to the lead.
- Both knees will be flexed during flight
- Now the center of mass is kept low during the movement without changing the pattern, and the young athlete is able to stay on the balls of the feet.
- The arms are no longer needed for balance and can be used to create momentum.

Kicking

Initial Stage:

Early in the life span, movements will be restricted to the kicking action alone (all leg). The trunk will remain erect, and the arms are used to maintain balance only. There is little backswing or follow through with the kick, and the motion is more of a push than a strike[16,26].

Intermediate Stage:

As one enters the elementary years, one should see a preparatory backswing; the kicking leg will remain bent. Although there is more of a follow-through, the child will only use the knee to follow through. This could stem from the difficulties encountered at this age in achieving dynamic balance in single support. The child at this stage may also take steps toward the ball, though these steps will be choppy and poorly timed.

Mature kicking:

- The arms will swing reciprocally during the kicking action as a result of rotary trunk involvement.
- The kick, instead of being initiated at the knee, is now powered through the hip.
- The trunk will flex during the follow-through, and the support leg will bend slightly at contact.
- Follow through is high and the support foot will rise to the toes and may actually leave the ground as a result of the forceful swing.
- The approach to the ball is either via several small steps or from a leap.

Here we have summarized some of the basic athletic movements and the likely developmental course. It is important to recognize that these patterns will no hold true for every child, and that the features of each stage will not always occur in parallel. This information is meant to be a general guideline for the practitioner to use in recognizing possible weaknesses in the child (ren) under his or her charge. The professional is cautioned to take care in attributing a perceived weakness or deficit to a specific cause and is advised to consult with the parent/guardian, and a qualified therapist or physician in the event that a profound deficit is observed.

Special Populations

We will review here some difficulties one may encounter when training children with mild disorders. This is just an introduction into three commonly encountered exceptionalities that a coach or trainer may have to deal with in an athletic setting. A more complete manual addressing special populations in athletic environments will be forthcoming from the IYCA.

"Clumsy" Children (Developmental Coordination Disorder)

Children with developmental coordination disorder may be diagnosed with one or more of the following: developmental dyspraxia (impaired organization of movement), minimal cerebral dysfunction, or deficits in sensory integration (the ability to use sensory information to solve problems and plan actions). It is estimated that as much as 6% of children in the U.S. between five and eleven years of age exhibit signs of this disorder[32]. It is evident that children with developmental coordination disorder[33], as assessed by the Movement ABC[34], are less adept at tasks that require proprioceptive input[35]. Children with this disorder will often become frustrated and avoid activities that involve motor skills, exacerbating the problem. If a trainer or a coach suspects that a child has some variation of this disorder, the parents should be notified, and the child should be assessed by a physical therapist.

The practitioner must work closely with parents in communicating to them that their child will need specialized attention, and will need to work through these problems. Additionally, as with very young children, the tasks should be simple initially to build confidence through multiple successes. The environment for training should be non-competitive due to already low self esteem, and the emphasis should be on enjoyment of activities. Many times, allowing the child to participate in designing the training environment/program can be beneficial.

Attention Deficit / Hyperactivity Disorder (ADHD)

Most people in today's society are aware of ADHD and the behavioral problems, as well as cognitive difficulties that accompany the disorder. However, few are informed of the physical motor deficits in children who suffer from this problem. A child with ADHD will likely have difficulty with sensory integration, proprioception (spatial knowledge of ones body) and establishment of limb dominance.

When training children with ADHD, it is best to give instructions step-by-step at first, rather than give multiple instructions all at once.

One thing that the practitioner can try is to increase slowly the number of steps instructed at a time. This should be done gradually. Training with children who suffer from ADHD is usually best accomplished in one-on-one situations, due to the tendency of the group to distract.

Deaf Children

Deaf children may have overall deficits in balance, as well as overall motor skill when compared to children of the same age[36, 37]. The practitioner must remain aware when working with the deaf child who has no other obvious deficits, that deafness itself is associated with a developmental delay in the acquisition of skills involving proprioception. This shows how important sensory integration is. If an individual is missing important information, such as that provided by auditory, visual or tactile stimuli, then sensory integration will be less efficient.

Conclusion

We have talked about some of the major movement skills that a child will assimilate during the course of normal development, and also some of the clues that the practitioner can use to assess whether a child is acquiring the proper movement patterns. We also have discussed some possible reasons why a child would not have acquired these skills, such as inactivity (deprivation) and developmental disorders. The practitioner must learn through a careful assessment and experience to differentiate between the normal range of abilities expected to be present in the normal, healthy population and when a child is truly developmentally delayed. Additionally, as mentioned in the introduction, many coaches and practitioners mistakenly identify a child as untalented when the child may simply be lagging behind in development. We also discussed briefly the societal influences that are so pivotal today in determining the course of development for children. Parents, educators, and practitioners alike must encourage children to engage in activities that will stimulate them to explore the environment and acquire these basic movements. These activities can include self-directed physical play, school sanctioned physical education, organized sports, outdoor activities such as hiking, surfing, skateboarding, etc. When it is recognized that a child has a developmental exceptionality, it is an imperative that a professional steps in and addresses these problems.

The practitioner is also encouraged to remain abreast of the current research and engage in regular discourse with other professionals in order to maintain the flow of information. If a practitioner is not well versed in dealing with the problem, he / she should seek help from someone qualified to address the particular disorder.

"Knowledge comes by eyes always open and working hands, and there is no knowledge that is not power." Jeremy Taylor.

References

[1] Van Beurden, E., et al. (2003)

[2] Clark, JE (1989)

[3] Haywood, KM. & Getchell, N. (2001)

[4] Thelen, E. (1995)

[5] Thelen, E. (1981)

[6] Thelen, E. (1987)

[7] McGraw, MB. (1963)

[8] Peiper, A. (1963)

[9] Keen, M. (1995)

[10] Molner, G. (1992)

[11] Sutherland, D., et. al.(1988)

[12] Williams, P. (1982)

[13] Hatzitaki,, V., et al. (2002)

[14] Williams, H. (1983)

[15] Gallahue, D. (1989)

[16] Winter, D. (1990)

[17] Streepey, J.W. & Angulo-Kinzler, R.M. (2002)

[18] Assaiante, C. (1998)

[19] Howland, DR. et al. (1995)

[20] Donatelle, J. (1977)

[21] Largo, R.H., et al. (2001)

[22] Riach, C. & Starkes, J. (1994)

[23] Ferrel, C., et al. (2001)

[24] Fayt, C., et al. (1993)

[25] Payne, V. (2002)

[26] Whitall, J. & Getchell, N. (1995)

[27] Whitall, J. & Clark, J.E. (1994)

[28] Clark, J.E., Phillips, S.J. & Petersen, R. (1989)

[29] Halverson, L.E., Robertson, M.A., Safrit M.J. & Roberts, T.W. (1977)

[30] Halverson, L.E. & Roberton, M.A. (1979)

[31] Fronske, H. & Blakemore, C. (1997)

[32] Cratt, BJ. (1995)

[33] Cantell, M., Smyth, M., & Ahonen, T. (1994)

[34] Henderson, S. & Sudgen, D. (1992)

[35] Smyth, M, & Mason, U. (1998)

[36] Wiegersma, P. & Van der Velde, A. (1983)

[37] Gayle, G.W. & Pohlman. R.L. (1990)

4

Speed Training and Movement Economy

Lee Taft

Regardless of age, speed training is probably the most fascinating component of sports. When an athlete displays speed on the playing field, it is eye catching to the spectators. Speed is known to change the outcome of a game in a single play. In the younger athlete, speed can be more impressive due to a lack of tactics used by the opponents to combat speed. Whether or no the speed is from the legs of a kickoff returnee in football, the arm of a major league pitcher, the feet of soccer player, or the untouchable serve of a tennis player, it impresses us all.

When looking at speed as it translates to most sporting events, it is seen to take place in a multitude of directions and actions, yet the 40 yard dash and the 100 meter dash are for ever seen as the standard of speed in sports.

In this chapter, speed will be treated for what it really is: a skill. This concept is ever so important to grasp as it relates to young athletes, especially pre-adolescents. Although the top-end linear speed needed to perform well in the 40 and 100 is used less often in most court, field, and other sports, it will be the foundation from which speed technique is taught. All young athletes should be taught how to run in a linear direction properly, as it is the foundation for multidirectional speed.

In a later section of this chapter, the developmental stages will be discussed in regard to speed training, but for the purpose of laying the foundation for speed development through proper technique, young athletes generally develop the capabilities for speed around the age of seven. During this stage, the most basic techniques that make running speed efficient should be the focus; having said that, the coming section on linear speed will outline in detail the phases of speed, and the fundamental mechanics that allow speed to become effortless. This next section will be the "101 of speed training". After this section there should be no doubt that speed is a skill.

Before beginning any workout a complete functional warm up and flexibility routine should be performed. This will prepare the athlete for increased activity to follow. The chapter on flexibility will explain in detail the proper methods of flexibility training.

Fundamental Mechanics of Sprinting

Although not an individual segment of mechanics in sprinting, posture is the foundation that allows the other techniques to be performed properly. Listed below are components of posture:

1. Erect body with hips under the center of mass
2. The head is looking straight with the chin slightly in.
3. The pelvis should be neutral or slightly posterior to allow for complete cycling of the legs.
4. Chest should be up and the shoulders back (neutral) to allow for proper swing action of the arms from the shoulder joint.

Once proper posture is established, the actions of the legs and the phases in which they should go through will be more efficient.

Leg Action

As mentioned during posture, the legs will complete a full cycle comprised of different phases. Competency in each of these phases increases the speed of the runner due to efficient movement. Let's take an in-depth look at the first phase of the support phases (ground contact), the push off phase or rear support phase.

Rear Support Phase

The rear support phase, or "push off phase", is one of the three sub-phases of the actual support phase, the other two being the anterior support and middle support phases. The most important phase of the support phase is the rear support phase or push off phase[1]. The act of moving forward is achieved by the alternating push off action during the rear support phase. The push off phase is characterized by full extension of the hip, knee, and ankle joints in a down and back action into the ground. "Due to the resistance of the track or ground this force, resulting from the exertion of the muscles, produces and effect in the opposite direction, which we call supporting reaction; this generates the push off force, kinetic energy, which acts on the body's center of gravity".[2] This action is also often referred to as Newton's Third Law of Action Reaction.

The push off doesn't only occur by the actions of the posterior muscles of the legs and hips. The body is coordinated in such a way that the actions of the opposing limbs aid in the force production. The opposite leg in this case is known as the free leg and is moving in the opposite direction. The free leg must create as much speed as possible to increase the force of the push off leg.

This will also get the rear support leg off the ground quicker. Remember, the actions of one limb effect the actions of the opposite limb (coordination). In order for the free leg to move quicker, it must shorten its lever arm by collapsing at the knee joint and bringing the heel into the buttocks as it pulls through. The thigh of the lead or free leg will get to a horizontal or parallel position as quickly as possible, which pulls the leg through faster. The actions of the arms, which will be addressed later, will have an impact in the push off force as well.

Non Support Phase

The body naturally transitions from the support phase and the first sub phase; the rear support phase, and moves into the non support phase which consists of both legs being in the air. This phase is characterized by the center of mass going through a slight forward and upward lift, created by the push off, and a forward and downward direction, created by gravity (explained in greater detail in the book "The East German Textbook of Athletics"), leading into the second sub phase of the support phase. The less the hips move up and down between the support and non support phase will result in greater linear speed. If watching from the lateral view of a sprinter, with the focus on the hips, it is possible to view the raising and lowering of the hips. The better the sprinter is the more difficult this action is to observe. It is advisable to videotape sprinters from all angles in order to use as a source of visual feedback for the coach and athlete.

Lead (anterior) Support Phase

The lead or anterior support phase is initiated by the downward and back cyclical action of the lead leg. In essence, the foot is pawing the ground. If the backward pawing action of the lead leg is not moving as quickly as the center of mass of the runner, this will cause a braking or slowing down action.

The lead foot should be in a dorsiflexed (ankle cocked and toe up position) in order to aid in the push off during the rear support phase. "Dorsiflexion of the foot recruits the calf (gastrocnemius) muscle into the running action[3]". As soon as the lead or free leg is in a high-knee position, the ankle should be dorsiflexed. "When the foot lands in the dorsiflexed position, the calf can be contracted, helping to propel the body forward by pushing backward on the running surface[4].

During the contact phase, the outer edge of the ball of the foot should contact first. "Then, under the impact of the body weight, the pressure area moves towards the inside of the foot and the whole ball of the foot makes contact with the ground[5].

It will be much more common to see many of the subtleties in young athletes, such as dropping of the hips due to lack of lower leg, foot, and ankle strength during contact; and rising too much of the hips during the push off phase. This is why speed training during pre and early adolescents should mainly focus on the skills of running and build the foundation for speed.

The Middle Support Phase

Basically, the middle support phase is responsible for maintaining foot speed as the leg travels under the center of mass. The ankle should be dorsiflexed as the weight of the body transfers from the outer half of the ball of the foot to the middle and eventually inner aspect of the ball of the foot in preparation for the rear support phase[6]. As the name describes, the middle support phase is responsible for making sure nothing goes wrong from contact of the anterior support phase to the push off of the rear support phase. Strength of the foot, ankle, and lower leg to maintain position will determine how quick the transition from touch down to take will be.

Summary of the Phases of the Leg Cycle

Posture will be the foundation for the different phases of the leg cycle. If the body is in too much of a forward lean the stride will suffer due to having to contact the ground early. If the hips are not under the center of mass allowing the legs to complete a full cycle the stride length will once again suffer and the potential for injuries due to poor orthopedic alignment will present itself in the future.

The actions of the two legs must be coordinated to display a smooth and effortless

running action. "Running should involve a rapid change of muscular contraction and relaxation[7]". The actions of hip extension during the rear-support phase and the actions of the

lead leg being pulled into hip flexion are critical in force production into the ground. As younger athletes mature, the muscular coordination to become fluid during the running cycle will become evident.

The lead leg support phase must demonstrate a pawing action of the foot against the ground to maintain body speed. The outside of the ball of the foot must contact the ground first and eventually roll to the whole ball of the foot as it travels under the body during the mid-stance support phase. When the lead leg is in the proper landing position, not creating a breaking action, the body slows down less during contact and allows the foot to get to the push off phase quicker.

It is important to teach young athletes to maintain posture while going through the proper leg-cycle mechanics during the early stages of development. This is critical for future success.

Arm Action

The role of the arms is usually mentioned briefly in most texts. In this chapter the arms will be given the importance they deserve.

It is commonly mentioned that the arms should drive straight forward and backward and avoid crossing the midline of the body; this is true. The problem with most literature on the arm action is it doesn't go much beyond that statement. In reality, the arms are as important, if not more important, in the force generation of the legs.

Starting from the beginning and most basic actions of the arm, it is important to list the obvious:

- *The arms should be bent at approximately 90^0 at the elbows.* This is true of when the elbows are at the side of the body and when the forward arm swing is about half to three quarters of the way completed, but when the arms near completion of the forward swing, the hands near the face, the angle of the arms should close down to approximately 80 and 85 degrees[8]. During the backward swing of the arms, as soon as the hands start passing the hips, the angle at the elbow opens to approximately 120 degrees. This is critical in improving force production in the legs.

The idea that the legs are the most important factor in determining their own speed is incorrect. The arms must match the driving force of the legs; in fact the arms actually initiate the action first. This is not to say the coordination is messed up by the arms moving too quickly. The comment simply means the action of the arms will dictate the actions of the legs. "A long time ago, Percy Cerutti wrote that runners don't run with their legs, they run ON their legs[9]". "In reality, they run with their arms![10]" This is more evident during the starting and acceleration phases of speed. "When Scientists completed neurological pattern related research, they found the arms do precede the legs slightly and all control does come from the arms[11]".

Although the arms do initiate the running action, the coordination, rhythm, and timing must take place to have a fluid running action. The arms and legs must compliment each other to produce the most force. As the rear support or push-off leg goes into extension, the recovery leg (high knee leg) must be quick and power into its position to aid the force into the ground of the push-off leg. The arm on the opposite side of the push-off leg must violently drive back in order to facilitate the knee drive of the recovery leg. This is why it is important to allow the athletes to open the arm up to 120 degrees during the backward swing. If this arm stays at 90 degrees and is too quick out of the backward swing, it will limit the force production of the push off leg. This is a perfect example of coordination, and how the arms do in fact lead the legs. The arms want to be quick but not so quick that the legs can't finish their job.

In finishing up the mechanics of arm action, it is important to understand the relationship of the shoulders to the arms. The arms should freely swing from the shoulder joint. If the shoulders elevate due to tightness, this will adversely affect the path of the arms swing as well as trigger a tightening response throughout the upper body. It is crucial that the athletes are taught at a young age how to swing the arms properly with relaxed shoulders.

Hands

Just like the shoulders have an impact on the relaxation of the upper body, so do the hands. Because the hands are at the most distal part of the arm, an important driver of force, the hands need to take an active part in the initiation of arm drive.

The hands are taught to be held in varying positions by different coaches. The most common approach is to have the hands relaxed with the thumb over the index finger as if lightly holding a piece of paper between the two fingers. The other commonly used technique of holding the hands during sprinting is to open the fingers out straight. The school of thought with most coaches is that the closed hand technique is to relax the forearm and therefore relax the sprinter. The open hand technique is said by many to initiate a more aggressive arm drive. "The real question is whether closed hands help or hinder power development during arm drive[12]". "Furthermore, is hand position a consistent neural trigger across all athlete[13]". The issue being raised in this last quote by Charlie Francis, one of the worlds finest track and field coaches, is do all athletes function the same neurologically? Will some athletes respond neurologically different to open or closed hands?

It is the role of the coach to experiment with the young athletes and find a hand position that works best for the individual. It is important to educate the athlete on the proper positions for either technique.

Stride Length and Stride Frequency as it Relates to Speed

To master sprinting mechanics the support and non-support phases must be understood and practiced by the athlete. The efficiency of sprinting is influenced by the mechanics such as posture, leg cycle, arm and hand actions, and shoulder position and relaxation, force generation into the ground and to get body parts into appropriate positions, neurological functions to fire
muscles quicker and more efficiently, and the length of the arms and legs. The two main components influenced by these above factors are stride length and stride frequency.

Stride Length

"Stride length is governed by the power the sprinter puts into the stride or the ground contact time[14]". This is why increasing strength will have a positive influence on sprinting speed. Another important component to the stride length is the angle at which force is applied into the ground. This angle changes from acceleration to top end speed, but none the less the angle of force application is important. "When an athlete's over stride, or place the landing foot too far forward of [his/her] center of mass, [he/she can] create braking forces that slow [him/her] down[15]". Many athletes make the mistake of trying to over stride in order to lengthen his/her stride. Simply by having proper leg cycle mechanics and posture along with increasing the force into the ground will improve stride length.

Stride Frequency

Stride frequency is determined by the number of strides taken in a given time frame or distance. Stride frequency, although can be improved with proper mechanics, is largely determined by the muscle composition of the athlete. If the athlete has a dominance of fast-twitch compared to slow-twitch muscle fibers, he/she will be able to produce faster actions. Although there is a ceiling on the amount of improvement that can be made with regard to the nervous system and muscle fiber type, it is possible to improve the efficiency of muscle firing with practice.

The other determining factor of stride frequency that can't be changed is limb length. It is important to remember in the case of pre-adolescent children, they will actually have a length change in their limbs. As they go through puberty and general developmental growth the arms and legs will increase in length. It is important for running technique to be established at a young age so the muscle memory can be established. There will need to be subtle changes made to the technique due to limb length as the athlete grows, as well as nervous system orientation due to a longer limb, but for the most part, teach them at a young age to establish a solid foundation.

Elements of Developing Linear Speed

Moving into the final area of pure linear speed development, it is important to realize the elements that go into the initiation of speed through the end result of top end speed.

The three main elements that will be discussed are:

1. Reaction time or speed
2. Starting time or movement speed
3. Frequency of movement speed

It is critical all three elements be developed to reach full potential in sprinting. The pre-adolescent athlete should practice the skills and components of these elements during the early stages of development in order to advance in the later stages.

Before discussing the basic three elements of this chapter, an outline of two of the top youth instructors will be discussed. This will surely reiterate the importance of certain elements all youth coaches should concentrate on.

Jozef (Joseph) Drabik, is a professor of Physical Education in Gdansk, Poland. He is known for actually working at ground level with young children. He sees first hand what the needs are of children, yet he backs it up with sound research.

The three elements Jozef focuses on are:

1. Reaction time
2. "Speed in a single simple movement[16]".
3. "Frequency of movements, determined in movement cycle per time units[17]".

Jozef puts a big emphasis on the many factors of the first element, reaction time. He breaks the reaction time into five components. 1) Time it takes for a stimulus to excite a receptor. 2) Time it takes for an impulse to travel to the CNS. 3) Time it takes to transmit impulses through the nervous path from sensory to motor centers and produce an effector signal. 4) Time it takes to transmit the effector signal from the CNS to the muscle. 5) The time that elapses between the arrival of the stimuli at the muscle's motor plate and the beginning of the muscle's contraction.[18]

The second element that Jozef emphasis is the speed of a single movement; this is basically the time it takes for a single body part to move a given distance. Finally, Jozef speaks of the frequency of movements. He States that this "has little susceptibility to improvement[19]". Basically, heredity plays a large role in the fast-twitch muscle fiber composition of each individual.

Another expert in the field of strength and conditioning is Tudor Bompa. Tudor is recognized for his training systems that have helped the eastern bloc countries to prominence in the early 1960's. He has spent many years developing programs and training for the youth population. The following is a brief outline of his elements of speed that must be trained. (Due to the definition of similar terms in Josef Drabiks' section this section will be brief.)

1. Reaction time
2. Frequency of movement per time unit
3. Speed of travel over a given distance[20]

Tudor says "The correlation between these three factors assists the assessment of the performance of an exercise requiring speed. Thus, in sprinting, the final outcome depends on the athlete's reaction at the start, the speed of travel throughout the body of the race (i.e. Force of propulsion) and his/her stride frequency[21]".

It should be obvious that the elements described by both Jozef and Tudor are consistent and critical to developing speed.

To expand on the topic as it will relate to linear speed in sport, the three elements will be further outlined.

The importance of reaction time in most sports is crucial. Although this section as been devoted to linear speed it is important to emphasis most sports are not linear based. The point is, when an athlete gets a stimulus from an opponent or a situation in a sport, a reaction of the neuromuscular system will occur. Immediately from this reaction, the athlete must orient the body to most efficiently move in the direction of travel (in sports where movement of the upper body or hands is the focus, the same principle applies). This is when the important acceleration speed comes into play. Finally, the athlete must develop the ability to repeatedly produce fast motions to achieve and maintain speed.

In the sport of tennis, a drop shot, if performed correctly, is a difficult shot to defend. Taking the three elements of speed and applying it to a drop shot situation in tennis, a tennis player would go through the following:

1. Recognize the drop shot is occurring and a large distance must be traveled. (the fact that there is a large distance to be covered will intensify the response from the CNS back to the muscles) This will immediately send a signal to the CNS. The CNS will send a signal back to the muscles to meet the demand and the intensity of the situation.
2. The body will align itself in order to produce force into the ground in the complete opposite direction of travel.
3. Finally, acceleration and frequency of movement will occur to move the body in the direction of the drop shot.

This is the basic sequence of events that occurs when an athlete must move quickly to a different position in sport. Practicing the three main elements by putting young athletes in situations where they must react and run is crucial to develop greater efficiency of speed.

Multi-Directional Speed

The role of pure linear speed technique in the development of young athletes is important to learn in order to build upon in later stages of development. It develops fundamental movement patterns that are the foundation to developing other speed movement patterns. Although it is the foundation of other speed movements—known as multi-directional speed, the skill of moving lateral, angular, backwards and any combination—that must be taught with sound principles. This is an important concept to understand due to the different loading patterns needed to change direction, stop, and retreat. So in essence, the athlete with the greatest linear top-end speed may not be the fastest athlete in a court sport, field sport, or any other activity requiring multiple changes of direction.

There probably has been a time in every coach's life when he/she has witnessed an athlete who is lightening quick, yet seems to get beat, runs by plays, and is always trailing the play. This is when the principles of controlling movements of multi-directional speed come into play.

1. **Balance**: Maintaining the center of gravity over the base of support with little to no movement is referred to as *static balance*. Static balance is seen in sports such as diving, archery, shooting, gymnastics, and skating. Static balance is important when the athlete is being judged on accuracy, posture, or strength. In many situations in sport this will not be the case. When an athlete is performing a cut or change of direction. The athlete's body weight and the angle of the leg that is planting into the ground will no longer be aligned in the vertical plane or along the line of gravity. The athlete needs the ability to perform *dynamic balance*. The athlete has the ability to regain balance at anytime.

2. **Swaying/Stabilizing**: When an athlete must make an aggressive change of direction or stop the feet and legs, he/she must create a stopping angle that halts momentum. When this occurs the muscles of the trunk must eccentrically control the desire of the upper body to continue in the original direction of travel. If the core is weak or unstable, the result is a swaying of the upper body. This negatively impacts the efficiency of movement.

3. **Excessive movement in the vertical plane**: The old saying holds true with speed of movement, "The shortest way from point A to point B is a straight line". The principle of excessive movement in the vertical plane can be seen in athletes who allow his/her body to rise up and down when trying to move in a horizontal direction. The most basic example is when a basketball player is performing a lateral shuffle and is allowing the hips to rise up and down on every push off (galloping). It is also obvious in novice sprinters.

4. **Excessive movement in the transverse plane**: This principle is seen most in the arm action of sprinting. The arms travel across the midline of the body rather than forward and backward. This is also obvious in athletes who don't allow the arms to pivot from the shoulder joint causing the shoulders to become active in the forward and backward arm swing. The body will rotate in the transverse plane causing an undesirable action.

5. **Rearing up/Shoulder elevation**: When an athlete needs to accelerate quickly out of a stationary position, the athlete will perform a plyo-Step—a quick alignment of the feet into the linear plane to create positive line of force into the ground, and in many cases the shoulders and chest will rise causing an arcing of the low back. This action depletes the energy or the ground reaction coming back from the ground and redirects it out of the anterior hips rather than through the body and out the shoulders and head.

6. **Premature planting**: When an athlete needs to stop, change directions, or perform a cut, the angle of the planting leg or foot needs to be wide enough to stop the athlete by handling the momentum of the athlete's body. When the athlete plants to soon, *Premature planting,* the momentum of the body will cause a stumbling or tripping over the planted foot. The angle

of the plant is determined through kinesthetic awareness and past experience of what is needed to control the speed of the body in any given situation.

7. **Force application/push the body away**: When an athlete needs to move in any direction, the push off needs to be down and away from the direction of travel. If the athlete wants to go horizontal the push off needs to allow this to occur. In other words, if the push off foot doesn't create a positive angle there will be *Excessive movement in the vertical plane or an uplift.* When an athlete is performing a lateral shuffle, if the push off occurs too far under the hips, this will rise the body taking away from the horizontal line of travel.

Neuromuscular Considerations of Multi-directional Movement

Multi-directional movement (balance, agility, quickness, body control) is developed with the aid of different systems of the nervous system and brain. The use of the eyes, special awareness of the head, and the bodies understanding of the location of its limbs in relation to each other are all critical in the understanding of athletic movement. The following information is from the text "Applied Anatomy and Biomechanics in Sport":

1. Visual receptors (the eyes): these provide information on the relative spatial location of objects in the field of view.
2. Vestibular apparatus: this provides the perception of movement of the head through the semicircular canal structures of the inner ear.
3. Kinesthetic receptors: these provide information regarding the relative location of one body part to another, the position of

the body in space and an awareness of the body's movements. These receptors include joint position receptors (Ruffini endings, Golgi receptors and paccinian corpuscles) as well as the muscle-length tension receptors (Golgi tendon organs and muscle spindles)[22]

Much of this information relates to the bodies ability to maintain balance and awareness. This is the critical element of multi-directional speed. Without balance, all other actions are stalled and uncoordinated.

In young children, the development of balance can't be overstated. It will determine how well he/she performs many athletic movements. The three mentioned structures (visual receptors, vestibular apparatus, and kinesthetic receptors) that must be developed to aid in balance and movement ability develop at different stages of growth and maturation. It has been shown through research that there are distinct stages or phases when balance becomes strongly dominant during development and other ages of development when balance is not the primary focus of development. Woolacott *et al. (1989),* as referenced in "Applied Anatomy and Biomechanics in Sport", state visual dominance in balance control appears to recur at transitional points in human development[23]. When a baby is first learning and experiencing movement the visual acuity is important.

"The ages of four to six years, however, represent a transitional period when stability often declines temporarily[24]". The child is experiencing many changes and the developments of
many systems are occurring in the body. "It is postulated that the child is attempting to integrate the various sensory information from all the above sources (visual, vestibular, and kinesthetic), not just the visual[25]".

According to Bloomfield, Ackland, and Elliot; "From 7 to 10 years and beyond, the child becomes more reliant upon kinesthetic and vestibular feedback in balance control[26]".

Josef Drabik states, "Those times when the child's organs and systems related to a particular ability are undergoing intensive development are the times when it is particularly effective to stress training that develops that ability[27]". If a child is in the pre-pubescent years concentrating on activities that will challenge the bodies systems to balance he/she will enhance the development of balance. According to Drabik, balance is developed during the sensitive periods of "ages 10 to 11 for boys and 9 to 10 for girls[28]". Drabik says "According to Protasova (1984) balance reaches its fully matured level between 12 and 14[29]".

It is obvious multi-directional speed training is more than just performing speed and quickness drills. There has been mention of one ability, balance, and it is plain to see there are many subsystems that must be developed within the brain and nervous system to attain great balance. Therefore, in order for multi-directional speed to be highly developed, it will be important to develop the systems of other abilities such as agility, coordination, flexibility, and strength. It is important to mention balance is the most important overall ability to establish great athletic ability. As mentioned earlier, if balance is not well developed, the ability to make quick, coordinated, and smooth movements will be stalled or delayed due to not being balanced.

Below is a list of abilities that make up multi-directional speed. Some of the abilities are dependent upon the other abilities such as balance and coordination to for optimum performance.

Balance

Balance has already been described and understood to be the primary ability that must be in established to allow the other abilities to perform well.

Speed

Speed comes from the ability to have a coordinated action between the arms and legs, intramuscular and inter-muscular coordination for appropriate contraction and relaxation of antagonists and agonists, dynamic flexibility, and strength.

Coordination

Coordination is necessary for other abilities to perform efficiently, but coordination must have certain factors occur or be available for it to be optimal.

Drabik in his book "Children and Sports Training" lists the following factors:

1. Intelligence of the athlete to be able to solve complex, unexpected motor tasks.
2. Systematic training to improve an athlete's kinesthetic sense and thus improve coordination, precision, and speed of movement.
3. Motor "erudition" (the store of acquired movement skills). Speed of learning and the ability to perfect movements depend on the size of one's stored experiences of movements.
4. Level of development of other motor abilities will directly affect the coordination of an athlete.[30]

Flexibility

The dynamic flexibility of an athlete will affect the ability to move the hips and legs freely to perform multi-directional speed movements. In young children dynamic flexibility is important to develop for increasing joint range of motion, but also for improving movement technique, and strength.

Agility

In order for agility to be developed in an athlete, balance, coordination, and flexibility must be developed. Agility encompasses speed and quickness within changing directions and speeds under control. The greater the athletes balance and coordination is developed the greater the agility will be.

Teaching Multi-directional Acceleration Techniques

It goes with out saying that if an athlete wishes to improve his/her skills in a particular sport, repeated correct practice will be necessary. The same holds true for developing athletic speed. The techniques that make up the speed skills need to be practiced often to develop muscle memory and experiences.

The skills that will be described below allow the athlete to smoothly transition from the reactive stimulus of speed, as described by Drabik and Bompa, into the starting and acceleratory aspect of speed. The stimulus immediately tells the body how to align itself with regard to several factors that will have an effect on acceleration:

1. The exact direction of travel
2. Which foot will be the push off leg and which foot will be the power leg and the direction the force will be applied?
3. How much force is needed to accelerate at a particular speed to accomplish the goal?
4. How aggressive the arm action needs to be to coordinate with the knee drive. This is directly related to the force needed at take off.
5. How much the shoulders need to drop in order to have a positive line of power from the push off leg through the head. This is determined once again by the speed needed to accomplish the goal.

It is important to remember that multi-directional speed is based off the reactive nature of the human body and the situations in sport. The athlete's ability to recognize the stimulus and gain feedback from the stimulus, coupled with the ability to apply the appropriate footwork skills to begin acceleration in the intended direction will be most successful. This is the random reactive nature of sport.

Let take a close look at the various skills and techniques that make up multi-directional acceleration:

Linear Acceleration

Linear acceleration has basically been described throughout this chapter, but the skills and techniques will be expanded in greater detail.

In order for an athlete to accelerate straight ahead, the stimulus received during the action of play will give certain feedback to the athlete:

1. What direction to travel, therefore how to initiate the foot placement.
2. The amount of force needed at push off to accomplish the goal.
3. The force needed by the arms to increase the force by the legs.
4. The amount of forward lean needed to aid in the acceleration.

The information received by an athlete is used quite differently by young pre-pubescent athletes in the age range of six to seven as compared to athletes ranging from fourteen to eighteen years old. The ultimate goal is to develop conditioned reflexes to a stimulus. "Children typically exhibit weak inhibition, poor concentration, high excitability, and generalization in their reaction to stimuli[31]". This is why children usually won't last long when it comes to an organized setting where they must concentrate on a particular task for any extended length of time. "These factors often cause improper reaction to external stimuli, especially in situations demanding quick adaptation or sudden changes of directions and of character of movement[32]". It is extremely important to understand these concepts when designing exercises that involve reaction to a stimulus.

Let's look at a linear acceleration skill that is in inherent to the reaction of a stimulus in sport.

Plyo Step

The plyo step, more popularly known as the false step, although the connotation of the word step wrongly depicts the true action, is becoming more and more recognized as the appropriate method taken during the initial stages of acceleration from an athletic or active athletic stance. The plyo step is only used in sports or activities when the direction of travel is unknown until a stimulus is given by the opponent or game situation. For example, a track athlete in a track stance would already be in an appropriate linear acceleration stance to accomplish the acceleration goal.

An article written by Todd Brown and Jason D. Vescovi in "The NSCA Journal on the Plyo Step", which they referred to as the "false step" (FS), researched three acceleration starts. The first being the "drop and go"; this technique has the athlete drop the hips and rotate the center of mass forward via the ankles and taking off with no false step. The second technique used was the "staggered step" (SS), which allowed the athletes to place one foot in front of the other to have a built in angle to push off with. Finally, the false step technique was used allowing the push off leg to quickly align itself behind the body for more horizontal force.

Jason and Todd wrote: "Using the FS was originally thought to be wasted notion and decreased the ability to accelerate, although inherently paradoxical, the information from Krann's group (2,3) (Krann, G.A., personal communication, 2003) suggests the FS holds the most promise to maximize performance during the first few steps of acceleration[33]. Jason and Todd went on to say "This natural movement demonstrates greater force development with the shortest impulse time[34]. The plyo step ultimately is the appropriate skill when an athlete is in a random directional reaction state.

To clarify why the term "false step" incorrectly describes the action of the plyo step, it is important to understand what a step is. A step occurs when the hips travel the distance from the push off of one foot to the landing of the other foot. The definition of a step in "The American Heritage Dictionary" is, "The single complete movement of raising and putting down one foot in the act of walking[35]. This definition applies to backward walking and or running as well.

During the Plyo step, the hips should not travel back at all. If it were a true step, the lead leg would actually push the body back into the step. This is not the case at all. The push off leg (Plyo step) and the lead leg or power leg simultaneously lifts off the ground momentarily as they prepare for their actions. Listed below are actions occurring during the plyo step for linear acceleration.

   i. The push off leg is aligned directly behind the body, but should not cross the midline of the body.
   ii. The upper body and shoulders assume a forward lean to line up with the angle of the push off leg.
   iii. The opposite leg, which is now the power leg, prepares to produce an aggressive push off down

and back into the ground. This occurs by lifting the knee as close to 90 degrees as possible with a dorsiflexed ankle.

iv. The arms are preparing to produce an aggressive backward action to increase the amount of force produced by the push off and power leg. This is accomplished by driving the same side arm of the raised knee back aggressively allowing the force of the knee lift to transfer into the push off leg.

Once the plyo step has occurred and horizontal acceleration is underway, the skill of acceleration now takes place.

In order for the body to continue to accelerate, there must be greater forces applied into the ground initially to get the body moving. Once the body is moving, the frequency of the applied force becomes greater, yet the intensity of the force decreases due to the increased velocity of the body. The techniques that allow this to occur are as follows:

1. Each leg will push down and back into the ground to produce horizontal acceleration.
2. The hip, knee, and ankle of the push off leg will go into triple extension to produce as much force as possible.
3. The ankle of the lead leg will be in dorsi-flexion while the knee will be flexed to create a shorter lever and a quicker recovery.
4. The lead leg hip will get into the flexed position, at least to 90 degrees, as quickly as possible in order to increase the push off power of the opposite leg and to allow greater force when it drives down and back.

5. The arms will be in opposition of the legs with a strong emphasis on driving back behind the hips to increase force production from the legs.

The athlete should be trying to push his/her body forward with each and every stride until the goal of accelerating is met. As mentioned earlier, the rate of force needed and the aggressiveness of the acceleration are determined by the stimulus during play. In tennis, if the ball lands five feet in front of you, your intensity during acceleration will be much different than if the ball lands fifteen feet in front of you—especially if the ball is at the same height and speed of the ball that landing five feet in front of you.

Lateral Acceleration

Athletic Stance

Before getting into all the lateral movement patterns and techniques, we must start with the foundation: the athletic stance.

The athletic stance, to most coaches and athletes, is taken for granted. The time spent on it is minimal, yet it is the foundation for all multi-directional movement. The athletic stance must be treated as importantly as the other skills of movement.

To understand the reason for the athletic stance let's take a look at why we use it.

In sports where the initial movement out of the athletic stance is undetermined until a direction occurs by the opponent, the athletic stance allows athletes to move in any direction quickly. Obviously, if the athlete knew without question the direction of travel, the standing or down track stance would be best.

Let's view the basic guidelines of the athletic stance:

1. Feet wider than shoulder width with the ankles dorsiflexed (ankles locked).
2. Feet straight to slightly turned in with the pressure on the ball of the big toe.
3. Knees are slightly angled to the inside to create a down and out pressure. It is important to realize the pressure is out; it is not only created by pushing the knees in and down.
4. The shoulders are lined up over the knees and the knees are over the feet.
5. The back should be flat with the head up.

It is important to remember the stance will be slightly different according to the sport and position.

Most court and field sports consist of lateral movement. Lateral movement can be broken down into three movement skills:

1. *Lateral shuffles*: This is commonly seen in basketball. A defensive player will move side to side with no turning of the hips or shoulders.
2. *Crossovers*: This technique is performed as to keep the athlete's upper body oriented to the ball or opponent yet allowing the hips and lower body to rotate in the direction of travel. This is used to gain more speed.
3. *Lateral shuffle crossover combination*: Being able to transition quickly from the shuffle to the crossover is vital in most sports. The athlete must be able to keep proper defensive positioning by accelerating and decelerating to maintain optimal positioning

In order for an athlete to be able to master these techniques, the skill of lateral movement must be mastered. As in linear acceleration, the body and its limbs must be put in optimal angles for proper execution. Listed below are the body positions and the related skill:

1. *Dorsiflexed ankle*: This allows for quick and powerful push offs from the feet. This is why it is important to have the feet turned in (internal rotation) slightly during the lateral shuffle. If the feet are turned outward (externally rotated) the heels will be the source of contact and push off. Imagine sprinting full speed with only your heels touching.

2. *Knees to the inside upon push off*: In order for the force generated by the hips and legs to be positively directed into the ground there must be proper alignment from the source of the power to the source accepting the power (the ground). If the knees are kept vertical over the knees as in squatting, the power from the hips will be lost out the side of the knee. It is important not to allow the knees to drop inside the angle of force either. This will decrease power and increase risk of injury just as much as having the knees to the outside.

3. *Maintaining a level hip height*: If the goal is to go from point A to point B, any excessive movement in the vertical plane will diminish lateral speed. Keep the hips calm by moving the feet and legs under the hips.

4. *Avoiding shoulder sway in the sagittal and frontal planes*: The shoulders must stay calm allowing the athlete to move efficiently. If the shoulders drop forward or sideways during lateral movement, the

athlete will take himself/herself out of optimal sporting positions.

5. *Use the arms to help produce force during the lateral shuffle*: When an athlete shuffles laterally, the arms will rise during push off and lower into the body during the recover of the legs. This helps to produce force into the ground by producing a counter action (arms up creates a stronger push off).

Lateral Deceleration and Change of Direction

When an athlete needs to stop and or change directions while moving laterally the ability to apply the following techniques is essential for success:

1. Placing the outside leg (stopping leg) on a large enough angle to handle the momentum of the body coming into the stop. This angle must not be too wide to cause slippage.

2. The ankle needs to be dorsiflexed and the foot needs to be straight to slightly turn in. If the athlete is up high on the ball of the foot, the ankle is susceptible to rolling over.

3. The knee needs to be inside of the vertical plane, over the plant foot, and in direct alignment with the force coming from the ground up through the foot, knee, and hip. This will align the knee between the hip and the foot; which is the line of power.

4. The shoulders should remain inside of the vertical plane of the plant leg knee. If the shoulders sway, this slows the change of direction or lengthens the time it takes to stop.

5. The hips need to settle as little as possible to allow the change of direction to be quick. The hips should primarily drop due to

the plant leg being outside the hips which naturally lowers the hips.

When speaking about deceleration it would be remise not to mention the importance of proper deceleration training to avoid injury and increase performance.

It is well known that many injuries occur to the knees when poor deceleration during cutting or landing is used. The ACL injury is most common during poor positioning of the feet and knees during these skills. "The ACL is most vulnerable when the knee is pointing inward and the foot is pointing outward with the torso falling forward. Therefore, one common position that can lead to an ACL tear is when the knee is fixed around 20 degrees of flexion, almost straight, the torso is leaning forward, the thigh is internally rotated, shin externally rotated and the foot is pronated[36]. The potential for the positions described to occur are high in many athletes, especially female. "The quadriceps and hamstring are attempting to control the deceleration of the knee, but the position places overload on the ACL[37]. The ACL is obviously a bad injury to have an athlete experience, but it is not the only injury that can occur during deceleration. Ankle injuries, hip injuries, and hip are also common to cutting and landing skills.

In order to reduce the potential for injuries, proper technique and strength training need to be a part of every training program. The most common weakness, that caused the position described above with an ACL tear, is the valgus position of the knee. The mistake that is most commonly made by beginning trainers and coaches is to strengthen only the muscles that surround the knee, because that is the site of the injury. The area of most concern is going to be the musculature around the hip and core. "Hip weakness can exacerbate the anatomical alignment problems. Additional internal rotation of the knee can occur too far and too fast it the hip abductors and hip external rotators are not functional[38]. These are not the only muscles surrounding the hip and core that can lead to poor alignment. "Weak lower abdominals and poor muscular control can lead to a forward pelvic tilt[39]". In order to reduce the potential for injury, it is important to strengthen the gluteus medius, lower abdominals, external rotators of the hip, quads and hamstrings.

The other issue in dealing with prevention of injury is the technique during landing and cutting. As mentioned above, the ACL injury occurs when the knee goes into valgus and there is outward foot rotation and pronation. It is important to teach athlete to line the knees up over the feet in order to keep the line of force going through the joints. This is done progressively and at increasing intensities.

The other important technique to teach, which will reduce the potential for ankle injuries, is the technique of dorsiflexion during contact. When an athlete is on the balls of his/her feet and the heels are elevated quite high, the ankle joint is more susceptible to lateral movement. When the athlete is taught to dorsiflex the ankle, he/she strengthens the joint and therefore reduces the potential for injury. The dorsiflexed position also creates a quicker push off during cutting or jumping.

Special Techniques of Multi-directional Speed

Hip Turn

It goes without saying that if an athlete has the ability to accelerate out of any stance and in any direction quickly, he/she will have an advantage. One of the mistakes in the field of sports performance is the implementation of drills with out teaching the proper techniques to execute the drills, also making the drills strictly rehearsed and not random and reactive.

In most field and court sports, acceleration occurs in virtually every direction and angle possible. It is common practice for coaches and trainers to teach acceleration or "first step" speed moving forward on all angles. It was mentioned earlier that the Plyo step is the most efficient and effective techniques to use out of the athletic stance to move in a forward or angular direction. What is not as commonly taught, or correctly taught, is the "first step" or acceleration moving straight or angled backwards.

A common defensive technique is to retreat while continuing to keep body orientation and vision on the opponent or ball. The most common technique that has been taught for years during the initial movement backward was to "pivot" by keeping one foot planted and opening up the hips and swinging the free leg back. This technique is important for sports like basketball, where if the pivot foot is lifted it is a violation of the rules. Other than this example, the pivot is not the most advantageous technique to induce an explosive quick first step in a retreat technique. Let's look at a list of reasons why the pivot is not the most effective technique to initiate a first step with:

1. In order for a push off to be effective, the angle must be down and back. The pivot tends to position the knees directly over the feet, which creates a vertical line of power.
2. The pivot creates friction between the surface and the footwear of the athlete. This has a slowing down effect. If the athlete is on a grassy surface and is wearing cleats, the potential for ankle, knee, and hip injury is increased.
3. The pivot, although taught, does not take into consideration the natural instinct of the reaction of the body to align itself for a quick get a way. If a person was being chased by a bear, it is unlikely that a pivot would be used to get away.
4. The pivot doesn't allow for the plyometric action incurred by forcefully pushing the foot into the ground. The foot never leaves the ground during a pivot.

5. The pivot doesn't allow for the natural force angle to be created from the foot up through the hip and therefore doesn't allow for the shoulders to be out in front of the site of force between the foot and the ground.

Just as the plyo step is a reactive technique out of an athletic stance, the technique to initiate a retreat first step, known as a hip turn, is also a reactive technique.

The hip turn is performed by quickly and aggressively rotating the hips and legs so the feet can be placed in the complete opposite direction of the intended direction of travel. In order for the hip turn technique to be performed correctly, there must be an instantaneous lifting of both feet off the ground in order for the hips to rotate quickly and smoothly. It is not a jumping action. It is a minimal rising of the legs via a hip and knee flexion. The leg that will perform the push off will be placed out from under the hips and at an angle that will allow for horizontal acceleration with minimal vertical lift. The opposite leg will swing the hips open and flex at the knee and hip in preparation for a power step down and back under the hips. The shoulders must begin a lean in the direction of travel and in straight alignment with the push off leg. The head and eyes will be positioned to most effectively perform the game situation.

Let's take a look at a more detailed list of the actions of the hip turn and why it is the more effective technique in retreating for speed:

1. The hip turn is initiated by a random reaction and stimulus given by an opponent or game situation. This stimulus gives the athlete the feedback to know where to place the feet, how much intensity is needed to initiate the hip turn and first step,

the direction the push off leg will be placed, and what footwork will be used once the hip turn is completed.

2. The ankle needs to be dori-flexed and the foot needs to be pointed straight ahead or slightly inward toward the direction the hips are facing. This keeps the feet pointing in the same direction as the knees.

3. The knees need to be in direct alignment with the feet and the hips and on the line of power from the reaction back from the ground forces. This force needs to travel straight up the ankle, knee, and hip to promote a safe and powerful push off.

4. The shoulders need to start leaning in the direction of travel in order for a smooth acceleration to take place. Now the shoulder position will change according to the footwork needed after the hip turn and the tactics during the play.

The important thing to remember is, during the hip turn, the athlete wants to reduce the ball or opponents advantage of moving first. If the athlete is always behind the ball or opponent due to a fast initial movement by the ball or opponent, he/she will always be at a big disadvantage. The hip turn can and will reduce the offensive advantage if used properly.

Finally, the hip turn is basically the plyo step used behind the frontal plane. It allows for the same quick reactive movements of the plyo step, yet it is done behind the frontal plane.

The Crossover

The crossover is another technique that gives an athlete an advantage in reducing the opponent's offensive advantage. In sports where moving laterally is an important skill to master, many coaches and trainers don't teach the different techniques to improve lateral movement.

Lateral movement isn't just about staying parallel and shuffling the feet. It is about staying oriented and in position to negate the offensive player's intent to pass by, or to stay in position to catch or field the ball.

The athlete must be taught the techniques needed to match the speed of the opponent or ball, yet not lose important body positioning during the play. One of these techniques is the *lateral shuffle*. This technique allows the athlete to stay completely square to the play and move by pushing off with the power leg and clearing the lead leg, with minimal pulling of the lead leg. The other technique that is used laterally is known as the *crossover* technique. This technique is more commonly taught in sports such as football because it is a fundamental skill for linebackers and cornerbacks to use. In sports such as tennis, basketball, and soccer, it is not directly taught as a skill by most coaches.

The crossover is performed by allowing the hips to turn to around 45 degrees or more in the direction of travel. This immediately allows the trail leg to crossover the hips and act as it would in linear running. The shoulder stay oriented to the play at hand. The lead leg also acts as if it were in normal linear running mechanics. The arms are also allowed to move freely to help increase the coordination of the arms and legs (this is subject to the sport and if implemented, is in the hand of the athlete).

The crossover technique will be used when more speed is needed to maintain good defensive positioning during a play. The athlete must be taught this technique in order to reduce the potential of getting beat by an offensive player or situation.

It is important to be able to combine the technique of crossing over and shuffling. In sports such as tennis, the combination of both is critical to performance.

Directional Step

The *Directional step* is a technique used during the initiation of linear acceleration out of an athletic stance and running to the right or left (i.e. a baseball player stealing second base). The goal of the directional step is to allow the hips to open, which allows the upper body to turn freely, and to let the lead leg prepare for the power step.

The technique will be outlined in greater detail below for the directional step:

1. Once the athlete determines which direction he/she will be traveling, the push off leg, leg furthest from the direction of travel, will push the hips and upper body in the direction of travel. This may occur using a plyo step if the athlete is using an active athletic stance or a pure stationary push off from a static athletic stance.

2. At the same time the upper body will rotate quickly allowing for a good shoulder lean.

3. The lead leg will take the directional step by turning the foot in the direction of travel and flexing at the hip, knee, and ankle in preparation for an aggressive power step down and back into the ground.

4. The push off leg, leg furthest from the direction of travel, must get the body started over the power step leg. If this doesn't occur, the tendency is to reach with the directional step and contact the heel first, which is a breaking action.

5. As soon as the lead leg pushes off the body it is not in linear acceleration.

The reason this techniques has been named the directional step is due to the turning of the lead foot in the direction of travel and the initiation of acceleration in that direction.

Summary of Multi-Directional Speed

Being a good mover in athletics has to do with an entire body system being developed from a young age and the experiences the system has been exposed to. Understanding that certain abilities develop at different stages of development, it is important to expose athletes at a young age to as many diverse movement patterns and skills as possible in order to create motor pathways for the system to call upon in later development.

Multi-directional speed is the result of several skills and techniques being learned and practiced to create an efficient pattern of movement. The key to being a good mover, aside from developing the skills of movement, is being able to match the sport situation with appropriate movement skills as often as necessary to accomplish a task. In other words, if an athlete is quick laterally, but can't stop and change direction with control and quickness, he/she is not considered an efficient mover. Being able to combine several movement skills with varying speeds and directions changes is the ultimate goal of multi-directional speed.

It is the job of the coach and trainer to prepare the athlete for these situations by systematically introducing more advanced movement skills and techniques and placing the athlete in random reactive situations to employ the newly learned skills.

Role of Age in Developing Speed

When an athlete is mature and has trained for several years the method of training will be far more advanced than that of a child. This section of the chapter will describe the basic foundations that should occur depending on the age of the athlete.

Speed training is more than going out and doing drills when referring to children. "The sensitive periods for developing speed are between the ages of seven and nine for both sexes and additionally for girls between ten and eleven[40]". Mike Gattone of USOC Coaching and Sports Sciences says, "The most intense improvements (in speed) occur between 14 and 17 years[41]". Mike goes on to say "The most significant improvements in muscular reaction speed occur between 7 and 11 years of age, and reaction speed to difficult movement sequences improves between 11 and 16 years[42]". He finishes by saying "improvements in movement frequency occur most significantly between ages 10 and 13[43]".

It is important to realize there are slight differences in the sensitive periods of development between boys and girls. These stages of development will vary depending on the individual as well. Josef Drabik says "Around the age of 14 the roads of speed development for boys and girls divide[44]". Drabik also says "Boys' speed keeps increasing until 18 whole girls' speed results after 15 as a rule are progressively worse[45]". Finally, Drabik states "Girls have their last acceleration of speed improvement at age 13 or 14[46]".

It is important for coaches to realize employing improper training methods with children will decrease the potential for improvement of speed. Conversely, if proper training occurs during appropriate stages of development an increase of speed can be realized.

It is of greater importance to focus on technique of movements and increasing frequency of movements while athletes are pre-pubertal. It has also been shown increased aerobic capacity in prepubescent children will aid in the development of speed due to the need to produce energy via help from the aerobic system. As the athletes mature, the need for greater reliance on the anaerobic system as the energy source for speed is greater. "The ability to produce energy with an adequate supply of oxygen for children, there is a strong correlation between VO_2max and speed of running (MacDougall et al.1983) [47]".

Exercises for Developing Speed in Prepubescent and Adolescent Athletes

Basically, young children should learn speed through games and relay type activities. Techniques can be taught during this time. It is important to make it enjoyable in order to keep the interest of the children. As the athletes reach early adolescents, the focus should still be fun, but more attention to detail and skill can be slightly engaged. Obviously, as an older adolescent age is reached, the athletes need to use more structured speed training.

Another important point to mention is the role of fatigue. Children should not be practicing speed techniques in a fatigues state. It will surely result in poor mechanics. As the athlete matures, training in a slightly fatigues state will build speed endurance. It is still important not to allow technique to suffer.

Probably the biggest mistake made by most coaches is attempting to increase pure speed, yet prescribing drills that are longer than seven to ten seconds. Once the time frame becomes too long, the system that is used for maximum speed, Phosphate system, is no longer emphasized. The other important issue is to allow for appropriate rest periods in order for the muscles to replace CP, its energy needs.

In Summary

As mentioned in the opening paragraph, speed is one of the most fascinating abilities of athleticism. It can change a game in one play. Although speed is genetically determined for the most part, it certainly can be increased with proper training at appropriate stages.

In order for any athlete to improve at anything, the skills and techniques of that skill must be mastered. The ultimate goal is for an athlete to perform a skill as close to perfect, for that athlete, with unconscious ability. All the rehearsed and planned technique work lays the groundwork for the ability to perform in a random and reactive state, known as sport.

It will be important to teach athletes for multi-directional speed in a random reactive state as much as possible. The skills of multi-directional speed can be corrected during live drills. This is much like teaching sport skills during a live scrimmage or game.

The eventual goal is to prepare the athlete to recognize and make corrections of movement technique on the fly. When an athlete is able to do this, the coach has prepared the athlete well.

Finally, Speed training in itself isn't enough to make a complete athlete, or reach optimal speed. The athlete must train other abilities such as strength and flexibility, have proper nutrition and regeneration, and train the mental aspect of learning speed. So, assess your athletes, create a plan, implement and teach your plan.

References

[1] Gerhardt & Schmolinsky (1992)

[2] Gerhardt & Schmolinsky (1992)

[3] Dunton, R. (2003)

[4] Dunton, R. (2003)

[5] Gerhardt & Schmolinsky (1992)

[6] Gerhardt & Schmolinsky (1992)

[7] Gerhardt & Schmolinsky (1992)

[8] Gerhardt & Schmolinsky (1992)

[9] USA Track and Field Level 1 Curriculum

[10] USA Track and Field Level 1 Curriculum

[11] Francis, C. & Patterson, P. (1992)

[12] Francis, C. & Patterson, P. (1992)

[13] Francis, C. & Patterson, P. (1992)

[14] Rogers, J. (2000)

[15] Rogers, J. (2000)

[16] Drabik, J. (1996)

[17] Drabik, J. (1996)

[18] Drabik, J. (1996)

[19] Drabik, J. (1996)

[20] Bompa, T. (1994)

[21] Bompa, T. (1994)

[22] J. Bloomfield, Ackland, T.R., Elliott B.C. (1994)

[23] J. Bloomfield, Ackland, T.R., Elliott B.C. (1994)

[24] J. Bloomfield, Ackland, T.R., Elliott B.C. (1994)

[25] J. Bloomfield, Ackland, T.R., Elliott B.C. (1994)

[26] J. Bloomfield, Ackland, T.R., Elliott B.C. (1994)

[27] Drabik, J. (1996)

[28] Drabik, J. (1996)

[29] Drabik, J. (1996)

[30] Drabik, J. (1996)

[31] Drabik, J. (1996)

[32] Drabik, J. (1996)

[33] Brown, T. & Vescovi, J. (2004)

[34] Brown, T. & Vescovi, J. (2004)

[35] The American Heritage Dictionary (1983)

[36] London, J.K., Jenkins, W. & Loudon, K.L. (1996)

[37] London, J.K., Jenkins, W. & Loudon, K.L. (1996)

[38] London, J.K., Jenkins, W. & Loudon, K.L. (1996)

[39] London, J.K., Jenkins, W. & Loudon, K.L. (1996)

[40] Drabik, J. (1996)

[41] Gattone, M. (2004)

[42] Gattone, M. (2004)

[43] Gattone, M. (2004)

[44] Drabik, J. (1996)

[45] Drabik, J. (1996)

[46] Drabik, J. (1996)

[47] Drabik, J. (1996)

5

Practical Application of Strength and Power Development

Bill Hartman

The inclusion of strength and power training as a component of a total sports training program has become an integral component in the developmental process for young athletes. Once believed to be ineffective for developing strength in the young athlete and unsafe due to a high risk of injury, empirical evidence and research has demonstrated that strength and power training is not only safe and effective but also beneficial to a young athlete's health, performance, and general development.

To be successful an appropriate strength and power training must consider the influences of body type, age, stage of physical development, sensitive periods, level of performance, and prior or current training status. The selection of an age-appropriate program along with methods and means are also dependent on the desired adaptations in physiology and performance, as each will provide the young athlete with a specific training effect.

The purpose of this chapter is to provide the athlete, coach, trainer, and parent with foundational information in regard to understanding the adaptations associated with the proper design and application of a strength and power training program for young athletes.

Types of Strength and Power Training

A number of training methods are utilized in the design of strength and power programs for young athletes. The following will provide a brief description of the most common methods and their derivatives as they are used to develop the young athlete.

Powerlifting

Powerlifting is a competitive strength sport; the goal is to lift the most weight possible in a one repetition maximum lift. The competitive lifts are limited to the squat, the bench press, and deadlift (97,8). Because the methods utilized to develop the powerlifting athlete are specific to developing maximal strength, many sports training programs will include similar methods. Weights lifted in training and competition at a high level frequently require lifting maximal and near-maximal loads in excess of two to three times bodyweight (15).

Weightlifting

Weightlifting is frequently referred to as "Olympic weightlifting" to distinguish it from the common term of weight lifting. Weightlifting is a competitive, skilled power sport with a goal of lifting the most weight possible in a one repetition maximum lift. The competitive lifts are limited to the clean and jerk and the snatch (8, 97). Derivatives of the competition lifts are frequently used to assist in the development of the competitive lifts. Examples of the derivatives of the competitive lifts include the power clean, power snatch, the jerk, and the push press. Because of the higher power outputs developed and the mechanical specificity to many power-based sports demonstrated in the competitive lifts and their derivatives, these methods are frequently included in sports training programs (97).

Bodybuilding

Bodybuilding is a sport based on the aesthetic development of the skeletal muscles. There are no competitive lifts in the sport of bodybuilding, although it does rely primarily on the lifting of weights with the intention of increasing muscular hypertrophy in a proportionate manner (8, 97). The methods utilized to develop hypertrophy may be beneficial in the development of some athletes as gains in muscle mass frequently result in increased strength; however, hypertrophy alone is rarely beneficial. Theses methods are rarely beneficial to very young athletes who lack the hormonal environment necessary for muscle hypertrophy (34).

Strength Training

Strength training is a non-competitive use of progressive resistance exercise in an effort to improve physical abilities such as strength, power, and endurance (97). Body weight, elastic bands, free weights, and strength training machines may provide resistances in such methods. Sports training programs typically include a component of strength training with method and exercise selection, dependent on the sport in question (8).

Plyometrics

Plyometrics, shock training, is a method of training designed to improve explosive strength and rate of force development (8). Activities typically emphasize the application of the stretch-shortening cycle that consists of a lengthening muscle contraction providing enhancement to the immediately following shortening contraction (51). Jumping, bounding, and medicine ball throws can be considered plyometric forms of training.

Weight Training

Weight training is a non-competitive activity that utilizes methods similar to strength training but tends to be less formalized training with a goal of general conditioning (8). Body weight, elastic bands, free weights, and strength training machines may provide resistances in such methods.

Physiological Concepts in the Programming of Strength Training for the Young Athlete

A brief examination of scientific and popular literature clearly shows an infinite variety of loading parameters and training strategies that have been successful in increasing strength, power, and muscular hypertrophy in an adult population. Because of physiological differences in the development of children and adolescents, it cannot be assumed that exercise programming which is successful for adults will be successful in younger athletes. The following section will examine the physiological considerations in the programming and organization of strength and power training exercises in an effort to determine useful principles that coaches and trainers can apply to their own programs utilized to improve performance and prevent injury in young athletes.

Sensitive Periods

Physiological changes, in the muscular and nervous systems, progress in a predictable manner throughout a young athlete's growth and development from childhood to adolescence (52). Because of this fact, there are periods of development when a young athlete's physiology is more adaptable to a specific form of training stimulus. This period of training is most effective when programming targets a specific ability that is developing rather than one that is already matured (26). Drabik defines these periods of physiological development as "sensitive periods." He further stresses the importance of these periods by indicating the result of not developing ability at the optimal time will result in a permanent loss of fitness and athletic potential (26, 54). Sensitive periods differ between males and females due to the differing rates of biological development (26).

Fig. 1 Sensitive Periods by Age (Adapted from 26, 27)

Age	7-8		8-9		9-10		10-11		11-12		12-13		13-14		14-15		15-16		16-17	
	F	M	F	M	F	M	F	M	F	M	F	M	F	M	F	M	F	M	F	M
Absolute Strength	L		L	L			H	L	M					M		L	H	L		H
Speed	H	H	H	H	M	L	H						H			L	L			
Speed-Strength	L				H				H	L	H		L	M	M					
Strength-endurance			M		H		H		H	H								M		
Anaerobic Endurance			L	H	M		M	H	H			H				M			L	
Flexibility	L				L	H			M				M	H	H				H	H

H = Highest Rate of Development

M= Moderate Rate of Development

L= Low Rate of Development

Muscular Hypertrophy Adaptations to Training

A young athlete will naturally gain muscle mass and strength as he or she grows and develops via natural maturation processes. In comparing body composition in children at 8 years of age and teenagers at 15 years of age, 27% of the children's body composition consists of muscle mass and the teenagers' body composition consists of 33% muscle mass (27). With increasing natural body weight and total muscle mass, young athletes will obviously demonstrate greater absolute strength (90).

The natural increases in muscle mass and body weight are typically associated with the normal increases in anabolic hormones associated with puberty and adolescence (52). These changes in muscle mass are typically more pronounced in males than female to the larger secretion of testosterone which is 10 to 30 times greater in males than females (52). The increase in muscle mass can also be augmented via strength training in the 12-16 year old age bracket (27).

Because of these hormonal differences in pubertal and adolescent athletes compared to children, muscular hypertrophy with training may occur (63), but is atypical.

For instance, in a comparison between ten year old gymnasts who had undergone intensive gymnastics training and ten year old untrained controls measurable, but not significant, increases in maximum force and muscle mass were indicated (40). It was also indicated that the measured increases in force could not be associated entirely with the gains in muscle cross-sectional area (40), therefore, training programs designed to increase muscle mass in children are not typically recommended.

Neural Adaptations to Strength Training

In general, the younger the athlete the less able the athlete is able to fully activate his or her neuromuscular system. (40, 4, 48, 39, 82). Natural growth and development improves this ability as it has been shown that adolescent males are better able to activate the nervous system than prepubescent males (40). Comparisons to adults also show higher contractile speeds in favor of the adults over children (4).

A summary of the neuromuscular limitations during maximum muscle action in children in comparison to adolescents and adults is as follows:

- Longer electromechanical delay (time from onset of EMG activity to muscle tension) (4)

- Less eccentric EMG activity for the same amount of concentric force (82)

- Restricted eccentric capabilities (48)

- Decreased motor unit activation (39)

- Decreased muscle coordination (73)

In direct comparisons of strength-trained versus untrained athletes, the strength-trained athletes demonstrate improved abilities that off-set these limitations. A summary of the benefits of a strength training program for young athletes are as follows:

- Increased motor unit activation (73, 40)

- Greater percent recruitment of fast-twitch motor units during maximum voluntary contractions (40)

- Increased motor skill and coordination (73)

- Increased spatial and/or temporal recruitment of motor units (40)

As the potential for increased speed of movement, coordination, flexibility, and technique is greatest during the early periods of athletic development (27), the value and importance of a properly designed strength and conditioning program becomes clear from these comparisons.

Energy System Development and Recovery

Children are shown to rely less on glycolytic energy production in comparison to adults due to its lack of efficiency (45). This results in a lower production and accumulation of lactic acid during intensive efforts in comparison to pubescents and adults (45, 74).

Therefore, children rely more heavily on their oxidative capacity (74, 93) consuming as much as 10% more oxygen per unit body mass than adults (93). The result of greater dependence on oxidative capacity allows for greater phospho-creatine resynthesis during activity at a rate of up to two times faster than adults (74).

In a comparison between prepubescents, pubescents, and adults performing 10 x 10 second sprints separated by either 30 seconds, 1 minute, or 5 minute rest periods, the prepubescents were able to maintain their peak power output with just 30 second rest periods. The pubescents and adults required the 5 minute rest period to maintain peak power output (74).

This concept should be considered during program design involving interval type activities as prepubescents will require a shorter rest period in comparison to older athletes (74).

Strength Development, Gender, and Age Considerations

The physical loads of training clearly can improve strength regardless of age, however, some age and gender related differences exist that may influence the selection of exercises and program design to optimize balanced development of the young athlete. "The selection of strength exercises for juveniles and youths must provide a harmonious development of the musculature and sufficient strength development in conformity with the means, appropriate for this age group." (27)

In a comparison between eight year-old boys and girls, no significant differences are found in regard to isometric trunk strength or dynamic strength of the extremities. There was, however, a 17% difference in isometric hand-grip strength in favor of eight year-old boys (90).

Increases in the strength of the trunk and extremities tend to be non-uniform. In the ten to fourteen year-old age group, lower extremity extensor strength naturally increases by 85% in comparison to the shoulder girdle which only increases by 24% (27). Intensively trained ten to thirteen year-old female gymnasts, figure skaters, and ballet dancers, were found to have significantly greater muscle cross-section of the trunk musculature in comparison to untrained controls, specifically of the psoas, multifidus, and erector spinae. This increased muscle cross-section was strongly correlated with greater trunk flexion and extension force and endurance (72).

Relative strength should be emphasized in the thirteen to fifteen year-old age bracket (27). Thirteen year-old males demonstrate greater absolute strength and relative strength in comparison to thirteen year-old females except in comparison of knee extension strength (90). Interestingly, untrained thirteen year-old females demonstrate greater absolute strength than untrained eight year-old females, however, when corrected for relative trunk strength, the eight year-old females were stronger. This may have been due to a generally lower level of physical activity for the older females (90). Regardless, the above information clearly demonstrates benefits of a properly designed training program.

General Guidelines in the Organization of Strength Training of Young Athletes

The success of any training program depends on the foundational principles upon which it is based. The following guidelines provide a framework from which parents, trainers, and coaches may draw from in the design of effective strength training programs. They are in no particular order of importance.

All participants of a training program should undergo a detailed functional and orthopedic assessment. This will allow the identification of any unique postural abnormalities that may need to be addressed via corrective exercise or orthopedic conditions that may influence performance or predispose the athlete to injury during training (26). If necessary, consult with a medical professional before beginning a sport-specific training program (42).

Training should be designed with the intension that improvement will occur over a period of years (27). Training will follow a series of specific stages, based on the chronological, biological, and psychological development of the young athlete. Drabik organizes these stages into general strength, directed strength, and special strength. General strength exercises promote all-around athletic development and prepare the athlete for more intensive training to come. Directed strength exercises utilize similar muscle groups to those utilized in a particular sport. Special strength exercises are those performed through a similar range of motion and at similar speed to those of a particular sport. None of these stages should be avoided nor rushed through (26).

The initial stages of training should be general in nature using a variety of activities. Activities that include the training of strength, speed, flexibility, coordination, dexterity, and the skills of generating maximum effort in a minimum of time as well as the relaxation of muscles to produce skilled movement should be included (26, 27, 42). Zatsiorsky goes as far as recommending following a "3 year rule" in which a young athlete undergoes at least three years of general physical preparation (GPP) prior to performing strength specific exercises with a barbell (103). Even in young athletes who choose to pursue a single sport, as much as 80% of their total training time should consist of generalize physical activities (27).

Continue to utilize general physical preparation activities throughout an athlete's development. For ages twelve to fourteen, up to 80% of training should consist of GPP. For ages fourteen to seventeen, up to 50% of training should consist of GPP. For ages seventeen to twenty, up to 35% of training should consist of GPP (27).

Use body weight for resistance before adding external loads (26, 42). Common sense would dictate that if a young athlete were unable to control his or her own body weight during dynamic activities external loads would be unnecessary. When additional loads may be necessary for activities such as throwing, medicine balls may be appropriate (26).

Prioritize the strength development of the larger trunk musculature and muscles required for maintenance of posture (103,42,26, 52). This would include the hips, back, thighs, and abdominal muscles.

Emphasize the use of repetitive methods to develop dynamic strength (103, 26). This may consist of using the athlete's body weight or light loads for as many as thirty repetitions in some cases (54, 26).

Exercises may also be performed at maximal speed when necessary to a point of technical failure. This would be the point where the athlete is unable to maintain the designated speed of the exercises prescribed or proper technique (54).

Emphasize dynamic concentric contractions over eccentric contractions in younger athletes (26, 42). There is an age-related increase in eccentric force production that becomes more adult-like during puberty (81). This would place the optimal age to initiate eccentric loading at eleven to thirteen for females and thirteen to fifteen for males (42).

Alternate the body part being exercised to avoid excessive local fatigue and maintain technique (26). For example, a squat may be followed by an upper body throw followed by a run.

Emphasize technique and increase loads in small increments (26, 103, 42). Loads should be sufficient to allow performance of each repetition with good technique throughout the appropriate range of motion and at the appropriate speed.

Provide sufficient rest and recovery (26). Adequate recovery is necessary to prevent injuries, allow for maintenance of technique, and to provide sufficient resources for normal growth and development.

Strength Qualities Defined

Strength can be defined as "the ability of a given muscle or group of muscles to generate muscular force under specific conditions." (85) Special attention should be given to the latter portion of this definition in that depending on external conditions the production of, demonstration of, and description of strength will be variable. The type of movement, muscle action, external resistance, and speed of movement will all influence how strength is described, and more importantly, how proper selection of strength training means and methods are selected to develop the proper strength qualities in young athletes.

Muscle Action

Muscle action may be demonstrated and described as those that result in movement, or dynamic muscle actions, and those that result in no movement, or static muscle actions. In a static muscle action, also called **isometric contractions**, force is produced, however, no external movement is occurs (26, 84, 51, 103). Dynamic muscle actions result in either lengthening of the muscle while it produces force, or **eccentric or yielding contractions**; or shortening of the muscle while it produces force, or **concentric or overcoming contractions** (84, 103).

Muscle Action	Movement type	Change in Muscle Length
Isometric	Static	None
Concentric	Dynamic	Decrease
Eccentric	Dynamic	Increase

Effect of External Resistance on Strength

External resistance determines whether a muscular effort is maximal or sub-maximal. An external force resulting in the voluntary maximal muscular effort is considered a demonstration of **maximal strength** (84, 85). An example of this type of effort would be the maximum weight an athlete is capable lifting from the floor in a deadlift.

Because muscle action can vary when the athlete encounters external force, maximal strength can be defined as **maximal concentric strength, maximal isometric strength and maximal eccentric strength**. **Absolute strength** is often confused with maximal strength and can be defined as "the greatest amount of force that an individual can display in a given moment." (26) In sports activities, the closest one typically comes to achieving the demonstration his or her absolute strength is during a task in which an involuntary reflexive action augments the force produced by a muscle (84). This may occur in activities such as landing from a maximum jump height.

Relative strength is another form of describing maximal strength. An athlete's maximal strength divided by his or her body weight determines the athlete's relative strength (26, 84, 85). It is most commonly used when comparing athletes of different body size.

Relative strength = Maximal strength ÷ Body weight

Effect of Speed of Movement on Strength

The rate at which strength is demonstrated or work is performed is called **power** (85, 51). It is most commonly calculated using the equation:

$$Power = \frac{Force \times Distance}{Time} = Force \times Velocity$$

Or more simply

$$Power = strength \times speed$$

As one can identify from the equation, power has two primary components which include both the load and the speed of movement. When an athlete attempts to move a heavy load quickly, the athlete is considered to be demonstrating **strength-speed**. An example of a strength-speed activity would be performing a power clean with 80% of the athlete's one-repetition maximum (85, 26). When an athlete attempts to move a small external load quickly or performs an unloaded movement, the athlete is considered to be demonstrating **speed-strength** (85, 26). An example of a speed-strength activity would be throwing a regulation 5 oz. baseball or cycling the legs during sprint activity.

Explosive strength is "the ability to produce maximal force in a minimum of time" (85, 103). Explosive strength development is important as in most athletic activities requiring power expression, an athlete rarely has sufficient time to demonstrate his or her maximal strength. Activities such as jumping in track & field and throwing rely heavily on an athlete's explosive strength. Explosive strength is usually measured by an athlete's **rate of force development (RFD)** (85, 51).

For example:

Athlete A is capable of bench pressing 200 pounds in 5 seconds.
Athlete B is capable of bench pressing 200 pounds in 3 seconds.

Therefore, athlete B is said to have greater explosive strength and a higher RFD.
It is important to note that an athlete's maximal strength and RFD are not correlated (103). This means that just because an athlete is stronger than another his RFD is not necessarily higher.

For example:

Athlete A can bench press 300 pounds for a maximum and can bench press 200 pounds in 5 seconds.
Athlete B can bench press 250 pounds for a maximum and can bench press 200 pounds in 3 seconds.

Therefore, athlete B has a greater RFD. If competing in the same athletic activity where speed of movement is important and assuming equal skill between the two athletes, athlete B will most likely be more successful.

Effect of Duration on Strength

"The ability to effectively maintain muscular function under work conditions of long duration" is referred to **strength-endurance** (84, 85). This form of strength can be demonstrated under static, dynamic, or explosive conditions (85). Activities such as maintain a body position or hold in wrestling would require high levels of static-strength-endurance. Bicycling or distance running would require high levels of dynamic-strength-endurance. Top speed sprinting would require high levels of explosive-strength-endurance.

Other Factors that Influence Strength Expression in Young Athletes

- Natural (untrained) relative strength is achieved by age 16-17 years of age and is maintained until 41-50 years of age (27).

- Early physically developing athletes are better suited for sports involving strength and speed (36).

- Concentric force correlates to muscle cross-sectional area (48).

- Concentric, isometric, and eccentric force decline at the same rate with advancing fatigue (48).

- Speed-strength potential depends on strength, speed, technique, flexibility, coordination, and skill to relax muscles and produce volitional effort and are most effectively developed before the age of 14 (27).

- Rapid growth may influence the ability to generate power and alter coordination (36).

- Speed-strength qualities are one of the most important aims for young athletes in activities in which power is the basic quality (27).

- Body height increases faster than muscle mass, therefore, speed-strength activities such as running and jumping may be recommended rather than standard strength exercises (26).

- Speed-strength naturally increases in young athletes in the 11-14 years of age range (26).

- Speed-strength of females stabilizes or decreases at 14 years of age (26).

- Explosive strength of males naturally increases with age and reaches a maximum rate of development at 15-17 years of age and continues to increase until 25 years of age (26).

- Explosive strength of females naturally increases until 14 years of age (26).

Influence of Body Type on Strength and Power Training for Young Athletes

There is no single factor or variable that can predict an athlete's success in any particular sport (52). An athlete's level of interest and motivation, coaching influences, current level of skills, quality and quantity of practice all contribute and influence motor skill development (11). However, in sports requiring the demonstration of various levels of speed, strength, and power, the young athlete's body type may be a significant factor to determine his or her success in the sport of their choosing (59).

In adults, body type, or more specifically, somatotype, can account for 25-60% of an athlete's success in competitive sports. Correlations also exist in younger athletes as to specific motor skill ability (11). Especially in the case of the young athlete, the perceived ideal body type is not an adequate predictor of speed, strength, or power performance, but an athlete's performance may be hindered by the lack of the perceived ideal physique (5).

As an example of how body type can influence speed, strength, and power performance, one need look no further than any Olympic games. Select any event or sport and you will see drastic similarities in body type among the athletes (95). Throwers of heavy implements such as the shot put and discus all possess great height, broad shoulders, broad waist, heavy musculature, and moderate amounts of body fat. In sharp contrast, long and high jumpers present with a much more linear physique with much lower body fat and an almost sinewy muscularity. That's not to say that a shot putter is less explosive than a high jumper, yet it is the contrast in physique that significantly influences ultimate performance.

This influence of physique trickles down to youth sports as well. American youth football programs are the perfect example of how physique plays a role in athletic performance. Offensive and defensive lineman tend to possess the largest physiques, running backs tend to be shorter in stature, and receivers tend to be more linear in physique much like their adult counterparts in college and professional football.

In this section, we will briefly examine some of the normal physiological changes associated with growth of the young athlete. We will also examine the process of identifying and describing the young athlete's somatotype (body type). Using these concepts we will then examine the relationship of how somatotype influences performance in activities that require speed, strength, and power.

Through greater understanding of the influences of somatotype, the parent, coach, or trainer can then utilize the guidelines to understand how the young athlete will respond to various activities and applications of strength and power training. It may also assist int the development of a selection process to place young athletes in activities, sports, or player positions to allow the athlete to contribute and excel to the best of their abilities with the highest level of success and minimize the risk of injury.

Somatotype

Somatotyping is a physique rating system used to identify body types and to organize them into categories associated with various levels of genetic potential or limitation for specific activities. The most common classification system comes from the work of William Sheldon who classified body types into three basic categories: endomorphic, mesomorphic, and ectomorphic (59).

An individual is genetically programmed via physical development to demonstrate components of each of these three body types. The individual may demonstrate a predominance of one body type or a variable balance of all three types which is usually the case (59). There does appear to be some controversy as to whether somatotype is stable with increasing age (95, 53) or it is variable as an individual grows and develops (59, 53).

Endomorph

The endomorph is typically described as an individual with a larger body size with a soft or rounded appearance. Musculature also tends to be underdeveloped (59, 88, 9). Endomorphy is also associated with a predominance of the digestive organs (59) and a moderately high association with percent body fat (11). Skeletal structure shows a large ratio of pelvic breadth to height ratio and a smaller shoulder breath to height and shoulder breadth to pelvic breadth ratio. This may favor the development of muscle mass in the lower body due to the greater pelvic breadth (53).

Mesomorph

The mesomorph is typically described as an individual with well-developed musculature and a mature appearance. Body shape tends to be rectangular with muscle bone and connective tissue being predominant. The skin tends to be described as thick (59, 88) and there is a balanced association with percent body fat (11). Posture tends to be upright with height and breadth being intermediate (9). Skeletal structure shows a larger shoulder to height ratio as well as a larger shoulder breadth to pelvic breadth ratio (53).

Ectomorph

The ectomorph is typically described as an individual who is thin and usually tall. They tend to be lightly muscled and characterized by a linearity or fragility of build and a young appearance. Ectomorphy is also negatively associated with high levels of percent body fat (11). Posture tends to be described as slouched (59, 88, 9, 53). Skeletal structure shows a smaller ratio of pelvic breadth to height as well as a smaller ratio of shoulder breadth to height (53).

It is obvious through general observation of larger groups of young athletes that rarely does a single body type predominate. Rather most young athletes present with a combination of the above three body types and variable skeletal structures resulting in a full spectrum of body types from endomorph, endo-mesomorph, meso-endomorph, mesomorph, meso-ectomorph, ecto-mesomorph, and ectomorph (80).

Somatotype and Developmental Changes

Many factors associated with somatotype are related to growth and maturity. Some physical changes may also not affect somatotype (11). Variation in somatotype will also depend on the differences in the timing and rate of change associated with the adolescent growth spurt and stages of sexual maturity (59).The following will provide some generalizations as to the predominance of body type by normal growth and development.

Children tend to be less endomorphic and more ectomorphic as they grow toward adolescence (11).

Mesomorphy tends to predominate in boys more so than girls while endomorphy tends to predominate in girls moreso than boys (59, 21, 11).

During adolescence females tend to be more ectomorphic and males tend to be more endo-mesomorphic with all moving toward endomorphy with age (11, 77).

Mesomorphs and ectomorphs tend to be late maturers (11).

Somatotype and Training Related Changes

A common concern with parents is the affect that sports training will affect normal growth and development of their child. Work done by Malina & Bielicki indicates that sports training during puberty or the adolescent growth spurt does not influence the predetermined body size, height attained, or rate or timing of somatic, sexual, or skeletal maturity (65, 58).

Somatotype may (59, 11) or may not (36) be altered by intensive sports training. For instance, there is an association with metabolic fitness level and body type in both adults and young athletes (47). The most common change is associated with a decrease in body fat which would influence a change toward decreasing endomorphy (59, 9). However, training and any other environmental influences must be continued to maintain these changes in somatotype (59,11).

In a study involving junior weightlifters, at twelve and fourteen years of age, weightlifters were found to weight more than same aged runners or untrained controls. At age sixteen, weightlifters' body weights were significantly more than their running and untrained counterparts (27). This may indicate a natural selection toward mesomorphy for athletes choosing sports related to strength and power training and a training specific change during puberty and early adolescence.

Somatotype and Strength and Power Training

Somatotype and qualities such as body proportions, limb length, and body segment length are significant factors in the performance of strength and power training activities with strength being directly related to overall body size and chronological age (11).

Endomorphy, Strength, and Power

Athletes with a predominance of endomorphic qualities have strong correlations with activities requiring functional strength, isometric strength, stability (11) and producing larger magnitude of force especially when attempting to overcome the stability of another athlete. (9).

Because of their larger body mass, during the application of strength training activities it may be necessary to utilize training loads that are greater than those for normal weight children. In a study comparing nine year old children of normal weight children and overweight children (endomorphic), using the same relative loads up to 70% of the child's one repetition maximum did not produce a significant training effect in the overweight group compared to the normal weight group (31).

Aerobic capacity, running performance, agility, and jumping performance is significantly reduced due to greater fat mass (7, 11).

Therefore, care should be taken when programming repetitive running and jumping activities favoring lower volumes.

Endomorphs tend to perform favorably in weightlifting, weighted throws, and sports in which they must overcome the stability of another athlete such as an interior lineman in American football or wrestling.

Mesomorphy, Strength, and Power

Mesomorphy represents the ultimate athletic somatotypic contribution having positive associations with most categories of athletic performance including power, speed, strength, and endurance (78,11). According to the Medford Boys Growth Study, outstanding junior high school athletes tended toward mesomorphy with a secondary ectomorphy toward sports such as basketball or a secondary endomorphy toward sports such as American football (78).

Mesomorphs in the twelve to nineteen age group show good correlations for functional strength and to a lesser extent trunk and explosive strength, flexibility and running speed (11). Mesomorphy is also associated with a superior ability to withstand prolonged muscular and cardiovascular efforts according to Morehouse & Miller (80).

Ectomorphy, Strength, and Power

Whereas the endomorphs and mesomorphs demonstrate greater levels of absolute strength, athletes with strong ectomorphic qualities tend to demonstrate greater levels of relative strength due to lower total body mass. Their tendency for longer limbs also provides biomechanical advantages for power related activities (9). Ectomorphs tend to have superior performance in all variation of horizontal and vertical jumps, speed, agility, and reaction time (9, 78, 83, 44, 11).

Somatotype and Injury Potential

The effect of somatotype on injury potential appears to be related to the sport in question. For instance, a study that investigated the incidence of injury and somatotype for national level Netball players showed that while somatotype did influence player position it did not affect the incidence of injury. (44)

A similar study that looked at the injury potential of national soccer players based on their somatotype showed that increased injury rates increased as body types move from stronger, sturdier mesomorphs toward the more fragile ectomorphs. (80)

While these two studies involve more mature athletes, it may be assumed that younger athletes will experience the same relative loads and forces in the performance of sports of similar relative intensity. Therefore, precautions in player positioning and the athletes tolerance to loads, forces, and training intensities should be considered.

Injuries rarely occur during free-play activities with most acute injuries occurring in cases of overuse in preadolescents during sports such as weightlifting, throwing, and skating; and lower work capacity and endurance in young athletes. (11)

Strength and Power Testing for the Young Athlete

Strength and power testing for the young athlete provides the coach, trainer, or parent with information in regard to the athlete's current level of physical abilities. The results of these tests may then be utilized to determine the level of importance for strength and power activities in the athlete's training program, to establish an athlete's current level of abilities, to monitor the athlete's progress in a specific training program, or to monitor the rehabilitation process in the injured athlete (79)

There is a broad array of activities and tests that may be used to establish a young athlete's status in regard to strength and power performance. Field tests that include performance against external resistance or body weight, running, jumping, agility, and throwing may all be used to develop standards of performance for individual athletes and groups of athletes. Regardless of the test used or the outcomes recorded by the athletes, it is important to note that there is no single test or level of performance during a test that can clearly predict an athlete's potential level of performance or tolerance to sports-related training. (52)

Jump Tests

The standing long jump for distance and vertical jump tests for height provide indicators of a young athlete's preparedness for speed-strength, explosive strength, and power activities. (59,27, 54) Performance in such tests improves linearly with age up to the age of 14 without specific jump training with the largest increase coming between the ages of 11 and 14 years of age. (27) Males may see increases up to age 18. (59)

Sprinting Tests

Short sprint tests such as a 30 to 60 meter sprints provide indicators of a young athlete's linear speed. (59, 26, 54) Performance in such tests will see rapid increases from ages 5 to 8 and ongoing increases to age 18 for boys and 13 to 14 for girls. (59)

Agility Tests

Agility tests such as 10-yard shuttle runs provide indicators of a young athlete's ability to change direction quickly. (59, 26, 54) Performance in such tests see rapid increases in performance from age 5 to 8 and ongoing improvements up to the age of 18 for boys and 13 to 14 for girls. (59)

Strength and Strength-Endurance Tests

Tests such as total number of one-legged squats, push-ups, pull-ups or static tests requiring the maintenance of a fixed posture provide indicators of strength and strength-endurance. The flexed arm hang in which the young athlete holds him or herself suspended from a bar with the arms flexed to greater than 90 degrees is an example of a static strength endurance test. (59, 26) Strength-endurance during such tests increases linearly with age up to 13 to 14 to boys and 16 to 17 for girls. (59)

Upper Body Power Tests

Throws for distance such as an overhead softball throw or a medicine ball throw provide indicators of upper body power. (59, 54) Performance in such tests increases linearly for boys up to age 18 and only slightly for girls from age 6 to 14 years of age. (59)

Abdominal Strength and Strength-Endurance Tests

The number of sit-ups performed is a common test providing indicators of abdominal strength and strength-endurance. (59, 54) Performance increases linearly from age 6 to 13 for boys and 6 to 14 for girls. (59) There may also be some worth in testing the abdominals isometrically as this type of contraction occurs frequently in sport. (90)

Grip Tests

Isometric grip tests are simple and highly reliable tests that can provide a generalized measure of static strength in young athletes and a specific measure for athletes in sports that require significant grip strength. (59, 69, 96) Grip strength improves linearly with age for boys up to age 13 to 14 at which time there is a significant increase. Grip strength for girls increases linearly up to age 16 to 17. (59) Minimal differences are found between boys and girls up to age 8. (90) Norms for grip strength are provided in the following table.

Average hand grip strength in young people in pounds(Adapted from 60)

Boys

Age	6-7	8-9	10-11	12-13	14-15	16-17
Right	32.5	41.9	53.9	58.7	77.3	94.0
Left	30.7	39.0	48.4	55.4	64.4	78.5

Girls

Age	6-7	8-9	10-11	12-13	14-15	16-17
Right	28.6	35.3	49.7	56.8	58.1	67.3
Left	27.1	33.0	45.2	50.9	49.3	56.9

Maximal Strength Testing

Maximal strength testing for young athletes is a controversial subject with experts voicing opinions for and against. (16) In a study performed on 96 children from age six to twelve years of age in which each child performed a one repetition maximum (1 RM) test for one upper body exercise and one lower body exercise on child-sized weight training machines, the results showed that no injuries occurred during the testing and that the children showed no adverse reactions to the testing protocols. (29) While this study certainly indicates that 1RM testing may be performed safely under such conditions, the limitations of the study in that tests were performed on weight training machines that restrict movement and provide additional stability puts questionable value on such information.

The knowledge of a qualified athlete's 1RM in a specific lift may be helpful in determining the appropriate training loads for a specific exercise to induce a training effect or in determining the response to a previous training protocol. (6, 79) The results of 1 RM testing may be acquired by direct testing of the athlete's ability to lift a 1 RM load or by performing a multiple repetition test and estimating the 1RM.

While there are regression equations that can effectively predict a 1RM load based on the number of repetitions performed at a specific weight, these tend to be somewhat inconvenient as a unique equation is required for each exercise. (24) A simpler and equally effective method may be to estimate an athlete's 1 RM lift based on the number of repetitions performed with a weight as a percentage of the true 1 RM. The chart below provides such an estimate:

Percent of 1 RM and repetitions completed (Adapted from 6)

Repetitions Completed	Percent of 1 RM
1	100
2	95
3	93
4	90
5	87
6	85
7	83
8	80
9	77
10	75
11	70
12	67
15	65

Based on the number of repetitions completed, the percentage of 1 RM is determined. By dividing the weight used in the testing situation by the percentage of 1 RM, the estimated 1 RM is calculated as below:

Weight lifted: 200 pounds

Number of repetitions completed: 5

Estimated percentage of 1 RM (from chart): 87% (0.87)

200 ÷ 0.87 = **229.89 pounds**

14

Organization of Training for the Young Athlete

Successful development of the young athlete is dependent on a systematic approach that includes a broad range of general activities, or multi-lateral training, focused attention to developing a mastery of specific exercise techniques, and consideration of the proper application of exercises intensity. According to S. M. Vaitsekhovsky in *The Coaches Book*, this should be a period of "comparatively prolonged initial training, excluding forced elements." (62)

The next sections will provide the parent, trainer, or coach with background and general recommendations in strength and power program design for young athletes based on general divisions of prepubescent and adolescent growth and developmental periods.

Prepubescent Athletic Development

The importance of a properly designed strength, power, and conditioning program for the prepubescent athlete cannot be understated. In the prepubescent athlete, all athletic abilities correlate highly with one another. Therefore, an increase in strength will result in an increase in speed, agility, and endurance. (54) Motor skill, flexibility, and other neuromuscular traits that are developed prior to the onset of hormonal changes during puberty also increases the young athletes ability to tolerate training at higher intensities and volumes as he or she matures. (34) Properly applied age-specific strength training programs have been shown to benefit children as young as 6 years old. (10)

Prepubescent Program Design Considerations

Priority of training must be given to the sensitive periods of the development of motor qualities of young athletes to assure ultimate performance during later stages of maturity. The following will provide specifics to improve exercise selection and overall program design.

Motor Skill Rate of Development by age (26, 27)

Age	Motor Skill Rate of Development
7-8	Highest for speed (26) and quick flexion/extension of extremities and trunk (27)
8-9	Highest for speed and general endurance (26) Moderate for quick movements (27) and dynamic strength-endurance (26) especially trunk extension (27)
9-10	Highest for flexibility (26, 27), speed-strength, static/dynamic strength-endurance (26) Moderate for quick movements (27)
10-11	High for dynamic strength-endurance (26), anaerobic endurance, and general endurance (27) Moderate for strength and speed-strength development of legs and trunk (27)
11-12	Highest for static/dynamic strength-endurance (26), torso flexion strength-endurance (27) Moderate for flexibility (26)
12-13	Highest for anaerobic endurance (26, 27) High for strength-endurance (27)

Strength and power exercises can be used to correct postural deficiencies in prepubescent athletes. Due to short attention spans, excises typically used in postural correction programs may be inappropriate for children. Therefore, incorporating static and dynamic movements that influence strength in a lengthened or shortened range of motion are more appropriate. (54) Examples of such exercises are bear crawls to improve static postural strength, overhead soccer throws to increase shoulder mobility and trunk extension range of motion, or a high step-up to increase hip mobility.

Prepubescent Training Intensity, Volume, and Frequency

Research indicates a broad variability of loads that may elicit a training effect in prepubescent athletes. In general, appropriate loads are those that emphasize higher repetition protocols have demonstrated the most success.

For example, a study among untrained eight year old children compared a heavily loaded group performing six to eight repetition loads in a chest press exercise, a moderately loaded group performing thirteen to fifteen repetitions per set of chest press, a complexed group that performed six to eight repetitions per set of chest press immediately followed by six to eight medicine ball chest passes, and a group that performed thirteen to fifteen medicine ball chest passes. Results showed that only the moderately loaded group (thirteen to fifteen repetitions of chest press) and the complexed group (six to eight repetitions of chest press and 6-8 repetitions of chest passes) significantly increased the number of repetition that they could perform with their previous one repetition maximum performed prior to training. (28)

A second study of nine to eleven year old boys utilized an initial ten week training phase of ten to twelve repetition (~70-75% 1 RM) maximum loads followed by a ten week phase of five to seven repetition maximum loads (~80-85% 1 RM). While overall one repetition maximum strength increased significantly in both the bench press and leg press exercises after twenty weeks, a greater increase in strength was noted during the first ten week training phase that emphasized higher repetitions. (73)

Regardless of the training protocol utilized external resistances used should be the minimum required to elicit a training effect. For children, initial training loads may extend from no external loads to 50-60% 1 RM (42) although performance may be enhanced using loads a low as 20% of 1 RM. (103) According to the American Academy of Pediatrician's Committee on Sports Medicine and Fitness, seven to eight year old children can safely perform strength training exercises that emphasize weights that can be lifted for twelve to fifteen repetitions. (26)

The use of lighter resistances or body weight may be used to develop strength-endurance (26) or at high speeds and include activities directly utilized in specific sports. (54)
Exercises should be discontinued when the athlete is unable to maintain the prescribed technique or speed. (54)

Strength training frequency for prepubescent athletes in the literature tends to be consistent showing that two to three training sessions per week with a volume of one to three sets of six to ten exercises would elicit significant gains in strength. (26, 98, 71, 73, 28, 89, 103, 10) To progress, prepubescent athletes should be able to perform two to three sets of fifteen repetitions for exercises in three consecutive training sessions before weight is increased. (26, 10) Increases in load should be as little as one to three pounds (0.5 to 1.5 kg) (26) or up to 5-10% of the current load (10) keeping in mind the general rule of performing exercises with the minimal load required to produce a training effect.

Suggested Activities

It is general consensus that body weight provides sufficient resistance when initiating a strength and power training program for prepubescents. (26, 42, 10, 30) Activities may include but are not limited to sprinting, jumping, crawling, climbing, push-up variations, hanging, and pull-ups. To maintain interest, these activities may be arranged in complexes which combine exercises or obstacle courses. (26)

Multi-joint exercises such as squat variations and presses may be introduced on an individual basis as the young athlete demonstrates proficiency of technique. Complex exercises such as Olympic weightlifting variations may also be introdued. Loads for such exercises should consist of very light weights or no weight using a broomstick with emphasis on learning proper technique and developing skill. (26, 30) Medicine balls, barbells, and dumbbells may be utilized when externally loading is appropriate. (26)

Athletes as young as ten years old may learn the techniques associated with track and field such as long jumping and high jumping. (26) Competitive situations should be avoided until the time where the athlete is able to understand and demonstrate proper technique. The outcome of such competitive situations should be considered of low importance. (54)

Adolescent Athletic Development

The adolescent period represents an ideal time for strength training of the young athlete due to the increase in sex hormones associated with this stage of development. (42, 41) Increases in strength during this period of development show a "strong positive relationship" with higher levels of sports performance. The hormonal changes promote an improved ability of the body to repair itself, increase strength, increase muscle mass, and increase the density of bones, ligaments, and tendons. (52) Strength training should emphasize increases in relative strength (27) noting a progressive increase in relative eccentric torque with age. (81)

Adolescent Program Design Considerations

Priority of training must be given to the sensitive periods of the development of motor qualities of young athletes to assure ultimate performance during later stages of maturity. The following will provide specifics to improve exercise selection and overall program design.

Motor Skill Rate of Development by age (26, 27)

Age	Motor Skill Rate of Development
13-14	Highest for speed (26) and flexibility (26, 27) High for strength (27) and static endurance especially arm flexion Moderate for speed-strength (26)
14-15	Highest for static strength-endurance (26, 27) Moderate (26) to High (27) for speed-strength and general endurance Moderate for strength (27)
15-16	Highest for flexibility (26, 27) Moderate (26) to high for strength-endurance (27) Moderate (27) to low (26) for speed
16-17	Highest for strength, static strength-endurance (26, 27)

The ultimate goal of the early adolescent training period is to continue to develop a solid foundation of speed, strength, and endurance in preparation for future specialization in a specific sport or sports. Because intensities and volumes of strength and power training remain fairly low, it is unnecessary to program complex periodization schemes until the age of specialization. This age varies by sport but typically occurs at approximately fifteen years of age. (54)

Latter stage hormonal responses to strength training in adolescents are similar to that of adults. This indicates that these young athletes may be more tolerant to higher training volumes than previously thought. (34)

Adolescent Training Intensity, Volume, and Frequency

The first stage of the adolescent period of development should reflect the programming initiated in the prepubescent period with an emphasis on general physical preparation. Of the entire training program, only 20% of training should be comprised of specialized strength training with an emphasis on technique. (27)

The optimal intensity of loading for this first stage is raised only slightly from the prepubescent period using loads up to 60% of 1 RM. Recommended training volume at this intensity allows the completion of 3 sets for at least 10-12 repetitions per set with one exercise performed per body part. (26) Strength-specific training should be performed 2-3 times per week with at least one day of recovery between training days. (27, 26) Loads may be progressed when the athlete is capable of performing an exercise for three sets of twelve repetitions in three consecutive training sessions. (26)

As the adolescent stage progresses loads of 70% 1 RM have been shown to produce the greatest rate of development in the squat and strength-speed exercises. (27, 62) Exercises should be performed three times per week and remain limited to one exercise per body part for three to four sets of seven to eleven repetitions. Loads may be progressed when the athlete is able to perform three to twelve repetitions in three consecutive workouts. (26)

In the latter stages of the adolescent period of development loads of 50 to 80% of 1 RM may be used. Typical frequency may remain at three times per week with two exercises per body part for four to six sets of six to ten repetitions. Loads may be increased when the athlete is able to perform four sets of ten repetitions in two consecutive workouts. (26) Loads up to 90% 1 RM in latter stages of this developmental group have been shown to produce the greatest rate of development in the squat and strength-speed exercises (27, 62) and 70% of 1 RM loads are ideal for increasing speed-strength. (27) For sixteen to eighteen year old athletes, training at 90 % of 1 RM should be performed no more than one time per week for one to two repetitions per set for a maximum of four total reps per training session. (27)

Suggested Activities

The initial stages of the adolescent training period should continue with the general developmental nature of the prepubescent period. Strength training exercises are performed in a slower, controlled manner than the specific speed of the sports for which they are training. (26) Practice of multi-joint exercises such as Olympic weightlifting variations, squats, and presses may be performed progressed over a period of months using a broomstick, a metal pole, and light weight to assure ongoing development of technique. (30)

As the athlete grows and develops into the latter stages of the adolescent period, exercises may become more directed to include not only general strength exercises performed at higher intensity, but also directed strength training exercises that more closely approximate the dynamic components of a specific sport. These exercises may include explosive lifts and squats as well as various throws and jumps. (26) Directed exercises are then followed by special exercises that approximate the same speed, range of motion, and temporal dynamics of a specific sport. (26) Training technique must be closely monitored at all time as it is a valuable indicator of training stress. (34)

Benefits of Strength and Power Training for Young Athletes

The application and benefits of strength and power training has been examined extensively in the adult athletic population. Unfortunately, conflicting anecdotal information tends to rule discussion of strength and power training for the young athlete. The following section intends to examine some of the misconceptions in regard to the risks and benefits of strength and power training for the young athlete.

Protective Mechanisms of Strength and Power Training for Young Athletes

It stands to reason that increased strength and power development in the young athlete is beneficial to sports performance. As previously noted, strength levels in the prepubescent athlete is correlated to all physical qualities of strength, power and endurance. (54) Development of physical traits in the period of development are also foundational to further improvements in performance as the athlete matures, thus improving the ultimate potential development of the athlete. (34)

Unlike the prepubescent athlete, the adolescent athlete may benefit further from the additional hormonally based benefits of strength related to hypertrophy, muscle endurance, and injury prevention. (27, 72, 34, 32, 97) Increased strength may allow athletes to avoid competitive situations in which injury is more likely (32), and it seems likely that a muscle more resistant to fatigue is also more resistant to injury. (97)

A study of fifty-six 9th grade females who underwent nine months of plyometric training not only showed an increase in knee extension strength training induced bone strength but also experienced a 27% improvement in medial/lateral balance and a 17% improvement in anterior/posterior balance which may reduce fall-related injuries. (101)

Another study of fifty-three female high school athletes who participated in a supervised six week training program agrees with this assumption. Their training program included plyometrics, strength training, and core/balance training resulting in significant improvement in performance parameters of vertical jump, single-leg hop distance, speed, bench press, squat, knee range of motion, and most importantly knee stability in comparison to controls. The measures of knee stability showed a 28% reduction in knee valgus torque and a 38% reduction in knee varus torque which would be associated with a reduced risk of injury. (64)

Beneficial Tissue Adaptations to Strength And Power Training in Young Athletes

Tendons, ligaments, cartilage, and other connective tissues increase in strength, weight, and thickness in response to physical activity. (32) This would certainly be indicative of a reduced injury risk, but it should be noted that such results are inconclusive in prepubescent studies. (12)

The effects on bone development are of particular interest due to the prevalence of osteoporosis in the older population. (See the Surgeon General's report on Bone Health and Osteoporosis at http://www.hhs.gov/surgeongeneral/news/speeches/10142004.htm)

The rate of bone acquisition decreases significantly after the age of 15-16 for females and seventeen to eighteen for males. After the onset of puberty there appears to be a limited effect on interventions associated with nutrient intake or physical activity on bone acquisition that may put the individual at risk for osteoporosis later in life. (33, 13) This implies that there may be a "window of opportunity" in the prepubescent and early pubertal stages of development to enhance the acquisition of bone mass via higher impact activities, and progressive loading through strength training. (31, 55) As much as 40% of postnatal bone strength is determined by the effect mechanical usage. (33)

A Finnish study of eight to twenty year old females showed that physical activity was the only factor associated with increased bone mineral content and density other than normal growth-related changes. The authors also recommended that physical activity associated with increased bone mass should begin early in life. (92)

The question of how early in life this type of training should begin may have been provided by a study of eighty-nine children from ages five to nine years. These children underwent supervised jumping drills over a period of seven months. Forces absorbed by these children during the drills were shown to be approximately eight times their body weight. Results showed an increase in bone mineral content of the femoral neck and lumbar spine implying that adaptations to bone are site-specific to the areas of loading. As a side note, not injuries were reported in this study and no effects on normal growth were noted. (35)

Site specificity of bone adaptations was also noted in twenty-four 9th grade male hockey players who participated in a full body weight training program over a period of eighteen months. Greater bone mass was found in the humerus and femur and was related to the magnitude of weight-bearing loading. (70) Similar results were found in 10 collegiate powerlifters who had been training for at least 2.5 years. Bone mineral density of the entire body, lumbar spine, arm, and pelvis were found to be greater than a matched control group. The study noted that there was an especially high correlation to bond mineral density of the lumbar spine and the weight lifted in the deadlift exercise which is known for significant loading of the back. (91)

Strength levels were also found to be a good predictor of bone mineral content in junior Olympic weightlifters between the ages of fifteen and twenty. Bone mineral content was found to be two standard deviations greater than controls and best predicted by the athlete's body weight and personal best lifting total. (94) A similar study on seventeen year old Olympic weightlifters who had been training for 2.7 years showed that the lifters bone density was greater than age-matched controls and adults. (22)

It would appear that greater external loading may be more beneficial than simply increasing activity levels. A comparison between bodybuilders, swimmers, runners, and controls showed that the bodybuilders had greater overall bone mineral content and density than the swimmers, runners, and controls. (43)

Injury Risk in Strength and Power Training

The risk of injury during the strength and power training of young athletes is a realistic and very serious concern. According to the U.S. Consumer Product Safety Commission via its National Electronic Injury Surveillance system, from 1991 to 1996 an estimated 20,940 to 26,120 injuries associated with weight lifting were reported in individual twenty-one years old and younger. **Most of these injuries were considered preventable due to a cause of improper technique, attempting maximal lifts, and unsupervised training.** (A.A of P position statement)

In a similar study in 1986, a breakdown of injuries by age group showed that of a total of 43,000 emergency room visits due to weight training injuries, 2,270 occurred in the two to four year old age group, 5,940 occurred in the five to fourteen year old age group, and 21,240 occurred in the 15024 year old age group. (76) In 1987, 8,543 weight lifting injuries occurred in the zero to fourteen years old age group. **40% of these injuries occurred in the home in unsupervised situations** (12)**, and young children were injured while playing in the weight room or when weight plates were dropped.** (76)

As an example of athletes who utilize strength and power training to improve performance, a study of 354 football players showed a total of twenty-five strength training-related injuries for a rate of 7.1%. (76)

In contrast, a study of seventy-one competitive adolescent power lifters showed a much higher injury rate of 39%. (15)

As a frame of reference, 3% to 11% of all school-aged children will experience a sports-related injury. (102) In 1985, a total of 5.6 million sports-related injuries were reported in the under twenty year old age group. (76)

Sports Injuries per 100 participant hours in school sports (adapted from 46)

Track and Field	0.57
Basketball	0.03
Football	0.10
Gymnastics	0.044
Physical Education (United Kingdom)	0.18
Powerlifting	0.0027
Rugby (United Kingdom)	1.92
Soccer (United Kingdom)	6.20
Tennis	0.001
Volleyball	0.0013
Weightlifting (United Kingdom)	0.0017
Weight Training (United Kingdom)	0.0035

In consideration of the above information, it is clear that injuries related to strength and power training and activities do occur, but the rate is comparable to many accepted childhood and adolescent sports and activities. (97)

Types of Injury

There are two basic types of injury associated with any form of sports training. The first is an acute injury associated with an obvious direct trauma. The second is an overuse or repetitive strain injury. (49,86) Overuse or repetitive strain injuries typically present as tendonitis, bursitis, or apophysitis of the tendon insertion. (49)

Potential Contributing Factors for Injury in Young Athletes (23,86,49)	
Acute Injury	Overuse/Repetitive Strain Injury
Lack of physical maturity	Heavy work or pace
Improper equipment	Training Errors
Environmental Factors	Inadequate work/rest ratios
-playing surface	Poor instruction/training/supervision
-damaged/unsecured equipment	Poor conditioning
Training Errors	Anatomical malalignment
-poor technique	Footwear
-poor program design	Playing surface
Excessive Parental Expectations	Prior injury or disease state
Poor supervision	Growth spurt

Fractures

Fractures associated with training are commonly associated with falls or the dropping of weights. (76,8) Due to skeletal immaturity, young athletes may also be susceptible to spinal conditions such as pars interarticularis stress fractures, spondylolysis, or spondylolisthesis during weightlifting. (8, 97)

Back Pain

While there are numerous contributing factors, weakness of the back extensor muscles relative to the flexors may be a possible contributing factor in young athletes with low back pain associated with strength training. (68, 97) A study of forty-three females and fifty-three males ages ten to nineteen showed that those who complained of low back pain within the last year were also shown to have stronger back flexors than extensors. (68) Inappropriate exercise selection and loading parameters has also been implicated. (14)

Cardiac Injury

While there is a significant rise in blood pressure during repetitive strength training exercise (12, 97, 66), there is no indications that intensive sports training, strength training, or competitive weightlifting results any negative effects on cardiovascular fitness (12), injury to the heart (2), or chronic high blood pressure in young athletes. (12, 97) A study in which eight children performed bench presses to exhaustion at 60%, 75%, 90%, and 100% of 1RM showed that cardiovascular responses of heart rate and blood pressure were similar to those of adults. (66)

Growth Plate Injury

Because the growth plate is weaker than the bone and ligaments are two to five times stronger than the epiphysis (57), the loading and forces absorbed during strength and power training may predispose young athletes to growth plate injury. (17, 2) Damage to the growth plates, or epiphysis, of bones is a common concern as this type of injury may potentially result in abnormal or arrested bone growth. (36)

There have been such injuries reported in adolescent weightlifters, however few cases have been reported in preadolescents. (37) It is important to note that even though this type of injury exists, there is no evidence that growth complications associated with epiphyseal fractures are excessive in young athletes training at higher levels of competition or at higher intensities. (2, 12, 97)

In a fourteen week study of eighteen, eight year old males who participated in a supervised strength training program results showed significant strength gains and no physeal or epiphyseal injuries. According to Dr. Avery Faigenbaum, "Growth plate injuries have not occurred in any youth strength training study that followed established training guidelines." (25)

General Guidelines to Prevent Injury during Strength and Power Training

- Planning of training programs must take into consideration the level of physical maturation of the athlete. (57)

- Incomparison to expert lifters, novice weight lifters tend to use techniques that predispose the athlete to injury. (56) It is imperative that proper technique be emphasized at all times during strength and power training exercise. (76, 12, 97)

- Avoid maximal loads or large increases in loading or activity in developing athletes. (97)

- Horseplay should never be tolerated in the weight room. (76)

- Supervision by a qualified instructor must be provided at all times. (97)

Controversies in Strength and Power Training

There are numerous controversies in regard to strength and power training for young athletes. Evidence to support these controversies is often sparse or nonexistent. The following section will briefly examine some of the available literature.

Loss of Flexibility due to Strength Training

The belief that strength training reduces flexibility is long standing. Decades ago, sports coaches instructed their players to avoid strength training for fear that they would become "muscle bound" and lose flexibility resulting in lower levels of performance.

Studies on adults and strength training show that flexibility can increase (100) or remain unchanged (99) even when specific flexibility exercises are not performed. A review of the literature in regard to young athletes and strength training showed no evidence that children lose flexibility with strength training. (38)

Strength training may actually be beneficial to increasing flexibility. Strength training exercises performed through the full range of motion with a progressive emphasis on the application of the loading in the range of limited motion during the eccentric contraction will increase both active and passive flexibility. (85, 1) For this reason and because of the extreme ranges of motion experienced in training, Olympic weightlifters tend to be some of the most flexible of all athletes. (85)

The Stunting of Growth Resulting from Strength and Power Training

The stunting of normal growth due to strength and power training is also a long standing belief. In this case, there are conflicting results when examining young athletes involved in intensive training.

For instance, young gymnasts were studied over five years with athletes ranging from seven to sixteen years of age. In comparison to norms, these young athletes were found to have a slower growth rate and delayed menarche. (67) In another study, a group of eighty-three gymnasts from ages five to fifteen were shown to have shorter leg length than controls, however leg length velocity increased at the same rate. This would imply that perhaps the gymnasts in question gravitated toward activities to which their natural physical attributes are found to be of benefit. (67)

One case in which gymnasts were observed to demonstrate stunted leg growth may have been the result of the interruption of normal hypothalamus-pituitary-gonadal axis as a result of intensive training of twenty-two hours per week. (67) In such situations, other factors such as genetic or nutritional status must also be considered as potential influences. (57)

In conflict to the above examples, thirty-two prepubescents who underwent fourteen weeks of supervised strength training were found to have a greater increase in height in comparison to controls although the increase was not statistically significant. (75)   Another group of prepubescents ages five to nine performed jumping drills that required them to absorb forces up to eight times their body weight experienced no effect on their normal growth. (35)   It should also be noted that young males participating in intensive training for sports such as cycling, rowing, and hockey experienced no effects on normal growth. (57)

The Effectiveness of Machine based Strength Training

The effectiveness of machine-based training has caused a great deal of confusion among coaches, parents, and athletes. This is primarily due to concerns over the risk of injury associated with free weight strength training even though the risk of injury is no greater than many other accepted activities. (38, See INJURY RISK IN STRENGTH AND POWER TRAINING

As far as effectiveness of transfer to sport performance, machine-based training may fall short in comparison to free weights. Free weights demonstrate greater mechanical specificity because of the need for the athlete to stabilize the bar rather than having stability being provided by the guiding mechanism of the strength machine. (87) There are also indications of greater muscle recruitment in free weight training

(61, 87) as well as greater muscle electrical activity in the stabilizing muscles during free weight exercises (61) which implies greater joint strength. (87)

There are also issues related to training economy. With machine-based training, muscles or groups of muscles tend to be isolated from others to complete the exercise requiring numerous exercises to be performed, whereas free weight allows the training of more muscles with fewer exercises. (87) This is also advantageous to coaches and trainers who have limited time to include strength training as a component of their sports training programs.

Explosive Lifts are Dangerous

Even though the training of explosive lifts shows an injury rate comparable or lower than many accepted sports activities, many coaches and trainers continue to avoid their use in training there to be a higher risk of injury. (See INJURY RISK IN STRENGTH AND POWER TRAINING) This may be an unfounded belief.

In a comparison between standing vertical jumps, drop jumps from 42 cm and 63 cm, and 75-90% of 1RM power cleans, vertical jump and drop jump landing ground reaction forces were found to be greater than the catch phase of the power clean. The authors also noted that all landings were two-footed landings in the experiment and that these forces are often absorbed on one foot during normal sporting activities. These results indicate the use of explosive lifts in training are less stressful to the musculoskeletal system than many commonly performed jumps. (18)

The explosive lifts are technical in nature and require a great deal of practice under direct supervision of a qualified coach to assure quality of training and to prevent injury. In the training of young weight lifters, it is common that the first few months of training consist only of learning the technical aspects of the lifts using a wooden dowel or a metal pole before any weight is added to the lifts. (27)

Position Papers Regarding Strength and Power Training for Young Athletes

The following are summaries or excerpts from the position papers presented by the American Academy of Pediatrics, USA Weightlifting Sports Science Committee, the National Strength and Conditioning Association, and the American College of Sports Medicine.

AMERICAN ACADEMY OF PEDIATRICS: Strength Training by Children and Adolescents

Recommendations:

1. Strength training programs for preadolescents and adolescents can be safe and effective if proper resistance training techniques and safety precautions are followed.

2. Preadolescents and adolescents should avoid competitive weight lifting, powerlifting, bodybuilding, and maximal lifts until they reach physical and skeletal maturity.

3. When pediatricians are asked to recommend or evaluate strength training programs for children and adolescents, the following issues should be considered:

   a. Before beginning a formal strength training program, a medical evaluation should be performed by a pediatrician. If indicated, a referral may be made to a sports medicine physician who is familiar with various strength training methods as well as risks and benefits in preadolescents and adolescents.

b. Aerobic conditioning should be coupled with resistance training if general health benefits are the goal.

c. Strength training programs should include a warm-up and cool-down component.

d. Specific strength training exercises should be learned initially with no load (resistance). Once the exercise skill has been mastered, incremental loads can be added.

e. Progressive resistance exercise requires successful completion of 8 to 15 repetitions in good form before increasing weight or resistance.

f. A general strengthening program should address all major muscle groups and exercise through the complete range of motion.

g. Any sign of injury or illness from strength training should be evaluated before continuing the exercise in question.

To read the entire policy statement and full references, please see Pediatrics Vol. 107 No. 6 June 2001

AMERICAN COLLEGE OF SPORTS MEDICINE: Plyometric Training for Children and Adolescents (written for the American College of Sports Medicine by Avery D. Faigenbaum, Ed. D. and Donald A. Chu, Ph.D., PT, ATC)

Plyometric have been previously thought of as a method of conditioning reserved for adult athletes, the American College of Sports Medicine (ACSM) contends that plyometric training is a safe, beneficial and fun activity for children and adolescents provided that the program is properly designed and supervised.

Regular participation in a plyometric training program may also help to strengthen bones, facilitate weight control, and prevent injuries.

With qualified coaching and age-appropriate instruction, plyometric training can be a safe, effective and fun method of training for children and teenagers who have developed an adequate baseline of strength.

Plyometric training should begin with simple, lower intensity drills and progress to higher intensity drills over time.

Beginning with one to three sets of six to ten repetitions on one upper body exercise and one lower body exercise twice per week on nonconsecutive days seems reasonable.

Children and adolescents should be provided with specific information on proper exercise technique, rate of progression, and safe training procedures (e.g., warm-up and cool-down).

Plyometrics are not intended to be a stand-alone exercise program and should be incorporated into a well-designed overall conditioning program that also includes strength, aerobic, flexibility, and agility training.

The contention that plyometrics are inappropriate for boys and girls is not consistent with the needs of children and teenagers or their physical abilities.

Reprinted with permission of the American College of Sports Medicine, "Plyometric Training for Children and Adolescents," December 2001, www.acsm.org

USA Weightlifting Sports Science Committee Position Statement: Weight Training and Competition in Youth Populations

Recommendations:

- Based on the available medical and scientific data the committee recommends:

• Weightlifting training programs and competitions for children should be conducted by well-trained adults. Ideally, the supervising staff should be certified to coach and certified in first-aid. The American Academy of Pediatrics proposes that it is essential that all staff working with children should be trained in supervising strength training through completion of programs from universities or professional organizations.

• Weight training should take place in facilities equipped to support safe training practices.

• Skill based weightlifting programs that include a wide variety of general athletic preparation are appropriate for children and can commence between the ages of nine and twelve years of age.

• Total exercise training time should not exceed fifteen hours per week.

• Utilization of maximal weights, although no data currently establishes a clear-cut relationship, may place that child athlete at risk of injury. As such, these loads should be used cautiously and applied only as part of a regimented training program for technically proficient athletes. Each attempt must be supervised and safety measures must be in place. Excellence in technique should be emphasized rather than amount of weight lifted.

• All USA Weightlifting training centers (Olympic Training Center and Regional Development Centers) are urged to maintain a record of injuries incurred during training at their facilities. This information can be used by USA Weightlifting Sports Science and Sports Medicine Committees to more precisely establish the degree of risk associated with training for weightlifting competition.

To read the entire position statement, please see www.usaweightlifting.org

NATIONAL STRENGTH AND CONDITIONING ASSOCIATION (NSCA)
YOUTH RESISTANCE TRAININIG: Position Statement Paper and Literature Review

It is the current position of the NSCA that:

A properly designed and supervised resistance training program is safe for children.

A properly designed and supervised resistance training program can increase strength in children.

A properly designed and supervised resistance training program can help to enhance the motor fitness skills and sports performance in children.

A properly designed and supervised resistance training program can help prevent injuries in youth sports and recreational activities.

A properly designed and supervised resistance training program can help to improve and psychosocial well-being of children.

A properly designed and supervised resistance training program can enhance the overall health of children.

To read the entire policy statement and full references, please see Strength and Conditioning: Vol. 18, No. 6, pp. 62-76 or www.nsca-lift.org

STRENGTH AND POWER TRAINING RESOURCES

American College of Sports Medicine
401 W. Michigan St.
Indianapolis, IN 46202
(317) 637-9200
(317) 634-7817 (FAX)
www.acsm.org

American Orthopedic Society for Sports Medicine
6300 North River Rd.
Rosemont, IL 60018
(847) 292-4900
(847) 292-4905 (FAX)
www.sportsmed.org

International Youth Conditioning Association
109 White Oak Ct. #9
Schaumburg, IL 60195
(847) 885-0493
info@iyca.org
www.iyca.org

National Athletic Trainers Association
2952 Stemmons Freeway
Dallas, Texas 75247
(800) 879-6282
(214) 637 2206
www.nata.org

National Strength and Conditioning Association
1885 Bob Johnson Drive
Colorado Springs, CO 80906
(719) 698-1692
(719) 632-6367 (FAX)
www.nsca-lift.org

Pediatric Orthopedic Society of North America
6300 North River Road, Suite 727
Rosemont, IL 60018-4226
(847) 698-1692
(847) 823-0536 (FAX)
www.posna.org

USA Weightlifting, Inc.
1 Olympic Plaza
Colorado Springs, CO 80909
(719) 866-4508
(719) 866-4741
www.usaweightlifting.org

References

1. Alter, J. (2004)
2. American Academy of Pediatrics Committee on Sports Medicine and Fitness. (2000)
3. American Academy of Pediatrics Committee on Sports Medicine and Fitness. (2001)
4. Asai, H. & Aoki, J. (1996)
5. Avlonitou, E. (1994)
6. Baechle, T., Earle, R. & Wathen, D. (2000)
7. Bale, P., Mayhew, J.L., Piper, F.C., Ball T.E., Willman, M.K. (1992)
8. Basford, JR. (1985)
9. Battinelli, T. (2000)
10. Benjamin, H. & Glow, K. (2003)
11. Birrer, R. & Levine, R. (1987)
12. Blimkie, CJ. (1993)
13. Bonjour, J.Q., Theinzt, G. & Bucks, B. (1991)
14. Brady, T.A, Cahill, B.R. & Bodnar, L.M. (1982)
15. Brown, E.W. & Kimball, R.G. (1983)
16. Brown, L.E. (1998)
17. Bruns, W. & Maffulli, N. (2000)
18. Burkhardt, E., Barton, B. & Garhammer, J. (1990)
19. Caine, D., Howe, W., Ross, W. & Bergman, G. (1997)
20. Cheng, J.C., Maffulli, N., Leung, S.S., Lee, W.T. & Chan, K.M. (1999)
21. Cheng-Ye Ji & Seiji Ohsawa. (1996)
22. Conroy, B.P., Craemer, W.J., Maresh, C.M., Fleck, S.J., Stone, M.H., Fry, A.C., Miller, P.D. & Dalsky, G.P. (1993)
23. Cook, P. & Leit, M. (1995)
24. Dohoney, P., Chromiak, J., Lemire, D., Abadie, B. & Kovacs, C. (2002)
25. Dowshen, S (Reviewer). (2001)
26. Drabik, J. (1996)
27. Dvorkin, LS. (1992)
28. Faigenbaum, A.D., Loud, R.L., O'Connell, J., Glover, S., O'Connell, J. & Westcott, W.L. (2001)
29. Faigenbaum, A.D., Milliken, L.A. & Westcott, W.L. (2003)
30. Faigenbaum, A.D., Kraemer, W.J., et. al. (1996)
31. Falk, B. Sadres, E., Constantini, N., Zigel, L., Lidor R. & Eliakim, A. (2002)
32. Fleck, S.J. & Falkel, J.E. (1986)
33. Frost, H.M. & Schonau, E. (2000)
34. Fry, A.C. & Schilling, B.K. (2002)
35. Fuchs, R.K., Bauer, J.J. & Snow, C.M. (2001)
36. Gibson, B.
37. Gumbs, V.L., Segal, D., Halligan, J.B. & Lower, G. (1982)
38. Guy, J.A. & Micheli, L.J. (2001)
39. Halin, R., Germain, P., Bercier, S., Kapitaniak, B. & Buttelli, O. (2003)
40. Halin, R., Germain, P., Buttelli, O. & Kapitaniak, B. (2002)
41. Hansen, L., Bangsbo, J., Twisk, J. & Klausen, K. (1999)
42. Hartmann, J. & Tunneman, H. (2000)

43. Heinrich, C.H., Going, S.B., Pamenter, R.W., Perry, C.D., Boyden, T.W. & Lohman, T.G. (1990)
44. Hopper, DM. (1997)
45. Inbar, O. & Bar-OR, O. (1986)
46. Jones, L., Eksten, F. & Fleschler, A. (2001)
47. Katzmarzyk, P.T., Malina, R.M., Song, T.M.K. & Bouchard, C. (1998)
48. Kawakami, Y., Kanehisa, H., Ikegawa, S. & Fukunaga, T. (1993)
49. Kidd, P.S., McCoy, C. & Steenbergen, L. (2000)
50. Kilgore, L, et. al. (2001)
51. Komi, P.V. & Knuttgen, H.G. (2003)
52. Kraemer, W. & Fleck, S. (2005)
53. Kurilla, M. (2003)
54. Kurtz, T. (2001)
55. MacKelvie, K.J., Khan, K.M. & McKay, H.A. (2002)
56. Madsen, N,. & McLaughlin, T. (1984)
57. Maffulli, N. & Pintore, E. (1990)
58. Malina, R.M. & Bielicki, T. (1996)
59. Malina, R., Bouchard, C. & Bar-Or, O. (2004)
60. Mathiowetz, V., Kashman N., Volland G., Weber K., Dowe M. & Rogers S. (1985)
61. McCaw, S.T. & Friday, J.J. (1994)
62. Medvedyev, A.S. (1989)
63. Mersch, F. & Stoboy, H. (1989)
64. Myer, G.D., Ford, K.R., Palumbo, J.P. & Hewett, T.E. (2005)
65. Nariyama, K., Hauspie, R.C. & Mino, T. (2001)
66. Nau, K.L., Katch, V.L., Beekman, R.H. & Dick, M. (1990)
67. Naughton, G., Farpour-Lambert, N.J., Carlson, J., Bradley, M. & Van Praagh, E. (2000)
68. Newcomer, K. & Sinaki, M. (1996)
69. Newman, D.G., Pearn, J., Barnes, A., Young, C.M., Kehoe, M. & Newman, J. (1984)
70. Nordstrom, P., Thorsen, K., Bergstrom, E. & Lorentzon, R. (1996)
71. Ozmun, J.C., Mikesky, A.E. & Surburg, P.R. (1994)
72. Peltonen, J.E., Taimela, S., Erkintalo, M., Salminen, J.J., Oksanen A. & Kujala, U.M. (1998)
73. Ramsay, J.A., Blimkie, C.J., Smith, K., Garner, S., MacDougall, J.D. & Sale, D.G. (1994)
74. Ratel, S., Bedu, M., Hennegrave, A., Dore, E. & Duche, P. (2002)
75. Rians, C.B., Weltman, A., Cahill, B.R., Janney, C.A., Tippett, S.R. & Katch, F.I. (1987)
76. Risser, W.L. (1991)
77. Rosique, J., Rebato, E., Apraiz, A.G. & Pacheco, J.L. (1994)
78. Ross, W.D. & Day, J.A. (1972)
79. Sale, D. (1991)
80. Salokun, S.O. (1994)
81. Seger, J.Y. & Thorstensson, A. (2000)
82. Seger, J.Y. & Thorstensson, A. (1994)
83. Sharma, S.S. & Dixit, N.K. (1985)
84. Siff, M.C. (2000)
85. Siff, M.C. (2003)
86. Stanitski, C.L. (1989)
87. Stone, MH. (1982)
88. Suler, J. (2002)

89. Suman, O., Spies, R., Celis, M., Mlcak, R. & Herndon, D.N. (2001)

90. Sunnegardh, J., Bratteby, L.E., Nordesjo, L.O. & Nordgren, B. (1988)

91. Tsuzuku, S., Ikegami, Y. & Yabe, K. (1998)

92. Uusi-rasi, K., Haapasalo, H., Kannus, P., Pasanen, M., Sievanen, H., Oja, P. & Vuori, I. (1997)

93. Villagra, F., Cooke, C.B. & McDonagh, M.J. (1993)

94. Virvidakis, K., Georgiou, E., Korkotsidis, A., Ntalles, K. & Proukakis, C. (1990)

95. Viviani, F., Casagrande, G. & Toniutto, F. (1993)

96. Waldo, BR. (1996)

97. Webb, D.R. (1990)

98. Weltman, A., Janney, C., Rians, C.B., Strand, K., Berg, B., Tippitt, S., Wise, J., Cahill, B.R. & Katch, F.I. (1986)

99. Wiemann, K. & Hahn, K. (1997)

100. Wilmore, J.H., Parr, R.B., Girandola, R.N., Ward, P., Vodak, P.A., Barstow, T.J., Pipes, T.V., Romero, G.T. & Leslie, P. (1978)

101. Witzke, K.A. & Snow, C.M. (2000)

102. Zariczny, B., Shattuck, L.J.M., Mast, T.A., Robertson, R.V. & D'Elia, G. (1980)

103. Zatsiorsky, V.M. (1995)

6

The Science and Application of Development Flexibility

Dr. Evan Osar and Tony Reynolds

The notion that flexibility refers merely to "the range of motion at a particular joint" has been a subject of considerable disagreement[5]. Many consider this definition a somewhat limited description of the complexities that truly define flexibility. Since flexibility encompasses all components of the musculoskeletal and neuromuscular systems; exhibits both static and dynamic characteristics; is time, speed, and joint angle dependant; and defines range of motion, the IYCA has adopted the following definition of flexibility:

> *Flexibility is the ability to produce and reproduce efficient static and dynamic movements at speed over an optimal pain free range of motion[1,2,78].*

Many times, true expression of flexibility encompasses multiple joint structures simultaneously. Thus, this definition could be expanded to include:

> *With the proficient coordination of multiple joint structures as they contribute to an overall motion[3, 78].*

This proficient coordination is concomitant to the seamless integration of single and multi-joint agonists, antagonists, stabilizers, neutralizers, and synergists as they collective generate movement. Therefore, close consideration must be given to the actions of adjacent joints, and the contribution of all muscles comprising those joint, when discussing flexibility and range of motion for a specific joint.

Although flexibility is often viewed as a systemic value, it should be regarded as a joint specific characteristic. This specificity is relative not only to a particular joint on a given side of the body (if bilaterally oriented), but also by the speed of motion and joint configuration during a particular motion[4].

Flexibility requirements vary by not only occupation or sport, but more specifically by the mobility demands of a given sporting position or profession. Thus, common patterns and requirements of flexibility exist because of the inherently unique joint actions frequently utilized in habitual tasks[5]. This will help to quantify flexibility and range of motion requirements as they relate to the individual.

Chief Constituents of Flexibility

Alter cites over thirty-two factors contributing to flexibility in a given range of motion[5]. Thus, many closely associated structural, functional, and varied factors must be considered when adaptive change is required.

Factors such as joint structure, contractile and connective tissue composition, pennation angle, insertion points, body fat (forming mechanical wedges reducing range of motion), type of movement, and environmental and tissue temperatures all constitute structural factors of flexibility[5,78]. Consequently, these factors provide the mechanical means and limitations of movement.

Functional contributions come primarily from the neuromuscular system. These factors include neurogenic contractions that are mediated by the cerebral cortex, and the in-involuntary reflex arcs that are moderated by the golgi tendon organs, muscle spindles, and joint mechanoreceptors.

Where as functional and structural factors mediate internal function and change within the body, the varied factors exhibit an external influence on the body. These factors include age, gender, ethnicity, pregnancy, training history, and pain threshold.

Connective Tissue

Connective tissue, as the name implies, serves to support and bind other tissues together. It is generally characterized by a complex mixture of specialized structural and functional protein fibrils embedded in a large tissue-specific three-dimensional extracellular matrix[52]. Protein fibrils are classified as collagenous and elastic and are arranged in a complex aggregating network[6]. The interfibril matrix is a compound gel like substance that acts as both a lubricant and glue for the protein fibrils.

There are three general classifications of connective tissue in the human body. Loose connective tissue is the most common type of connective tissue. It holds organs in place and attaches epithelial tissue to other underlying tissues. Loose connective tissue is named based on the structural "weave" and forms of its constituent fibers. Types of loose connective tissues are areolar and adipose tissue.

Dense or fibrous connective tissue is composed of large amounts of closely packed collagenous and elastin fibers. Unlike loose connective tissue, dense connective tissue exhibits a great structural rigidity, which makes it useful for binding muscles to bones and bones to other bones. Due to the function of this type of connective tissue, it is considered the most essential in determining range of motion. Structures such as tendons, ligaments, aponeuroses, deep fascia, dermis, and scars are composed of dense connective tissue. Of these structures the tendons, ligaments, and fascia provide the greatest concern with regards to stretching and flexibility, and will be discussed in detail later.

The third classification of connective tissue is specialized connective tissue. Specialized connective tissue can be broken down into three subcategories, cartilage, bone, and interestingly enough, blood. Aside from slight limitations imposed by joint cartilage, the structural composition of theses tissues does very little to alter range of motion.

Collagen

Collagen, with its reported fifteen to twenty-seven morphological-fibril variants[7,89], is an inextensible fibrous protein produced by fibroblasts. The collagen protein is the most abundant protein in the human body and constitutes approximately one third[10] of all proteins in vivo[11]. The substantial volume and integrity of this protein makes it the primary structural component of living tissue[12,10]. Although so many collagen variants exist, 80% to 90% of all collagen in the body is comprised of types I, II, and III.

With tensile strength of that of steel[13], type I collagen forms molecular cables that strengthen the tendons, ligaments, cartilage, fascia, bone, and skin. Type II collagen is composed of thinner fibrils and comprises 50% to 90% of the collagen found in hyaline-articular cartilage. Type II collagen thus provides cartilage it with its structural strength to resist pressure.

Different levels of the organizational hierarchy of collagen come together to form a highly ordered and stable fiber. The repeated sequence of the three amino acids glycine, proline, and hydroxyproline form polypeptide chains that are about 1400 amino acids long. These chains, which are called alpha chains, are tightly wound into a coiled right-handed triple helices bound together by hydrogen cross-links to make up tropocollagen molecules[52]. Several tropocollagen molecules are held together by covalent aldol cross-links to form collagen molecules. These molecules lay in parallel with a staggered overlap of about ¼ their total length and coalesce to form microfibrils. Microfibrils are analogous to the sarcomere of a muscle fiber and appear striated when viewed through an electron microscope. Sequentially, microfibrils or filaments are grouped together to make subfibrils. Bundles of subfibrils in turn form fibrils that combine into wavy bundles named fascicles[5].

The wavy arrangement of the fascicles is known as crimp[52]. The crimp acts as a shock absorber and allows the non-elastic material to exhibit a slight viscoelastic like behavior. Under tensile force, the wavy configuration straightens allowing the collagen structure to increase in physical length. Ordinarily, it takes a maximal contraction of the muscle to completely straighten the crimp[14]. If additional force Is applied and no more crimping is available to absorb the force, the intermolecular forces are exceeded and the tissue parts resulting a plastic deformation. With plastic deformation, permanent damage has resulted and the structural integrity of the collagen is diminished. Under normal conditions, the collagen will spring back to its natural wavy configuration when the force is removed[15].

It is also important to note the cross-links in collagen play a very important role in collagen stiffness. Since the cross-links help to create a strong rope like structure, intra-crosslink proximity and quantity directly affect tensile strength. Consequently, the more cross-links that exist and the closer the cross-links reside, the greater the elasticity will be for the collagen[16]. It has been hypothesized that the number of cross-links could be related to collagen turnover. If more collagen is being broken down than created, there will be a decrease in cross-links resulting in a decrease in structure tensile strength and integrity[5].

Elastin

The other major fibrous protein in the extracellular matrix of connective tissue is elastin. Elastin, also called elasticin, is a yellow fibrous crosslinked Glycoprotein found in various concentrations throughout the body. Where as collagen provides rigidity, elastin coils and recoils like a spring within the connective tissue and, thus, accounts for the elasticity of the skin, blood vessels, heart, lungs, intestines, tendons, and ligaments[52].

The biochemical arrangement of elastin is composed largely of non-polar amino acids. Similar to collagen, elastin is made up of approximately 33% glycine and 11% proline that unite to establish polypeptide chains[5]. These elements fuse into a non-striated mass of twisted rope like fibrils that form a rubbery network. Polypeptide chains are joined together by lysine derived tetrameric desmosine and isodesmosine cross-links. Cross-links are widely spaced and the intra-link regions are hydrophobic in nature. This creates an extremely mobile and highly extensible unit.

Unlike collagen, which is organized into dense fibrous bundles, elastin is somewhat amorphous and arranged in relaxed crosslinked coils. When elastic tissue is stretched, the elastin molecule is elongated into a more linear conformation. When the stretching force is released, the elastin returns to the more stable random-coil structure. This allows elastin to be very extensible with a breaking point of approximately 150% of its resting length[17].

Due to the contributions of elastin, it is considered a vital factor in determining available range of motion. On average, connective tissue is reported to provide 41% of overall resistance to stretch. However, the contribution of connective tissue is largely dependant on the relative proportions of collagen and elastin residing within the extracellular matrix[5,18]. Generally, collagen exists in much greater quantities, but the greater the ratio of elastin to collagen the more extensible connective tissue will be. Additionally, large amounts of elastin are found in the sarcolemma, (surface plasma membrane) of the muscle fiber and, thus, play a major role in determining its extensibility. The combined effects of elastin on contractile and non-contractile components ultimately determine the soft tissue limitations of range of motion.

Aside from being extensible, elastic fibers possess a great deal of elasticity. This elasticity helps to conserve energy by providing an energy free contribution to returning and maintaining dimensional homeostasis of the sarcomere. Furthermore, elastin helps to disseminate isolated stresses, assists in returning stretched organs back to normal shape, and helps protect the bodily tissues by absorbing excessive forces.

Ground Substance of Connective Tissue (AKA cement substances)

The extra-cellular space between cells and fibers, and inside joints, is filled with soluble, gel-like polymers composed of a hydrated network of proteins. The ground substance within the hydrated network is primarily glycosaminoglycans (GAGs) and proteoglycans[52].

Glycosaminoglycans, which are the most abundant heteropolysaccharide in the body, link to core proteins to form proteoglycans, or mucopolysaccharides. Tissues rich in proteoglycan molecules have a spongy, cushion-like quality and function like shock absorbers (e.g., cartilage, vertebral discs, and skin).

Water, which constitutes 60-70% of connective tissue content, is osmotically attracted to the extra-cellular matrix by the proteoglycans. The resultant hydration creates a swelling that results in a turgor pressure in the surrounding collagen network. Pressure from turgor helps the extra-cellular matrix resist compressive forces applied to tissues[52]. Additionally, water acts with hyaluronic acid as the principle connective tissue lubricant that in turn helps prevent excessive cross-linking.

Time and Rate Dependant Properties

The rigidity of connective tissue is dependant on its extensibility and elasticity. Extensibility refers to a materials ability to lengthen without regard to return. When people statically stretch, it is typically done to augment extensibility, thereby enhancing overall range of motion. Conversely, elasticity refers to the amount of counterforce in a material and is responsible for returning materials to their original shape. By definition, if a material is more elastic, it possesses a greater counterforce making it harder to extend. Like a rubber band, tissues of the body experience increased internal counterforce as they are elongated. This increase in counterforce results in proliferation of resistance during end ranges of motion. Consequently, the properties of dynamic flexibility are a direct result of tissue elasticity.

Connective tissue possesses some elasticity, that is, it stretches under a tensile load but fully returns when the load is removed. However, if the load exceeds a certain magnitude, some permanent or plastic deformation of the tissue may occur[19]. The point at which this permanent deformation occurs is called the yielding point for the tissue. Mechanically, the strength of connective tissue has to do with the maximum stress or strain it is able to withstand before experiencing plastic behavior. This stress, which represents the elastic limit of the tissue, is known as the yield strength of the tissue. Although no breakage of the tissue occurs, permanent changes in its dimensions develop. This is often seen in the ankle after a severe strain in which there is permanent lengthening of the ligaments resulting in chronic-joint instability. If an adequate amount of strain exists, the tissue will ultimately rupture. This strain is known as failure strain. Failure strength is different from tissue to tissue, and decreases with injury, immobility, and age.

Since connective tissues display both elastic and plastic characteristics, they are classified as viscoelastic. Unlike pure elastic and plastic materials, connective tissue elongation possesses time and rate-dependant characteristics. At low loads, these tissues exhibit elastic behavior that allows full restoration. Under high loads, connective tissue presents plastic behavior. When the Achilles tendon ruptures upon landing, even though it is not in an elongated state, it is due to the plastic properties of the tendon.

Stress Relaxation

Stress relaxation is a property of biological tissues that is related to their viscoelastic properties. To understand this concept, the stress-strain relationships for a spring and biological tissues, such as a fascia, can be compared. When an increased level of strain is suddenly applied to a spring, it results in a rapid stretch. The stress that is generated is proportional to its change in length, which is termed the Hookean behavior. Due to the structural composition of the steel used in the spring, the developed tension remains constant over time.

In contrast, when sudden strain is applied to a soft tissue such as fascia, the tension does not remain steady, but progressively deteriorates gradually over time. This decline in stress over time at a constant strain is termed stress relaxation. This property tends to differ considerably for different biological tissues and is directly related to differences in their structural components (e.g., collagen, elastin) and the arrangement of those components within the tissue. For example, the fascia, which possesses a greater elastin and lower collagen content, shows a higher degree of stress relaxation than the much stiffer tendon.

To understand the functional significance of this property, one only has to relate the ability of different tissues to display stress relaxation to their biological function. For instance, if stabilizing tissues within the joint expressed large levels of stress relaxation, the joint would become progressively unstable. Inversely, if deep fascia did not possess a moderate degree of stress relaxation, the resultant effect would be a decrease in contractile-tissue extensibility and decrease-joint range of motion.

Creep

When a rapid strain is applied and maintained to a connective tissue at a constant temperature, it will quickly deform and than continue to lengthen over a finite period during a process known as creep. In connective tissue, creep can be divided into three stages. The first stage, or primary creep, starts at a rapid rate and slows with time. Lengthening of the tissue during this stage is typically a result of straightening of the collagen crimp and partial realignment of the fibrils in the extra-cellular matrix.

During the second stage, creep has a relatively uniform rate. In general, motion of the long GAG chains begin fibril slippage between collagen-fibers increases, as well as intrafibril-turgor pressure with proportion to the number of crosslinks[27]. Deformation typically stops when the total internal stress and external tensile force ratios reach equilibrium[52]. During this stage, connective tissues approach their elastic limit but still restore to normal physiological or resting lengths upon cessation of external loading.

If tensile forces are great enough, the tissue will enter the third stage know as tertiary creep. During this stage, the collective intermolecular forces are subjugated and the tissue parts resulting a plastic deformation. With plastic deformation, permanent damage results and the structural integrity of the tissue is lessened. With continued deformation, the ultimate strength of the tissue is surpassed resulting in failure strain.

Under normal conditions (stages one and two), the elastic properties of the connective tissue provide a means of full restoration to resting dimensions. Although recovery is typically absolute, it takes place at a gradual rate resulting in a loss of energy expelled in the form of heat during a process known as hysteresis.

Connective Tissue Structures

On a molecular level, the physiological composition of connective tissues determines its overall extensibility and elasticity. Ultimately, tissue cross-sectional area and length provide the global restrictions on elongation; typically, the greater the cross-sectional area of a given tissue, the greater the potential for elongation under tensile stress. At the fibril level, the collagen-elastin ratio helps establish extensibility and elasticity. Tissues with a greater proportion of collagen, will exhibit greater levels of stiffness. Additionally, fibril orientation and density, collagen-fiber maturity, differences in ground substances, the level of hydration, and the number of inter and intra-fibril collagen cross-links greatly affects tissue compliance.

Tendons

Tendons are tough fibrous cords that attach muscle to bone. They are composed of varying amounts of collagen and elastin in a large extra-cellular components composed mostly of water, glycosaminoglycans, and proteoglycans. Approximately 86% of the collagen in tendons is type I with the presence of a much lesser degree of type II-V. These fibers exist in closely packed parallel collagenous bundles that fuse together in many places and provide the tendons with the greatest tensile strength and lowest viscoelastic properties of any connective tissue. The existences of small amounts of elastin contribute to shock absorbency and maintenance of collagenous crimp.

Tendons provide approximately 10% of resistance to movement[20]. Ultimately, this resistance is dependant on tendon strength and stiffness and is related to several factors. From a hierarchal perspective, density and quantity of stable cross-links within and between fibers determines the molecular limitations of elongation. Due to the nature of collagen, the closer the cross-links reside and the greater number that exists, the less extensible and stronger a tendon will be. On the fibril level, the ratio of collagen to elastin fibers and the number of stress-oriented fibers determines tendon strength. Tendons with greater amounts of elastin will possess a lower level of stiffness. Additionally, tendons with lower percentages of stress-oriented fibers tend to be less structurally sound. From a global perspective, tendon length and cross-sectional area determine the overall mechanical limitations of the tendon[5].

As the tendon gradually transitions to the bone, it first changes into unmineralized fibrocartilage, then to mineralized fibrocartilage, and then into bone[52]. As the tendon merges with the muscle, the collagen fibrils insert into deep recesses that are formed between finger-like endings of the muscle fiber. Within these recesses, the collagen fibers merge with actin fibers in the muscle sarcomere. The molecular changes in composition of the sarcomeres in this area cause them to be considerable less extensible. Additionally the configuration of the junction of membrane creates more of a shearing force than a tensile one. For these reasons, this tends to be the typical site for most muscle strain injuries[21].

Tendons serve a much bigger purpose than merely attaching muscle to bone. The crimp in the collagen fibers allow for the initial low stiffness and great elasticity. The resultant combination of these two properties is a passive spring like mechanism that allows the tendon to stretch 1% to 2%[22]. This mechanism results in the development and storage of elastic energy during normal stretch. Upon release of the tensile force, there is rapid and complete return of the crimp with only a

4% to 10% hysteresis (lose in energy). This phenomenon comprises the passive element of the serial elastic component. Therefore, it will be discussed in detail later in the chapter.

Ligaments

Ligaments bind bone to bone and in some instances blend into the joint capsule[52] to form a ligamentus sleeve. They function to prevent dislocation, stabilize the joint, and to limit range of motion. Ligaments are similar to tendons in hierarchical structure but they have a lower percentage of collagen and higher percentage of proteoglycan matrix[23]. Like tendons, ligaments are primarily made up of densely packed parallel or interlaced bundles of type I collagen, trace amounts of type III and VI collagen, and interspersed elastin fibrils[52]. Even though ligaments are typically composed of more elastic tissue than tendons, they usually contain a much greater percentage of collagenous tissue. This ratio can vary significantly depending on the stability/mobility requirements of the joint.

Ligaments are comprised of 80% to 90% ground substances. The ground substance consists of approximately .2% proteoglycans and glycoproteins, and 1% to 3% glycosaminoglycans[52], which is twice and much as tendons. Additionally, the fibril components are more randomly spaced within the ligamentus matrix. Even though the previous factors significantly increase the viscoelastic properties of the ligaments and joint capsules, these structures contribute to 47% of the soft tissues joint resistance[20]. This is more than four times that of the tendon.

Fascia

In gross anatomy, all fibrous connective tissue not otherwise specifically named is called fascia. More specifically, fascia is fibrous sheet of connective tissue that binds muscle together at multiple levels and binds the skin to the underlying structures. Fascia usually forms elastic membranous sheets of varying thickness and density that surrounds and protects all of the structures of the body. It lies in broad, continuous and contiguous sheets making it a major path for force conduction, or myofascial-force transmission[24]. Within this continuous network, fascia organizes the body through elaborate three-dimensional layers of webbing and provides compartmentalization of muscles and organs.

Fascia can be categorized into three distinctive types: 1) Superficial Fascia lies directly below the dermis and is thus called the hypodermis. It is composed of two layers, the fatty outer layer known as Camper's fascia, or the Panniculus adipose layer, and the more membranous inner layer or the Scarpa's fascia; 2) Subserous fascia, also known at extraperitoneal fascia, makes up the innermost lining around the body cavities. It surrounds and provides support for the viscera and serves as a glue to hold the peritoneum to the deep fascia of the abdominal wall or to the outer lining of the GI tract; 3) Deep fascia is a connective tissue mesh that infests the wall of the body peripherally out to the limbs, and around muscles. It is almost completely fibrous and of variable thickness. It constitutes up to 30% of muscles mass and is responsible approximately 41% of the total resistance to passive stretching. This makes deep fascia the second most important determining factor of range of motion[20].

Deep fascia is separated into groups depending on its location. The outer most stratum is the epimysium. It encases the entire muscle and separates the muscle from surrounding tissues and organs. The connective tissue fibers of the perimysium divide the skeletal muscle into a series of compartments, each containing a bundle of up to 150 muscle fibers called a fascicle[5]. The perimysium binds each fiber within a bundle to its immediate neighbor and interconnects fasciculi to epimysium. Although all levels of the deep fascia contribute to the resistance to passive stretching, due to its greater quantity, the perimysium is considered the biggest contributor[25].

When the muscle is at resting length, the collagen weave within the perimysium is slack. As the muscle elongates the weave first re-orientates aligning the collagen fibrils more along the line of force. After reorientation, the collagen fibrils become progressively taut and the perimysium becomes progressively stiffer.

Within a fascicle, the delicate connective tissue of the endomysium surrounds the individual skeletal muscle fibers and interconnects adjacent muscle fibers to each other and to the perimysium. The endomysium provides lubrication for fibers and fiber bundles and helps to maintain proper fibril alignment. The sarcolemma is a thin surface membrane that covers the sarcomere level of the entire fiber. Each sarcolemma has a single neuromuscular junction on its surface and is electrically independent of its neighboring fibers.

The collagen fibers of the endomysium and perimysium are interwoven and blend into one another. At each end of the muscle, the collagen fibers of the epimysium, perimysium, and endomysium come together and merge into tendon or the aponeuroses. Thus, these tissues provide a framework that enables active and passive forces to be transmitted by the whole tissue safely

Cartilage (Hyaline Articular Cartilage)

There are three major classifications of cartilage: 1) White fibrocartilage is an extremely tough tissue that is oriented in bundles depending upon the stresses acting on the cartilage. The collagenous bundles take up a direction parallel to the cartilage. Fibrocartilage is found in discs between the vertebrae, between the pubic bones, in front of the pelvic girdle and around the edges of the articular cavities, such as the glenoid cavity in the shoulder joint. This type of cartilage is housed between the adjacent vertebrae and absorbs the shocks that will otherwise damage and jar the bones when we move. It serves to form a firm joint between bones, yet still allows for a reasonable degree of movement. In articular cavities such as the ball-and-socket joints in the hip and shoulder regions, white fibrocartilage deepens the sockets to make dislocation less possible[52];   2) Elastic cartilage functions to strength, support, and maintain shape of such things as the ear lobe, epiglottis, and larynx. It is composed of collagenous fibers and abundant network of branched yellow-elastic fibers that run through the matrix in all directions[52]; 3) Hyaline-articular cartilage is a highly organized avascular tissue that covers the ends of the long bones and forms the joint surfaces. It also exists in the trachea, the larynx, the tip of the nose, and in the connection between the ribs and the breastbone. In human embryos, the skeleton first forms as hyaline-articular cartilage. This temporary cartilage acts as a model that is gradually replaced by bone through a process known as ossification as the embryo grows[52].

Its small cellular component consists primarily of chondrocytes and condroblasts. Chondrocytes are responsible for development of cartilage and maintenance of extra-cellular components. Between the cells that houses the fibril and interfibril components, is a large amount of rubbery matrix. The interwoven fibril component includes elastin and collage type II VI IX X and XI with 90% to 95% being type II[26]. The interfibril component is composed of proteoglycans, non-collagen proteoglycans, and 65% to 80% water. Hyaline-articular cartilage has the highest concentration of proteoglycans of all types of connective tissue[27].

Hyaline-articular cartilage is exceptionally strong, yet remains highly elastic and flexible in nature. It primarily functions to enable the smooth articulation of joint surfaces. It also allows the distribution and cushion of compressive, tensile, and shearing loads over the cross section of bones. It provides frictionless and wear-resistant surfaces for joint movement, and has one of the lowest coefficients of friction known for any surface-to-surface contact.

Contractile System

Skeletal muscle, also called striated muscle, embody an extremely sophisticated collection of proteins. It is difficult to appreciate the processes underling fibril extensibility without first understanding the organizational hierarchy of the entire muscle and the muscles relationship with active and passive generation of tension[28].

Organizational Hierarchy of Skeletal Muscle

The way in which skeletal muscle is organized is vital to its mechanical properties. Skeletal muscle, which is encased by the epimysium, is broken down into smaller constituents known as fascicles. Fascicles organize the thousands of very long, cylindrical cells called myofibers (muscle fibers) into bundles enclosed by the perimysium. Fascicles lie in parallel to one another ultimately forming the belly of the muscle. The myofibers, which are encased by the endomysium, run the entire length of the muscle but are broken down into repeating functional contractile units called sarcomeres. Ultimately, skeletal muscles extensibility is directly proportional to its length and thus its number of sarcomeres in series[29,28].

The sarcomere is an aggregate of proteins known as myofilaments. Myofilaments are the contractile elements of skeletal muscle and consist of actin, myosin, and titin filaments. The overlapping of these filaments gives the sarcomere its distinctive light (I-band) and dark (A-band) striations lending to the name striated muscle. The I-band runs from the Z-line, which is the connecting disc between adjacent sarcomeres, to the beginning of the myosin filament. Its primary constituents are the actin and titin filaments.

The A-band spans the length of the myosin filaments and consists of the myosin incased titin, the myosin filament, and the interdigitated actin filament. The A-band also houses two more regions that are distinct. The M-line represents the equator of the sarcomere and the attachment point for the titin filaments. The H-zone has a vacillating length and represents the portion of the myosin filament not interdigitated by the actin. Even though the H-zone changes in length, the A-band remains static. Therefore, sarcomere length changes occur in the I-band region.

Another point of interest is the aforementioned Z-line or Z-disc. The major subunit of the Z-disc is an intermediate protein filament known as desmin[30]. Desmin intermediate filaments are cytoskeletal structures located in the transverse plane of muscle fibers that appear to connect adjacent Z-disks in parallel. Unlike other prominent cytoskeletal structures in muscle, they are oriented in both the transverse and longitudinal planes of the cell. This dual orientation suggests the possibility that desmin may not only contribute to the mechanical properties in both the transverse and longitudinal planes, but may also integrate the transverse and longitudinal mechanical systems resulting in passive resistance to muscular elongation.

The Three Myofilaments

Actin (Thin) Filaments

Thin filaments are dynamic polymers whose ATP-driven assembly in the cell cytoplasm drives shape changes, cell locomotion, and chemotactic migration. The main component of the thin myofilament is a contractile protein called actin, which is a ubiquitous protein found in virtually all cells cytoskeleton. Each molecule of actin is composed of a globular protein that looks like a kidney bean and is much smaller than the myosin monomers. On each molecule is a myosin-binding site that upon exposure, attaches to the myosin crossbridge. Individual molecules of actin are linked together to form the actin filament. The actin filament is a long alpha helical arrangement of two chains of actin monomers. Although there is no directional symmetry to this helix, the filament does have a positive and negative end giving it polarity based on the direction of polymerization[28].

Because of the helical composition of the actin filament, a long groove is created along the filaments length. Located within the groove is the regulatory protein tropomyosin, which under resting conditions, blocks the binding sites on actin from myosin. Also located at intervals of about every seven actin molecules along the filament is the protein troponin. Troponin is the protein that is responsible for turning on contraction. Troponin is made up of three subunits. Troponin-C contains a calcium binding domain, troponin-T interacts with tropomyosin, and troponin-I can block the actin binding site from myosin. One set of three troponin subunits is associated with each molecule of Tropomyosin and is involved with the activity of seven actin molecules[28].

Myosin (Thick) Filaments

Although several types of myosin exist, myosin II—the form found in skeletal muscle—is typically referred to as conventional myosin. For the sake of this text, any mention of myosin refers to myosin type II. Myosin is a large motor protein that moves along the actin filaments while hydrolyzing ATP. Myosin includes two heavy chains, each with a globular motor domain that includes a binding site for ATP and a domain that interacts with actin.

At the molecular level, a molecule of myosin is asymmetrically shaped with a globular "motor" domain creating a golf club head-like structure that powers contraction. At the other end of the molecule is a long rod-like tail. Tail domains of myosin-heavy chains associate in a-helical coils forming bipolar complexes. These tails assemble into the thick filament forming its shaft, while the golf club like heads project around the shaft in a spiraling fashion[28].

The projecting heads known as cross bridges extend out away from the middle of the filament towards the thin myofilaments leaving the M-band portion void of these structures. Their anti-parallel arrangement gives the sarcomere symmetry down the middle, insuring that each half is a mirror image and is functionally identical.

Titin Filaments (Passive Tension)

Titin is the largest protein known in the human body stretching 30,000 amino acids long, weighing 3.5 megaDaltons, and constituting about 10% of myofibril mass[31]. In skeletal muscle, it is a giant cytoskeletal multimodular protein formed by as many as 300 immunoglobulin (Ig) - and fibronectin-like domains arranged in tandem that span half a sarcomere, extending from Z-line (amino terminus) to M-line (carboxy terminus)[5]. The carboxy-terminal part of the molecule extends through and is bound to the thick (myosin) filament in the A-band region of the sarcomere. Additionally, the I-band section of the molecule includes a PEVK domain. PEVK is an acronym that stands for Proline (P), Glutamate (E), Valine (V), and Lysine (K), which are the molecular constituents of this region[32].

A single titin molecule consists of random coils throughout the I-band structure providing it with its extensibility and elasticity[33]. Early phases of lengthening involve the straightening of the Ig-domain regions coils first. It takes only very small forces of a few picoNewtons to straighten the molecule from its coiled equilibrium state. If forces increase, the next phase is the disruption of the titin structure and the unraveling of its polypeptide chain, first in the loosely structured unique sequences and then in immunoglobulin- and fibronectin-like domains.

Under normal conditions, it is hypothesized that exposure of hydrophobic residues along the length of the titin filament during elongation results in a strong propensity to return to tonic length[34].

Since the titin fiber links each end of the thick filament to the Z-line, the elasticity causes resting tension when the myofibril is at normal physiological length. It also contributes to the extensibility and passive force development of quiescent skeletal-muscle fibers during stretch. The titin molecule also serves to maintain the central position of thick filaments between Z-lines and to help spread localized tension among several sarcomeres. Without titin, there would be force imbalances in the opposite halves of thick filaments during active contraction. Maybe the most important function of the titin filament is the passive resorting of sarcomere length after stretch[35,36].

It has been suggested that the length and size of titin fibers in the sarcomere, determine its tension threshold[37]. Furthermore, these factors determine the sarcomeres elastic limit. In general, muscles with larger titin isoforms will express lower levels of elasticity and greater extensibility. Since different muscle groups express different titin isoforms, they each have unique stress strain curves.

Sliding Filament Theory of Skeletal Muscle Contraction

Myofibril tension developed because of neuromuscular processes, directly affects muscular extensibility. Although the process of muscular contraction is still not fully understood, the theory developed in 1954 by H. E. Huxley and A. F. Huxley[39] coined the sliding filament theory, is still the foremost theory on skeletal muscle contraction.

Although the sarcomeres can shorten anywhere from 20% to50% of resting length and elongate up to 120% of resting length, measurements of the actin (H-zone to Z-line) and myosin (A-band) filaments demonstrate they do not change length during contraction and elongation. Since the actin and myosin fibers do not change their length but overlap and interdigitate, it is postulated that shortening in sarcomere length occurs because the cross bridges on the thicker myosin filaments attach to active sites on the actin molecule and thae pull on the actin filaments[38,39,40]. This pull creates a ratcheting effect that causes the two filaments to slide across each other during what has been termed the cross bridging cycle. As long as the force generating mechanism is active, this process will continue to repeat causing the Z-line to move toward the A-band narrowing and eventually eliminating the I-band and H-zone, while shortening the sarcomere. This shortening of the sarcomeres, all in series, causes shortening of the whole muscle fiber, and ultimately of the entire muscle itself.

A single contraction-relaxation cycle of a muscle fiber is known as a twitch. Fiber twitch duration varies from muscle to muscle and between motor units within the muscle, and lasts anywhere from 7.5 msec to 100 msec. Since normal activity requires sustained contraction, a single twitch will not produce motion. Rather, the summation of overlapping twitches becomes necessary to create enough fibril tension to produce motion.

Neurogenic Contraction

The generation of voluntary muscular tension in skeletal muscle is ultimately initiated by a peripheral nerve action potential that originates from the cerebral cortex. Located in the frontal lobe of the brain, the portion of the cerebral cortex dedicated to purposeful movement is known as the primary motor area. Within this region, the human body is laid out in a "map" type fashion with varying portions of the primary-motor area controlling particular parts of the body. Not anatomically correct, the body parts requiring fine control, and therefore anatomically smaller, have a proportionally greater portion of the primary motor area committed to their control.

Latent Phase

The latent period begins at stimulation and typically last two msec[28]. During this period, there is no tension development in the fiber. Electrical nerve messages, known as action potentials, commence within the primary motor area and travel down through the spinal cord in nerve fibers called the corticospinal tract. The name is derived from the pathways start and ending points or the cortex and spine respectively. The corticospinal tract is also referred to as the primary motor pathway. The nerves of the corticospinal tract lower through the spinal cord until they arrive at the appropriate level or point of the body part for which the original action potential was intended (i.e. signals directing motion of the arms will descend only as low as the thoracic region of the spine). Once the action potential arrives at the correct level of the spinal cord, it synapses with a second nerve known as an interneuron. The interneuron transfers the action potential to a third nerve cell called a motor neuron. The motor neuron sends an extension, known as an axon, from the spinal cord to the skeletal muscle. These axons run in bundles of nerve fibers known as peripheral nerves.

This action potential initiates the biochemical process of contraction that leads to the release of intracellular calcium and the eminent contractile process known as excitation-contraction coupling. Ultimately, the action potential is delivered by the motor neuron resulting in the release of acetylcholine, which diffuses across the synaptic cleft at the neuromuscular junction to the sarcolemma.

Once the stimulus diffuses across the synaptic cleft, it binds to its receptors on the motor end plate propagating an electrical signal that depolarizes the membrane and travels inward via the T-tubules. This not only increases cell membrane permeability, but also opens calcium channels in the sarcoplasmic reticulum allowing calcium to diffuse into the sarcoplasm. Calcium ions bind with troponin C molecules that reside on the active sites of the actin filaments physically causing the tropomyosin-troponin complex to move, exposing the myosin binding sites on the actin. At the same time, the ATP cross bridge complex is charged permitting an actomyosin complex.

Contraction Phase

This activates an enzyme component of the myosin filament called ATPase, which causes ATP hydrolysis to the intermediate state of ADP and P_i (inorganic phosphate), thereby energizing the myosin. The energy from the hydrolysis fuels the cocking of the myosin cross bridges and the consequent attachment to and pull on the actin, causing the filaments to slide. This cross bridging action is accompanied by the release of the ADP and the inorganic phosphate. The binding of a new ATP must then break the strong actomyosin cross bridge to the myosin cross bridge to allow for subsequent cross-bridging cycles. This chemical process continues as long as there are sufficient amounts of calcium and ATP present.

Relaxation Phase

Skeletal muscle is incapable of lengthening on its own and thus fibril elongation during relaxation is a completely passive process. Essentially, fibers relax when they are no longer receiving an impulse. The calcium and troponin combos separate and calcium is pumped back into the sarcoplasmic reticulum by the calcium activated ATPase enzyme. Since troponin and calcium no longer bond, the actin no longer has an affinity for the myosin allowing filament disassociation. As cross bridges detach and separate, the internal elastic force that accumulated during contraction is released and the elasticity of the connective tissue connecting the muscle to the bone helps restore the muscle to resting length.

Reflexive Considerations

The CNS is composed of the spinal cord and the brain. The spinal cord acts as a coordinating center responsible for processing simple involuntary reflexes. Likewise, the peripheral nervous system is made up of the cranial and two types of peripheral nerves. The sensory or afferent neurons send signals from the stimulus receptors (mechanoreceptors) to the CNS. The motor or efferent neurons run from the CNS to the muscle fibers. The nerve cell axon is the usually long process of a nerve fiber that generally conducts impulses away from the body of the nerve cell. It extends from the cell body to the muscle, where it divides into smaller branches. Each of the smaller branches terminates on the motor endplate of the muscle fiber. The motor neuron, more precisely the alpha motor neuron, and the muscle fiber complex are known as a motor unit[52]. The size of the motor unit determines the precision of its control. Motor units of some eye muscles innervate as few as six fibers, whereas motor units of the quadriceps may innervate up to 2000 fibers[41].

Mechanoreceptors

Three major types of mechanoreceptors influence range of motion[5]: 1) Golgi tendon organs (GTO) primarily read tension in the tendon; 2) Spindles read the change and rate of change of muscle fiber length. Typically, when GTO activity increases, it silence spindle activity; 3)Joint or articular mechanoreceptors sense joint position, amplitude, acceleration, and velocity of motion, joint stresses and pressures, and pain and irritation.

Spindles

Spindles are highly sensitive stretch receptors located in the muscle. Each spindle is comprised of three to ten intrafusal fibers encapsulated in a connective tissue capsule[78]. Both ends attach to the endomysium of the extrafusal fibers (normal contractile fibers) and therefore run parallel to them. This orientation causes the spindle to be sensitive to short variations of muscle elongation.

Thanks to the presence of two different types of intrafusal fibers within the spindle, the nervous system gets information on both the size and speed of the lengthening of the muscle. The neuromuscular spindle is highly sensitive to stretching stimulus. This causes a big variation in the frequency of the discharge of the afferent fibers. Nuclear bag fibers (NBF) house a non-contractile sack like structure in their equator region that contains an abundance of sarcoplasm and the cell nuclei. The polar ends of the fiber are striated contractile filaments that attach to the endomysium of the extrafusal fibers. Nuclear chain fibers (NCF) are thinner and shorter than NBF. Their non-contractile equator is a single chain like structure of nuclei that terminates into striated contractile filaments on either end of the fiber. These structures are often attached to the NBF.

The control over the sensitivity of the receptor is exerted by the alpha and gamma innervation system, which innervate the muscle and the spindle at different levels. The alpha motor neuron innervates the extrafusal fibers and caries signs from the central nervous system to the fibers. The alpha motor neuron and all of the fibers it innervates are called a motor unit. The gamma motor neuron, or gamma efferent neurons, innervate the equator region of each intrafusal fiber and conduct signals from the CNS to the intrafusal fibers that cause contraction of their polar ends.

There are two classifications of gamma-motor axons. Static-gamma axons increase the length sensitivity of primary-sensory neurons. Their stimulation elicits persistent static responses without significant concurrent influence on dynamic response[42]. Dynamic gamma-axon significantly increases the velocity sensitivity of the primary-sensory neuron. Their stimulation creates a very strong dynamic response of the muscle spindle accompanied by a minimal static response

Two types of sensory-afferent neurons invest the middle spindle and innervate the nuclear bag and chain fibers[42]. Primary endings, also know as large type Ia afferents and annulospiral endings spiral around the central region of the NBF and form side branches to the NCF. These endings are easily excited due to their very low stretch threshold and have both a phasic and a tonic response to elongation. The phasic response measures the rate or velocity of the stretch by changing the motor neuron impulse frequency during stretch. The frequency of discharge increases rapidly at commencement of the stretch, but when the stretched muscle reaches its new length, the frequency drops to an appropriate consistent level. Therefore, the tonic response provides neuromuscular feedback on the length of the muscle.

Secondary endings, also known as smaller type II afferents, form what is called branch or flower spray type endings, which are located near the equator of the NCF. They work together with the primary endings and fire in proportion to fiber length. When gamma efferent neurons cause contraction of the contractile ends of the NCF, the center region undergoes a passive stretch that causes the secondary endings to send information regarding fibril length to the CNS. Therefore, significant activation of the gamma motor neurons increases gamma drive from the CNS and drastically increases the amount of stretch perceived by the sensory endings.

Golgi Tendon Organs

Golgi tendon organs (GTO) are contraction-sensitive mechanoreceptors located in the aponeuroses of the musculotendinous junction that serve to protect the muscles, tendons, and ligaments from injury. They are oriented in series, or directly in line with the path of force from the muscle to the bone. This orientation in conjunction to their low threshold and appreciable dynamic sensibility, allows them the capability of signaling very small and rapid changes in contractile forces[43].

Anywhere from three to fifty extrafusal muscle fibers (contractile fibers) are attached to one GTO. In turn, each encapsulated GTO fiber is innervated by a large diameter, fast conducting, type Ib, afferent-nerve fiber[44]. When muscles contract and produce tension in the musculotendinous junction, the tendon organ straightens the collagen tissues. This compresses the nerve ending causing them to fire and send signals to the spine conveying the change and rate of change in tension. Although these sensors monitor are degrees of muscular tension[45], they are most sensitive to the active tension created by muscular contraction[5]. Only under extreme forces will passive muscular tension elicit a response.

Articular Mechanoreceptors

There are four types of articular mechanoreceptors located in all synovial joints. Each type is designated according to the morphology and behavior characteristics of the nerve ending. All four provide afferent feedback to the central nervous system and result in active muscular tension.

Type I mechanoreceptors are clusters of thinly encapsulated globular corpuscles (up to eight) located in the external layers of the fibrous joint capsules. These nerve endings are slow adapting and exhibit a low threshold allowing them to respond to small mechanical stress. They function to signal direction, amplitude, and velocity of active and passive movements in joints via regulation of joint pressure changes. This produces inhibition from nicoceptive afferents from type

IV receptors. They also facilitate CNS regulation of postural muscle tone and muscle tone during movement and therefore contribute to postural and kinesthetic sensation. These mechanoreceptors tend to be active at all times and fire impulses for the entire time they are stressed.

Type II mechanoreceptors are larger and thicker encapsulated-conical corpuscles (two to four corpuscles) located deeper in the fibrous joint capsule. They are considered acceleration or dynamic mechanoreceptors because they exhibit velocity dependant firing. Since they measure sudden changes in movement, they do not fire during immobilization or during rest.

Type III mechanoreceptors are thinly encapsulated corpuscles (largest of four major receptors) which exist in the joint capsule (intrinsic) and out of the joint capsule (extrinsic) in the ligaments. They are high-threshold, slow-adapting receptors that monitor direction of movement, and therefore are inactive in immobile joints. They respond to high tension in joint ligaments and become active during extreme ranges of motion. They produce profound inhibition of activity in some of the muscles functioning around the joint. This creates a reflexive breaking action to stop overstressing of the joint.

Type IV mechanoreceptors, or nociceptors, function as the pain receptor system of articular cartilage. They are non-encapsulated nerve endings that are active when articular tissues are subject to marked mechanical deformation or chemical irritation. There are two types of type IV receptors. Type IVa nociceptors are lattice like plexuses found in joint fat pads and throughout entire thickness of joint capsule but not in synovial tissue. Type IVb nociceptors are free nerve endings with no specialized structures and are found in the intrinsic and extrinsic ligaments of the joint.

Reflex Arcs

Unconscious responses to stimulus, otherwise know as reflexes, are the work of reflex arcs made up of mechanoreceptors, the CNS, and the spinal cord. They involve an involuntary reaction to a stimulus, an afferent sensory neuron to carry receptor signals about the effects of the stimulus to the spinal cord, and efferent sensory neurons to carry directional responses back to the muscle.

Myotatic (Stretch) Reflex

The myotatic reflex, also known as the stretch reflex, is a reflex that is mediated by the muscle spindles. It operates as a neural circuit geared toward maintaining optimal operating range of length in the muscle. When a muscle is stretched, the parallel spindles are elongated. The spindle stretch activates the primary and secondary sensory nerve endings (flower spray and annulospiral endings) which results in an action potential in their group Ia (primary) and II (secondary) sensory neurons. This action potential is sent to the spinal cord. If the threshold is surpassed by amount or speed of the stretch, the motor neuron fires an action potential, which returns to the muscle fiber via its axon, resulting in reflex contraction. If the response is phasic, there is an initial burst of action potential, which results in rapid increase in muscle tension proportional to velocity of stretch, as seen with the patellar reflex. Likewise, if the response is tonic, there will be a slow low frequency firing that lasts for the duration of stretch and is proportionally to amount of stretch[78].

Reciprocal Innervation

Reciprocal innervation, or the cross extensor reflexes, is a neural circuit that functions to orchestrate the contraction and relaxation process for oppositional muscles. When motor neurons to one muscle receive excitatory impulses telling it to contract, the cross extensor reflex provides a contra-lateral response to inhibit the antagonist. When the antagonist is contracted, the resulting inhibition of the agonist can result in an increased neurological extensibility of the agonist-muscular complex[78].

Although, the process of reciprocal innervation seems all-inclusive, it does not underlie all movement. Co-activation is the process of simultaneously contracting both the agonist and antagonist. While the agonist plays the role of the prime mover, the antagonist acts to stabilize the joint resulting in an increase in joint stiffness. A prime example of co-activation is the contraction of the hamstring to minimize anterior shear force in the knee during quadriceps-dominant knee extension. It is the complex and highly integrated interaction between reciprocal innervation and coactivation that results in efficient unobstructed movement.

Autogenic Inhibition

Autogenic inhibition, or the inverse stretch reflex, is responsible for the marked decrease in the tonic response of the stretch reflex that results in a sudden yielding of muscular resistance. Also known as the clasp-knife response and lengthening reaction, autogenic inhibition is a neural circuit thought to be arbitrated by the golgi tendon organs. As muscle tension increases and the GTO receptors in the aponeuroses are stimulated, they send an increasing number of signals via their group IIb afferents that terminate on the spinal cord. If the signaling is powerful enough to overcome the signaling of the muscle spindles, the CNS will then inhibit the efferent neurons innervating the contracting muscles causing a decrease in signal propagation. Since the muscles contraction is inhibited by its own receptors, it is called autogenic inhibition.

However, other avenues of research[43,44] have offered a second rational behind this process. It has been hypothesized that this process was actually mediated by the afferent input of the type II secondary endings of the muscle spindles and the type IV nociceptors located in the synovial joints when the muscular tension is the result of passive static stretch.

Since tendons are stiffer than muscle and the majority of the stretch is taken up by the muscle fiber first, the golgi tendon organs do not typically fire during stretch unless the tension becomes excessive. Therefore, the initial theory would not apply during passive static stretching. Although this is a logical summation, further research may be required to substantiate this view

Active and Passive Resistance to Stretch

When examining the soft tissues role in determining range of motion, all of the different tissues collective contributions must be considered. During stretching, total tension development is the product of both active and passive elements. Passive tension is void of neurogenic contraction and is provided by the parallel- and series-elastic components. Active tension depends on neural and mechanical properties of the muscle, thus is a product of the contractile component.

Parallel Elastic Component

In-vitro (outside of the body), a muscle fiber will shorten by approximately 10% of its resting length in vivo (in the body)[46]. Since the in-vitro fiber is void of neurogenic input, the shorting to its new equilibrium length is mostly due to passive forces of the parallel elastic component (PEC). As the name indicates, the PEC lies in parallel with the contractile mechanisms of the muscle[52]. All connective tissue surrounding the different levels of muscle tissue including the sarcolemma, sarcoplasm, epimysium, perimysium and endomysium connect to and constitutes the PEC

As alluded to in the previous paragraph, the PEC is responsible for passive tension in relaxed muscle at normal physiological length. As the sarcomeres shorten from their tonic length, the PEC becomes quiescent and no longer contributes to total tension. Likewise, as the muscle is stretched and the PEC progressively becomes tighter, passive tension develops in a non-linear pattern.

When the muscle is at resting length, the collagen weave within the perimysium is slack and the resting tension is from intrafibril-turgor pressure and the pull of elastin fibers. As the muscle elongates, the weave first re-orientates aligning the collagen fibrils more along the line of force. After re-orientation, the collagen fibrils become increasingly taut and the perimysium becomes progressively stiffer. Since the collagen fibrils of the different levels of the muscles fascia merge into the tendon or the aponeuroses sheath, the passive forces are safely transmitted from the whole muscle to the bone.

While in a lengthened state, the PEC contributes significantly to the storage of elastic energy. When a tensile force is quickly applied to a muscle (landing from a jump) and the muscle is stretched, the PEC absorbs much of the force in the form of elastic energy. This not only aids in mechanical efficiency of movement, but also helps to protect the sarcomeres and main body of the muscle from plastic deformation and microtrauma[52].

Series Elastic Component

The elastic elements that lie in direct line with the contractile component (CC) are justly known as the series elastic components (SEC). The SEC primarily consists of the tendon, which functions as a global passive component, and to a much lesser degree the titin filament, the myosin cross bridges and the Z-disc, which all function at the active level of the sarcomere[47,50].

As mentioned earlier in this chapter, tendons serve a much bigger purpose than merely attaching muscle to bone. The crimp in the collagen fibers allow for the initial low stiffness and great elasticity, which results in a passive spring like mechanism that allows the tendon to elongate by one to two percent. This causes the tendon to act much like a thick rubber band. If you attached one end of the rubber band to a moveable object to simulate the tendons attachment to the bone, and hooked the other to something moveable like your finger to simulate the muscle innervating the tendon, you would have a similar but extremely simplified system to emulate the musculotendinous unit.

As you pull on the rubber band with your finger, (much like when the sarcomeres contract and pull the tendon) the rubber band will stretch becoming progressively tauter (this would represent the straightening of the collagen crimp). When the internal resistive forces of the rubber band finally match the weight of the object, it will lift the object off the ground (movement of the bone). Interestingly, the faster you move your hand the more the rubber band will stretch before motion will occur or continue to occur. As a result, this phenomenon is rate dependant. The stretch experienced in the tendon results in the development and storage of elastic energy that provides passive recoil when tension is released.

On a molecular level, titin filaments provide a significant contribution to serial elasticity. The helical configuration of the titin filament uncoils under tensile force providing passive "retractibility". Since the titin fiber links each end of the thick filament to the Z-line, the elasticity causes passive tension when the myofibril is at normal physiological length and contributes to the passive force development of quiescent skeletal-muscle fibers during stretch. The titin filament also provides a contribution to the in-vitro shortening of the muscle fiber[48,49].

Two other molecular members of the SEC are the Z-disk and the myosin filament. The attachment of the titin filament to the Z-disk is thought to place localized stress on the disk. When the titin filament pulls, it distorts the disk causing a slight forward translation of the fiber along the line of the tensile force and a decrease in the lateral separation of the fibers. The elastic nature of the Z-disk results in a passive return to structural homeostasis[50].

The myosin filament forms a very strong chemical bond with the actin filament during the process of cross bridging. The resiliency of this bond is hypothesized to be strong enough to result in a stretch the tail domain between the globular head and the junction to the shaft prior to disassociation of myosin actin cross bridge[47].

Contractile Component

Where the PEC and the SEC provide passive resistance to stretch, the contractile component (CC) provides the active resistance to stretch. The CC consists of the actin and myosin filaments and their chemical cross bridges. Since the amount of force development is directly proportional to the number of active cross bridges, sarcomere length becomes vitally important[52,51]. Active tension during stretching is greatest at approximately 1.2-1.3 times the resting length. From this point to approximately 1.5 times resting length, the number of cross bridges decreases considerably until active tension ceases to exist. Since sarcomere length varies slightly throughout a muscle, especially toward the musculotendinous junction, some sarcomeres are still able to provide tension while others cannot.

The amount of active tension produced in the skeletal muscle as a whole is dependant on the frequency of stimulation and the number of muscle fibers stimulated. If a new action potential arrives and results in the incident of another twitch before the previous twitch finishes its relaxation phase, tension will build. When twitches build upon each other, it is known as summation of twitches, temporal summation, or wave summation. The frequency of the arrival of new action potentials and the concomitant summation of twitches ultimately determines the amount of tension. If the stimulation rate increases to the point that the relaxation phase is eliminated, complete tetanus will occur. Under normal conditions, all muscle fibers elicited during a contraction will reach complete tetanus[28].

When a motor unit is stimulated by an action potential, all of its innervated muscle fibers get stimulated. This is known as the all-or-none principle. Conversely, if all of the fibers in the muscle were recruited every time for every contraction, fine motor control would be impossible. Therefore, the total amount of muscular tension is regulated by the selection of the appropriate number of motor units necessary to carry out a give task.

In resting muscle, a small number of motor units always remain active. Although these contractions do not produce enough tension to initiate movement, they do cause a level of firmness in the muscle. This firmness is often referred to as muscle tone, and serves to stabilize bones and joints and aids in decreasing latency and accelerating recruitment speeds for reflex and voluntary contractions.

During stretching, protective subconscious and conscious neural drive causes motor unit activation and subsequent increases in active muscular tension. In severe situations, this can result in significant micro damage to the soft tissues associated. Under normal conditions, this process causes muscular fatigue and substrate depletion. For this reason, static stretching prior to dynamic activity can bring about adverse results.

Orthopedic Consideration

Joints, or articulations, are varying structures that house the complex connecting points of the bones of the body. Joints are much more than junctions where two or more bones meet. Rather they are an intricate assembly of bone; cartilage; ligament; synovium; and in some cases, muscle[52]. Joints serve several purposes. Initially, they are designed to bear weight and move the body through space. However, they also provide stability; mobility[52]; and in many cases, structural restrictions to ultimate range of motion.

Several of its structural constituents determine the ultimate range of motion of a specific joint. The first structural factor effecting joint range of motion is the proximity of muscular attachment to the axis of the joint. Due to the small effort arm created between the attachment and the axis of the joint, large motions create small changes in muscle length. Therefore, distal attachments close to the joint axis usually produce the greatest range of motion.

Passive insufficiency occurs when there is insufficient length or extensibility to permit a full range of motion to be produced at all of the joints crossed by the muscles. Since joints are linked together into a series known as the kinematic chain, motion at one of the joints in series is usually accompanied by motion in other joints[53]. This can create changes in the muscle length as it is stretched across adjacent joints. For instance, make a tight fist and try to flex your wrist. The loss of flexion results from passive insufficiency of the wrist extensors[52].

Sensory receptors provide feedback on joint position, pressure, and pain. Many times these receptors cause involuntary reactions resulting in rapid muscular contraction. These reflexes serve to decrease the likelihood of subluxation or dislocation, and protect the joint structures as they near end ranges of motion or become discommodious.

The last and most commonly discussed structural restriction is joint design. Joints are classified by the amount of movement allowed in the joint, which is typically dependent upon the function of the joint. Joints that serve a single function are the least complex and tend to focus primarily on stability. Synarthrodial joints are simple articulations that allow no movements. These fused joints serve to provide a stable juncture (such as those of the skull). Amphrarthrodial joints allow limited mobility and substantial stability such as the articulations of the spine.

The most commonly discussed type of joints is the diarthrodial joints. Diarthrodial joints, many times referred to as synovial joints, are the most complex of the joint structures. Under normal conditions, they allow maximal mobility with optimal stability.

There are six different types of diarthrodial joints. The hip and shoulder joints are known as ball and socket joints. They provide the greatest range of motion by allowing movement in three planes. Condyloid or ellipsoid joints move in only two planes as between the radial and carpal joints of the wrist. The elbow and knee are considered hinge joints. These joints allow motion in only one plane. Pivot joints allow rotation in one axis as between the first and second cervical vertebrae. The facet joints of the vertebrae constitute plane or gliding joints and allow only gliding type motions. The final type of synovial joint is the saddle joint. Saddle joints allow motion in two directions. An example of this type of joint is the carpal-metacarpal joints of the thumb.

Joint Design

Ultimately, the structural construction of the diarthrodial joint determines its mobility and stability. The end of each bone is covered with well-lubricated hyaline articular cartilage that allows for smooth union between bones. In some joints, this union is very tight fitting.

This results in a very strong and structurally stable joint. In other less stable joints, the junction is not so tight fitting and the stability is more dependant upon the ligaments and joint capsule.

In adults, hyaline cartilage is avascular and has no nerves or lymphatic channels. Its living cells are nourished by joint fluid, called synovial fluid, which also acts as extremely good lubrication. When the articular cartilage is damaged, it is repaired with scar tissue, which is mechanically inferior.

The joint is covered by the fluid filled ligamentus joint capsule known as the synovial sheath. This sheath provides a strong sleeve that helps hold the articulating bones together. The sleeve is oversized to allow for joint motion. It is nourished by blood vessels, which give it the ability to repair itself after injury. Ligaments are a specialized part of this sleeve and account for the primary stability of the joint. Many joints also have internal ligaments that contribute to support, such as the cruciate ligaments of the knee. In joints with poor articulations, the amount of ligamentus bracing a joint is very important to its stability.

The synovium is a specialized tissue that forms a membrane that is attached to the inside of the joint capsule. It produces synovial fluid, which functions as the primary lubricant for the joint and as the nutritional source for joint surface cartilage and meniscus cartilage.

Contained within approximately 10% of all synovial joints is a tough fibrous structure between bone ends called the meniscus. It absorbs shock, stabilizes the joint, and spreads the synovial fluid. The meniscus has no blood supply, no nerves, and no lymphatic channels making it unable to heal after damage.

Muscle tone tends to be the main stabilizing factor for most synovial joints. Muscle tone keeps the tendons that attach the muscles to the bones taut, reinforcing the related joints. As the joints near end-ranges of motion, they become more dependant on the innervating musculature for stability and become much more susceptible to dislocation.

Types of Synovial Joint Movements

Overall, synovial joints permit seventeen different types of motion, each of which has unique mobility characteristics. Each type of motion has reference to the anatomical position or the midline of the body and describes motion either away from or back to this position.

- Flexion: decreases the angle
- Extension: increases the angle
- Hyperextension: excessive extension beyond the anatomical position
- Dorsiflexion: bending at the ankle that rotates the foot upward toward the shin
- Plantar flexion: bending at ankle that rotates the foot downward away from the shin
- Abduction: moving a part away from the mid line in the frontal plane toward a 90-degree angle.
- Adduction: moving a part toward the midline in the frontal plane
- Rotation: moving a part around an axis
- Circumduction: moving a part so its distal end follows a circular path.
- Pronation: inward rotation of the forearm (turning the palm down)
- Supination : outward rotation of the forearm (turning the palm up)
- Eversion: turning the foot so the sole is out
- Inversion: turning the foot so the sole is in
- Retraction: a backward or pulling motion of the shoulder, scapula, and clavicle
- Protraction: a forward or pushing motion of the shoulder, scapula, and clavicle
- Elevation: raising a part up (shrugging the shoulders)
- Depression: lowering a part (drooping the shoulder)

It is also important to note that due to the complexities of movement and kinematic chain relationships, several types of motion can occur in a joint at one time. Moreover, different types of motion in adjoining joints usually accompany this. For instance, the simple task of taking a step forward involves hip flexion and external rotation of the lead leg and concomitant hip extension and internal rotation of the trail leg. Many times this is accompanied by a slight adduction of the front leg and abduction of the back leg as the pelvis tilts down away from the base leg (Trendelenberg gait).

Joint Positions

Joint position also plays a vital role in the amount of stability or mobility available at a joint. In the closed packed position, the joint surfaces become fully congruent, as the area of contact is maximal. No movement is possible in the joint structure since it is tightly compressed and the fibrous capsule and ligaments are spiralized and tense. This position is used during cutting or changing of direction where the ankle is dorsiflexed to maximize its stability and the transfer of power from the hip to the ground.

In the loose packed position, the articular surfaces are not congruent and the articular capsule is lax in some places. In this position, the joint capsule has greatest capacity and the joint structure is capable of the greatest amount of movement. Since this position provides the least amount of articular interference, it is used in joint play testing, such as the valgus and varus tests with the knee partially flexed.

Causes of joint stiffness

Several conditions may cause a short or long-term limitation to joint motion. If these conditions are present, it is typically advisable to avoid range of motion training. Disease can cause both permanent and short-term decreases in range of motion. Rheumatoid arthritis, an inflammatory condition of the joints caused by an autoimmune reaction, can prevent a joint from fully extending. Over time, this type of issue can produce contracture deformities, causing permanent inability to extend the joint beyond a certain fixed position.

Chronic injuries usually develop over an extended period. These injuries tend to occur when long-term training volume exceeds the joints capacity to experience adequate repair and recovery. They often result in degenerative conditions such as arthritic-type wear and tear, where the articular cartilage becomes worn leading to narrowed joint spaces. This type of degeneration is sometimes referred to as osteoarthritis.

Chronic muscle imbalances can also lead degenerative type injuries. Muscular imbalances can result in unequal or unbalanced muscular forces acting within the joint. This can shift the joints axis resulting in frictional damage or impingement. In extreme situations, muscular imbalances can also alter neuromuscular circuits via reciprocal inhibition (innervation) which leads to inhibition of antagonist's muscles. This inhibition can further perpetuate the imbalance and foster greater injury.

Growth & Flexibility Issues

Although much of the data pertaining to age and flexibility is conflicting due to focuses of research on specific joints or particular athletic disciplines, research clearly shows that flexibility changes during the ageing process. It is suggested that flexibility in young children is high and decreases during the school-aged years until puberty when it increases slightly again. This is however, a general statement considering flexibility may develop differently at varying age periods and dissimilarly for specific movements. Rather, flexibility is dependant on many interacting factors, such as ones level of preparation of training for sport, the quality and quantity of ones movements, ones physical environment, genetics, nutritional habits, and health and medical concerns[5].

While maturational development occurs at different rates and different levels for every person, there does appear to be some chronological commonalties that warrant discussion. Adolescences is a period of time that is typically associated with sudden gains in height and weight. Sometimes known as growth spurts, these changes in growth tend to occur between the ages of about ten-and-a-half to eighteen years, peaking around age fourteen. Both boys and girls usually undergo these changes. However, on average males usually experience them one to two years later than females.

The decline in flexibility observed in children entering into adolescence (see table 1) is in part due to bone growth. Bone grows at a much faster rate than muscle and results in increased tension in the muscle-tendon junctions of a given joint[54]. This increased passive tension will subsequently stimulate the creation of sarcomeres resulting in a decreased tightness[26,58]. Not all bones grow at the same rates and times during this period of development. This can lead to skewing of tests, such as the sit and reach that involve the ratio between the upper and lower extremities. In such cases, if the lower extremities grow faster than the upper extremities (the distance from the tips of the fingers to the bottom of the feet increases) it makes a favorable score harder to achieve.

Another possible reason for the decrease in flexibility over a lifetime can be explained at the molecular level. As age increases, the rigidity of collagen also increases. The fibers increase in diameter and become more crystalline, which leads stronger intermolecular bonds and an increased resistance to deformation. There is also a decrease in crimp and an increase in cross-links, which restricts extensibility via crimp extension or interfibril slippage[5].

There are also age related changes in elastin. Foremost, elastin production in the body ceases around age twelve to thirteen. After this period in time, there is a steady decrease in the elastin content of the body, primarily due to damage. The existing elastin fibrils become increasingly cross-linked, calcified and fragmented, and experience an increased proportion of chondroitin sulfate B and keratosulfate. This process leads to a slow degradation in their mechanical properties that result in a steady decrease of elasticity and extensibility.

The aging process is accompanied by an almost imperceptible decrease in the suppleness of the muscle. This loss seems to be heavily influenced by injury and poor or inadequate mobility. A decrease in muscle length resulting from a reduction in the number of myofibril sarcomeres, leads to physiologically shorting of the muscle. This is often experience in children who spend extended periods of time in the sitting position while in school. A common sitting position is one in which there is a "backward rotation of the pelvis so that the superior iliac spine lies well behind the pubis". This position causes slackness in the hamstring tendon, which will in turn cause the hamstring to shorten in an effort to take up the slack. This process seems to be less evident in children that lead a more active lifestyle[55].

Another age related change in muscle is an increase in muscle atrophy. With atrophy, there is evidence of the increased presence of fatty and collagenous fibers within the muscle concomitant to the decrease in cross sectional area. Although the increase in inextensible tissue occurs at many levels throughout the muscle, the increase for perimysium poses the biggest issue due to its overall contributions to resistance to passive and active stretch.

The neuromuscular system also experiences physiological changes with aging. Moreover, there is a decrease in the number of nerve cells innervating the muscular system[56]. This decrease can lead to a reduction in the active communication between the muscles and the CNS and can result in diminished reflex looping.

Decline In Flexibility		
Age Range	Test	Researchers
6-12	Sit and reach	Kendall and Kendall (1948); Koslow (1987)
6-15	Trunk and Neck Extension, Shoulder and Wrist Elevation, and Sit and Reach	Docherty and Bell (1988)
9-13	Shoulder Flexion and Extension	Koslow (1987)
10-15	Shoulder/Hip/Knee	Hupprich and Sigerseth (1950); Koslow (1987), Germain and Blair (1983),
Increase In Flexibility		
Age Range	Test	Researchers
5-10	Shoulder	Germain and Blair (1983)
8-16	Lateral Flexion (Spine)	Mellin and Poussa (1992)
13-17	Sit and reach	Kendall and Kendall (1948); Koslow (1987)

Table 1

Immobilization

Inactivity, whether it is from being sedentary or immobilization, can have an adverse affect on the tissues of the body. Disuse is associated with decreases in muscle mass, alterations of the structural and viscoelastic properties of connective tissue, changes in electrical and reflexive processes, and histochemical changes. Collectively, these changes may dramatically result in chronic loss of function and decreased range of motion.

Changes in Muscle

Physiological changes in muscle size and strength occur rapidly at the onset of disuse. Reduction in muscle mass is the product of a decrease in total muscle and fibril length and cross sectional area. Since actin and myosin filaments do not change length, changes in fibril length are seemingly the result of an adjustment in the number of serial sarcomeres[57,28]. Changes when immobilized in a shorten versus lengthened position have been report to alter the number of serial sarcomeres up to 20% and 40% respectively[29,57,57]. Since skeletal muscles, extensibility is directly proportional to its length and thus its number of sarcomeres in series, substantial changes in dynamic and static ranges of motion can occur because of immobilization and inactivity.

During immobilization, there is a significant reduction in muscle cross-sectional area (atrophy). Reports of muscle atrophy as high as 24.4% were shown to occur during eight weeks of immobilization with the majority, or 14.1% of atrophy occurring within the first two weeks[58]. After this point, the rate diminishes to a very slow rate by twenty-one days[59]. Although continued decreases in cross sectional area occur after this state, to what extent has yet to be defined.

Changes in strength and maximal-voluntary-contraction characteristics are also a byproduct of immobilization and disuse. Reports of decreased active expression of strength have been reported as high as 28% in six weeks[60]. Furthermore, the rate of tension development also changes considerably during inactivity. Bamman et al[61] showed a significant decrease in rate of torque development after fourteen days of bed rest. Duchateau[62] reported that the maximal rate of tension development was reduced by 24% in voluntary contractions after five weeks of bed rest.

Changes in Connective Tissue

When a joint is immobilized, the loss of muscle serial sarcomeres is accompanied by a down regulation of the collagen synthesis[63]. Although collagen synthesis slows, the proportion of connective tissue to contractile tissue increases. This results in reduced muscle compliance and a loss of range of joint motion[64,65].

During periods of immobilization, connective tissue in tendons, ligaments, muscles, capsules, and fascia experience significant changes in chemical make up. Of foremost importance is a reported 4.4% decrease in hydration. Since water provides turgor pressure within the collagen network, dehydration results in a decrease in intrafibril space. Furthermore, water acts with hyaluronic acid as the principle connective tissue lubricant. Through phases of low tissue hydration, the decrease in intrafibril space and increased friction can lead to the formation of additional cross-links. This will result in increased stiffness and a decrease in extensibility[5]. Additionally chemical changes occur in the form of a 40% decrease in hyaluronic acid, a 30% decrease in condroiten 4 and 6 sulfate[64,66,67,68].

Research has shown reductions in tendon stiffness as great as 32% and increases in hysteresis as high as 93.3% after twenty days of bed rest[69,70]. Furthermore, Noyes[71] demonstrated that knee joint immobilization for eight weeks significantly decreased the maximum failure load of the anterior crucial ligament

Electrical and Reflexive Changes

Neuromuscular adaptations to immobilization affect muscle function at many levels. Inactivity not only modifies the peripheral processes associated with contraction but also changes central and neural commands on involuntary and voluntary reactions. Maximal integrated EMG and overall mean power frequency are both decreased[69]. Duchateau and Hainaut[62] showed a 19% decrease in muscle surface action potential duration, a 15% decrease in amplitude, and a 26% decrease in total area in the adductor pollicis after six weeks of immobilization.

Tetanic tension in muscle is a fusion of a number of simple spasms into an apparently smooth, continuous effort. As the frequency of stimulation increases, the escalating tension generated in the muscle will rise to a peak known as maximal or peak tetanic tension (TTpeak). After immobilization, TTpeak differences existed between slow twitch and fast twitch muscle fibers. TTpeak declined 47% in slow twitch fibers and 28% in fast twitch fibers[59]. Additionally, electrically evoked max-tetanic contractions were reduced by 33%. Furthermore, peak rate of tension development and decline fell rapidly in the slow twitch and maintained in the fast twitch.

Reflex arcs associated with the muscle spindle also appear to be affected by inactivity. After three weeks of inactivity, Anderson et al[72] applied a tap to the Achilles tendon to initiate the myotatic stretch reflex. The tendon presented strong inhibition to the reflex indicating a reduction in spindle activation. Given that substantial decreases in tendon stiffness are associated with inactivity, this phenomenon may be the result of tendon distension. Since the tendon is more extensible, it will undergo a greater elongation at a faster rate before stretching the muscle to the point of activating the stretch reaction of the spindle.

Increasing Range of Motion

For decades, stretching of one form or another has been utilized as a means to increase range of motion and improve soft tissue compliance.

In theory, a more complaint tissue would be able to endure more strain. Since there would be more time and distance for the absorption of external forces, it would provide a cushioning effect that would lessen the potential for soft tissue disruption. Additionally, forms of stretching have demonstrated the propensity for delaying and decreasing the onset of muscular fatigue and soreness (DOM'S.)[73,78].

Increasing range of motion involves structural and functional tissue changes that promote an equal balance of mobility and stability under dynamic and static conditions. The quickest and most effective way to increase flexibility occurs through functional or neuromuscular means. By modifying the neuromuscular processes that control tension and length of the tissues in the muscle complex, you can almost immediately alter the length tension ratio of most musculotendinous units. Although the process is quick and efficient, it can be rapidly reversed if an ongoing means of training is not maintained.

The longer lasting way to improve flexibility and range of motion is via structural change. Structural change occurs in the contractile and connective tissues of the musculotendinous complex, especially the collagenous tissues in the fascia. These changes tend to occur much slower then the functional changes associated with the neuromuscular system, but tend to last much longer. The most permanent method of increasing range of motion involves stretching the joint capsule and ligaments. Although these changes tend to be almost permanent, promotion to the point of joint laxity can lead to joint damage, laxity, instability, and nerve and blood vessel damage. Therefore, attempts to increase range of motion via stretching the joint capsule and ligaments is not suggested[5].

Static versus Dynamic

Static flexibility represents a single measure in time of a static system. Therefore, many feel that it provides very little feedback about the changing behavior of the mechanical characteristics such as stiffness, elasticity, and viscosity of soft tissue. Conversely, dynamic flexibility represents the increase in resistance with muscle elongation for a given range of motion. Since this resistance (stiffness) can restrict the use of a given range of motion at normal or rapid speeds, it is viewed by many to be a more valuable measure of performance-based flexibility than static flexibility[5,74].

While insufficient evidence still exists to determine whether static and dynamic flex are two distinct properties or two aspects of the same flexibility component, plenty of research exists defining their differences. Iashvili[75] studied the effects of static verses dynamic flexibility on 200 participants. His research demonstrated that traditional static and passive stretching developed mainly passive flexibility. When stretching was combined with strength-type drills, it was considerably more effective in developing more sport specific active flexibility. Mortimer and Webster[76] found that dynamically trained athletes were able to manifest larger increases in the gain of long-latency myotatic pathways preceding movement and greater limb acceleration with greater rise time in agonist burst. This research demonstrated that dynamic flexibility might actually decrease Alpha-motor neural-pool excitability and more efficiently target the serial elastic components of the musculotendinous units.

Although more research needs to be conducted to support the benefits of performing dynamic activities rather than static stretching to warm up for sport, empirical evidence strongly substantiates its validity. While static stretching provides the obvious benefit of increasing soft tissue extensibility and passive flexibility, it does not always improve performance and decrease the potential for injury. Since static stretching increases connective tissue extensibility, it decreases its stiffness. Kubo et al[77] demonstrated that stretching alters the viscoelastic properties of the tendon. At five minutes of static stretching, stiffness decreased 8% and hysteresis increased 29%. After ten minutes of stretching, stiffness decreased 9% and hysteresis increased 34%. Therefore, when static stretching resulted in a decrease in elasticity and an increase in the time it took for the tissue to return to normal physiological length. The loss in stiffness and increase in hysteresis diminishes the ability of the PEC and SEC to store and return elastic energy.

Kubo et al.[77] demonstrated that resistance training increased tendon stiffness by 19% and decreased hysteresis by 17%. In addition, preliminary evidence suggests that strength can diminish for up to sixty minutes following a bout of static stretching[78,79,80] (Avela et al 1999, Vujnovich 1994). Therefore, a general assumption could be made that a combination of resistance and stretching type activities would better suit sporting performance than static stretching alone.

Research has shown that static stretching can result in the decrease in sensitivity of the stretch reflex. Furthermore, repeated and prolonged stretch modifies the titin in intrafusal fibers and directly decreases intrafusal-contraction force. Titin isoform change causes irregularity of filament overlap within extrafusal fibers. This may lead to increased compliance of sarcomeres through a decreased number of cross-bridges. This would ultimately lead to a decrease in external force response to stretch and a reduction in the mechanical effect on muscle spindle. Accordingly, modified titin isoforms would eventually cause altered stretch reflex sensitivity.

Malicious Points

With an increasing number of adolescents participating in youth sports, there exists a potential for an increased number of sport related injuries. It has been reported that injuries are the number one reason that students dropped out of competitive sports[81]. While there are numerous causes, flexibility is often cited as one of the major determinants in the causation of injuries in youth athletes. Significant flexibility is required around the hips and shoulders to perform many athletic tasks including throwing a baseball, serving a volleyball or swinging golf club. Under most normal situations, adolescent athletes enjoy the luxury of having full ranges of motion in the shoulder and hip regions. The increased flexibility provides the dual benefits of providing dynamic range of joint mobility while subsequently decreasing the likelihood of developing habitual postural alterations. While this potentially aids some aspects of performance (injury prevention) there are some potential drawbacks to the athlete. It has been observed clinically that many athletes possessing higher levels of flexibility actually have an increased susceptibility to injury. While this may seem contradictory to the accepted notions on injury prevention, there are several reasons for this. The most commonly accepted reason for this it that many youth athletes' exhibit decreased motor control in relation to the older athlete. Therefore, early program design for the youth athlete should focus on aspects such as basic movement patterns, coordination and general strength. This is accomplished best through games and playing. Flexibility comes as a result of using the body through its full range and potential. Only when specific alterations in joint range of motion or static posture are noted, should there be a specific focus on stretching.

Flexibility in the youth athlete decreases, especially in the hips and shoulders, as the athlete reaches puberty[82]. This occurs secondary to the significant growth of the long bones in the body relative to the soft tissue structures (i.e. muscles, tendons, fascia). This necessitates flexibility as part of a complete conditioning program. However, it is imperative that the athlete engages in the appropriate type of flexibility program to ensure proper length as well as motor control. See more on this subject in the section on functional flexibility.

Flexibility is important for the athlete regardless of his or her age. While the lack of flexibility is often cited as a cause of injury very few studies corroborate this theory. In fact, studies have demonstrated a higher incidence of injuries in those individuals that demonstrated both increased and decreased flexibility. Another determining factor regarding flexibility and the relationship to injury was imbalances between left and right sides. Flexibility variances of 15% or greater was just one of the factors reported to be a determining factors in the increased incidence of injuries in female collegiate athletes. Of particular interest, strength differences of 15% or more in the knee flexors or hip extensors from side to side also correlated to increased incidences of athletic injuries[83].

The following sections will focus on the shoulder and hip complexes as they relate to normal biomechanics and ranges of motion.

The Shoulder Complex

The following section is modified and adapted from Complete Shoulder and Upper Extremity Conditioning.

Biomechanics

The shoulder is a complex system of joints working together to allow for a large degree of mobility of the upper extremity. The shoulder functions to support the upper extremity and functions as a fulcrum for movement that allows for specific placement of the hand. It consists of the sternoclavicular, acromioclavicular, glenohumeral and scapulothoracic articulations. Since the shoulder complex lacks significant osseous and ligamentous support, it relies on soft tissues structures of the region for its support. These concepts are expanded below in the review of the four articulations of the shoulder complex.

Sternoclavicular

The sternoclavicular joint (SC) is the only bony attachment of the upper extremity to the axial skeleton. The SC joint is a relatively stable articulation and motion in this joint is somewhat limited in comparison to the other joints of the shoulder complex. However, rotation of the clavicle is important during any overhead motions of the arm. The clavicle is slightly "S" shaped and functions much like a bucket handle. During overhead motions involving the upper extremity, the clavicle at the SC joint is elevated and therefore assists in the first 30 degrees of upward rotation of the scapula[84]. Rotation of the clavicle assists in the last 30 degrees of scapular upward rotation[85].

Acromioclavicular

The acromioclavicular joint (AC) aids in the optimal positioning of the scapula. The AC joint is stabilized by the acromioclavicular and coracoclavicular ligaments although it is significantly less stable than the SC joint. Injuries to the AC joint usually involve tearing of one or more of the ligaments. A Grade I sprain is a tear or rupture in one of the ligaments, a Grade II sprain is a tear in two of the ligaments and a Grade III sprain is a complete rupture in both the acromioclavicular and coracoclavicular ligaments.

Glenohumeral joint

Although it has traditionally been classified as a ball and socket joint, the glenohumeral joint can be more correctly thought of as a golf ball on a tee. This arrangement allows for a tremendous amount of motion but it comes at the cost of stability. Therefore, the glenohumeral joint relies on the passive support that is supplied by the glenoid labrum, joint capsule and numerous ligaments of the shoulder. The glenoid labrum serves to create a greater depth to the gleniod fossa thereby deepening the contact area for the head of the humerus. The joint capsule is a fibrous structure that surrounds the head of the humerus and glenoid fossa and is twice the size of the humeral head[86]. The muscles of the rotator cuff and long head of the biceps blend intimately with the rotator cuff adding a dynamic component to this structure. The rotator cuff consists of four muscles: the supraspinatus, infraspinatus, teres minor and subscapularis. Each muscle serves a specific purpose in addition to depressing and stabilizing the humeral head in the glenoid cavity.

The function of the supraspinatus is to cause abduction of the humerus. Contraction of the suprsapinatus will depress the head of the humerus in the glenoid cavity which in turn causes abduction. This serves to counteract the upward translation (superiorly directed pull) created by the deltoid muscle on the humerus. Weakness of the supraspinatus causes a jamming of the supraspinatus tendon underneath the coraacromial roof as the humerus is pulled superiorly by the upward directed force of the deltoid.

The infraspinatus and teres minor externally rotate the humerus as the humerus nears 60-90 degrees of abduction and aid in depression of the humeral head during arm elevation thus helping to counteract the superior pull of the deltoid. This acts to rotate the greater tuberosity posteriorly and creates space for the supraspinatus tendon and subacromial bursa. Weakness in these muscles maintains the greater tubercle in an internally rotated position and may create an **impingement syndrome** involving the supraspinatus tendon, subacromial bursa and long head of the biceps against the coracoacromial roof. This also occurs if abduction begins with the humerus in an internally rotated position rather than a neutral humeral position as is seen with the upper crossed syndrome (tightness of the internal rotators of the glenohumeral joint) and with scapular misalignment. Individuals with this pattern will typically experience pain in the range of 70-130 degrees of abduction since this is where there is minimal space between the coracoacromial roof and the greater tubercle. The movement is usually pain free above 130 degrees since the humerus will begin to inferiorly translate at this time. This is known as the **painful arc**. Tightness in the external rotators of the shoulder and posterior capsule will lead to an anterior glide of the humerus in the glenoid cavity which often causes a perpetuation of many of the above conditions.

The subscapularis, the often forgotten member of the rotator cuff, causes internal rotation, depression, adduction and stabilization of the glenohumeral joint. It is an important muscle since it pulls the humerus posteriorly helping to offset the anterior directed pull of the teres minor and infraspinatus. It is often weak due to the over-dominance of the larger internal rotators mainly the pectoralis major and latissimus dorsi. Therefore, weakness in the subscapularis can contribute to impingement and anterior humeral glide syndromes of the shoulder.

While not considered part of the rotator cuff specifically, the biceps brachii deserves special mention due to its attachment through the joint capsule. The long head of the biceps originates from the superior lip of the glenoid labrum (supraglenoid tubercle), passes through the joint capsule and inserts into the radial tuberosity. In addition to its actions on the elbow, it functions as an anterior stabilizer of the humerus. The bicipital tendon sits along the bicipital groove of the humerus and allows the humerus to glide along it as it moves. Altered position of the shoulder, especially internal rotation of the humerus and abduction and/or anterior tilting of the scapula, create altered movements of the biceps tendon in the groove. Chronic irritation of the biceps tendon as it slides across, rather than in the bicipital groove may lead to **bicipital tenosynovitis** (inflammation of the synovial sheath of the biceps tendon).

Scapulothoracic

While the scapulothoracic articulation is not a true joint (it lacks ligamentous support, a joint capsule, a synovial membrane and synovial fluid), its relationship to the integrity of the shoulder complex is perhaps the most important. The scapula functions to place the humerus in space and position it in an optimal alignment which improves the function of the glenohumeral muscles. Neutral position of the scapula is located between the 2nd and 7th thoracic vertebral levels and approximately one to three inches from the midline of spine[87]. The scapula sits approximately 30 degrees off the coronal axis with the glenoid fossa facing anteriorly. This is referred to as the **scapular plane** and motion in this plane is often referred to as **scaption**. Scaption is thought to create less twisting of the joint capsule or impingement of the rotator cuff muscles. It is important to note that the scapular plane will change as the functional position of the shoulder changes[88]. Since it lacks the form closure of a more stable joint (ex. sacroiliac joint) and ligamentous integrity of most joint articulations, the scapulae relies heavily on the position thoracic spine and scapula stabilizers to maintain its position.

There are six general movements available at the scapulothoracic articulation; elevation, depression, adduction, abduction, upward and downward rotation. Accessory motions of the scapula that are often described in the literature include tilting, winging and flaring. Anterior and posterior tilting is associated with normal biomechanics of the scapula. Anterior tilting of the scapula occurs with GH extension while posterior tilting occurs with GH flexion. **Winging** of the scapula typically refers to an excessive anterior tilting of the scapula where the inferior angle is pulled away from the thorax while the superior aspect of the scapula remains in relative contact with the thorax. **Flaring** of the scapula refers to when the entire medial border of the scapula is lifted away from the thorax while the lateral aspect of the scapula remains in relative contact with the thorax.

TERMS	DEFINITION
Adduction	Referring to the scapulae approximating each other or moving closer towards the midline of the body. The adductors of the scapula include the middle trapezius and rhomboids.
Abduction	Referring to the scapulae moving away from each other or away from the midline of the body. The abductors of the scapula are the pectoralis minor and serratus anterior.
Depression	Lowering of the scapula in an inferior direction along the rib cage. The scapular depressors include the lower trapezius and latissimus dorsi posteriorly and the pectoralis minor anteriorly.
Downward rotation	Rotation of the scapula in a downward direction along the frontal plane of motion so that the glenoid fossa points towards the floor. The downward rotators of the scapula include the pectoralis minor and levator scapula.

Elevation	Raising of the scapula in a superior direction along the rib cage. The elevators of the scapula include the upper trapezius, levator scapula and rhomboids.
Protraction	Movement of a body region along the transverse plane of motion in an anterior direction; refers to the entire shoulder complex
Retraction	Movement of the body part along the transverse plane of motion in a posterior direction; refers to the entire shoulder complex
Upward rotation	Rotation in an upward direction along the rib cage so that the glenoid fossa points towards the ceiling. The upward rotators of the scapula include the upper and lower trapezius and the serratus anterior.

Description of scapular motion

Thoracic spine

The thoracic spine (T spine) should have a gentle kyphosis where the apex is approximately around vertebral level of T6-7. Proper biomechanics requires the upper T spine to extend as the shoulder goes into flexion, flex as it goes into extension and laterally deviate as it goes into abduction. Fixation or decrease in thoracic motion will result in decreased or compensatory motion of the shoulder complex. In addition to causing a decrease in shoulder flexion, an increase in the thoracic kyphosis (hyperkyphosis) will result in the scapula being placed in an abducted position as it follows the contour of the rib cage. Tightness/shortness in the pectoralis major, pectoralis minor, latissimus dorsi and teres major, in addition to weakness of the scapula stabilizers, additionally contribute to an abducted position. This creates an altered length-tension relationship and results in altered arthrokinematics of the glenohumeral joint and has been defined by Janda and others as the upper crossed syndrome (see section on posture for more on this topic). This posture is most commonly seen in the older population secondary to the compensatory osseous changes of the spine and soft tissue adaptations (shortening of the pectorals and upper rectus abdominus in addition to the anterior ligamentous structures and lengthening of the rhomboids, middle trapezius and thoracic erector spinae and posterior ligamentous structures). As has been discussed in the section on posture, a decrease in the thoracic kyphosis (hypokyphosis) is often seen in younger and athletic individuals thus creating a host of problems associated biomechanical alterations.

Biomechanics and Motor Control of the Scapula

Motion of the upper extremity requires coordination between the SC, AC, GH and ST articulations. Proper coordination is required to position all the aforementioned joints in the best biomechanical position in which to accept a load through the upper arm. This section will focus on the GH and ST regions. Movement between the GH and ST is often referred to as the **scapulohumeral rhythm**. For flexion and abduction, the GH joint contributes approximately 120° and 90-120° respectively with the remainder of the motion (180° total for both flexion and abduction) being contributed by scapular-thoracic motion[89]. The ratio of GH-ST motion is often referenced as a ratio of 2:1 where there is 2° of GH motion to every 1° of ST motion. These numbers are not always agreed upon by all experts in the field and may be purely theoretical as loads in the arm often alter this ratio as does individual differences. It has been suggested by Janda and others that during the first 90 degrees of GH abduction that the scapula should remain stable and contributes to the motion as the arm is lifted above 90 degrees. While all these numbers can be measured and argued about, the take home message is that the scapula should be stable during the initiation of arm motion and needs to elevate, posterior tilt and upwardly rotate to position the humerus in an optimal position for accepting a load through the upper extremity.

While assessment of the scapulohumeral rhythm is important, equally as important is the eccentric phase of the exercise or the return of the scapula to a resting neutral position. During the return from an overhead motion, the scapula should depress (minimally), anterior tilt (minimally) and rotate downwardly (return to a neutral position) and remain stable against the thorax. In essence, it should be the exact reversal of the flexion or abduction movements. It is common to see rapid deceleration, anterior tilting and/or excessive downward rotation of the scapula during the eccentric phase of motion. Another common movement fault is a more rapid movement of the scapula (into downward rotation and depression) than humeral motion rather than a synergistic deceleration of both structures. This often occurs secondary to altered scapular force couple relationships and glenohumeral muscles that are more stiff than their scapulothoracic counterparts.

While all muscles of the scapulothoracic region are vital to the optimal function of the upper limb, the muscles most associated with stabilization of the scapula are the rhomboids, serratus anterior and trapezius. The rhomboids act to adduct and downwardly rotate the scapula while the serratus anterior acts to abduct and upwardly rotate the scapula. The middle trapezius additionally causes adduction of the scapula. The upper trapezius and lower trapezius function as force couples and collectively cause upward rotation of the scapula and work as antagonists by causing elevation and depression of the scapula, respectively. The lower trapezius, serratus anterior and rhomboids are often lengthened and reciprocally inhibited by tightness in their antagonists (upper crossed syndrome). This leads to synergist dominance by the pectoralis major/minor, latissimus dorsi and levator scapula as they attempt to stabilize the scapula (synergist dominance). As the levator scapula assumes the role as a primary stabilizer of the scapula, it places a lateral flexion and compression stress on the cervical spine leading to neck injuries. Trigger points and myofascial pain syndromes often develop which further contribute to altered movement and scapular control. Weakness in the serratus anterior and tightness of the pectoralis minor will additionally cause winging of the scapula which is made more significant when a load is placed on the arm. This tends to be one of the major contributing factors of shoulder impingement injuries in overhead athletes.

Athletes and Shoulder Flexibility

Alterations in force couple relationships may occur secondary to multi-directional instabilities of the shoulder complex which often accompanies repetitive movement sports. Professional baseball players with no history of previous injury have demonstrated increased joint laxity in the dominant arm of both pitchers and positional athletes, although greater changes were noted in the pitchers[90]. While external rotation ranges of motion were greater in pitchers as compared to positional athletes, there was a decrease in internal rotation in the pitchers. Similarly, Little League baseball players showed a decrease in elevation and total ranges of motion in athletes occurring as early as the onset of puberty[91]. These ranges tended to decrease as the athlete's age increased. The most dramatic changes occurred between the ages of 13 and 14 year olds which incidentally, was the year before the peak incidences of Little League shoulder (fracture through the proximal humerus). Physeal changes, specifically retroversion of the head of the humerus, have been demonstrated in youth athletes with an increased frequency of throwing. This has been theorized to be one reason for the increased range of external rotation in the professional baseball pitchers. These studies highlight the need for both the proper assessment, conditioning and monitoring of the adolescent athlete involved in repetitive throwing (pitchers, quarterbacks, etc.).

These patterns are not exclusive to the throwing athlete. Similar patterns, increases in external and decreases in internal range of motion, are seen in tennis players as well[92]. Repeated microtraumas to the posterior capsule and external rotators leading to fibrotic changes in the structures may be one explanation for the changes in range of motion[93]. Alteration in ranges of motion in addition to changes in the mobility of the joint capsule of the shoulder have been shown to create a reflexive inhibition of the biceps brachii and pectoralis major and an increase in activation in the supraspinatus and infraspinatus which has been theorized to be compensatory reaction to the joint instability. These findings again suggest that a proper assessment is imperative prior to initiating a randomized or generic (one size fits all) stretching program for all overhead athletes.

Shoulder Range of Motion

Shoulder ranges of motion are located within the chart below along with the muscles producing those motions. It is important to recognize that these ranges are averages and variations will exist between individuals depending upon several factors including height, weight, muscle mass, gender and chosen athletic activity.

Shoulder	Movement	Range of motion	Muscle responsible for movement
	Flexion	170-180 $^{\circ}$	Anterior deltoid
			Pectoralis major (clavicular fibers)
			Coracobrachialis
			Biceps brachii (short head)
	Extension	45-60 $^{\circ}$	Latissimus dorsi
			Teres major
			Posterior deltoid
			Pectoralis major (lower costal fibers)
	Abduction	170-180 $^{\circ}$	Middle deltoid
			Supraspinatus
	Adduction	0 $^{\circ}$	Pectoralis major
			Latissimus dorsi
			Teres major
			Coracobrachialis
			Biceps (short head)
			Triceps (long head)
			Subscapularis, infraspinatus, teres minor
	External rotation	90 $^{\circ}$	Teres minor
			Infraspinatus
			Posterior deltoid

	Internal rotation	70 ⁰	Pectoralis major Latissimus dorsi Teres major Subscapularis Anterior deltoid
	Horizontal adduction		Pectoralis major (upper fibers) Coracobrachialis Biceps brachii (short head) Anterior deltoid
	Horizontal abduction		Posterior deltoid Teres minor Infraspinatus

Scapula

Upward rotation		Upper and lower trapezius
		Serratus anterior
Downward rotation		Rhomboids
		Levator scapula
Elevation		Upper trapezius
		Levator scapula
		Rhomboids
Depression		Lower trapezius
		Serratus anterior (lower fibers)
		Pectoralis minor
		Latissimus dorsi
		Teres major
		Lower fibers of pectoralis major
Abduction		Serratus anterior
Adduction		Middle trapezius
		Rhomboids

Anatomy of the Hip

The following section is modified and adapted with permission from Complete Hip and Lower Extremity Conditioning.

The hip joint is a classic example of a ball and socket joint articulation responsible for providing the lower extremity with a significant degree of mobility but more importantly a high degree of dynamic stability. It derives its stability from several sources including the depth of the acetabulum (hip socket) which is increased by the acetabular labrum, a fibrocartilagenous attachment surrounding the rim of the fossa. The hip joint is enclosed by a joint capsule that surrounds the articular surfaces and spans approximately to the neck of the femur. The joint capsule blends with several strong ligaments that add passive stability to the hip joint including the iliofemoral, pubofemoral and ischiofemoral ligaments and are expanded upon below. All three ligaments are vital in stabilizing and preventing excessive hip extension while simultaneously limiting hip abduction and are expanded upon below[94]. Other ligaments that add minimal support to the hip include the femoral arcuate ligaments and two located within the joint; the ligamentum teres and the transverse acetabular ligaments.

- Iliofemoral ligament: The iliofemoral ligament lies in an inverted Y-position attaching from the anterior inferior iliac spine and then dividing to attach distally to the superior and inferior aspects of the intertrochanteric line (in between the greater and lesser trochanters of the femur). It is the strongest ligament in the body.
- Pubofemoral ligament: The pubofemoral ligament extends from the superior pubic ramus of the pubic bone to attach laterally on the anterior aspect of the intertrochanteric line.
- Ischiofemoral ligament: The ischiofemoral ligament originates from the ischium just posterior to the acetabulum then wraps over the femoral neck to attach to the trochanteric fossa. This ligament assists in controlling internal rotation of the hip[95].

Muscles of the Hip

Due to the high forces placed upon the hip during many routine activities, the hip requires both static and dynamic stability from a variety of muscle and fascial attachments. For exampling, standing on one leg increases the weight on the hip by two and half times body weight while walking up stairs increases it by three times and forces often exceed four and a half time the body weight during running[96]. These forces are aptly dealt with by the many muscles that cross and attach to the hip joint. There are numerous muscles attaching directly to the hip joint that add dynamic stabilization to the hip including the psoas major, iliacus, gluteus minimus and medius, obturator externus, obturator internus, gemellus superior, gemellus inferior and piriformis. While not directly attaching to the hip joint, several additional muscles including the quadratus femoris, rectus femoris, sartorius, adductor complex, hamstrings, tensor fascia latae and gluteus maximus significantly influence hip function nonetheless.

Similar to the the links of a chain, the hip significantly affects and is affected by the adjoining articular linkages. Most notably, the hip is directly affected by the position of the pelvis. The pelvis is comprised of four bones; the two innominate attached anteriorly at the pubic symphysis and posteriorly to the sacrum and coccyx. The shape of the pelvis varies between individuals as well as between gender. For example, the female pelvis tends to be wider and shallower which potentially increases flexibility of the lumbo-pelvic-hip complex[97].

Pelvic alignment directly affects the hip by altering the position of the head of the femur in the acetabular fossa. An anterior rotation or tiliting of the pelvis tends to move the head of the femur towards the back of the fossa whereas a posterior rotation tends to move the head of the femur towards the front of the socket. Therefore, it is imperative to maintain a neutral position of the pelvis in order to maintain proper length tension relationships of the muscles affecting the hip joint. This concept is expanded upon below.

Neutral Alignment of the Pelvis

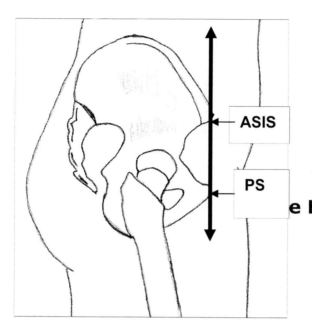

The pelvis is in a neutral alignment when the anterior superior iliac spine (ASIS) and public symphysis (PS) are in the same vertical plane. The pelvis is in an anterior tilt (rotation) when the ASIS is anterior to the PS symphysis. The pelvis is in a posterior tilt (rotation) when the ASIS falls posterior to the PS. Optimal length tension relationships of the muscles of the lumbo-pelvic-hip complex occur when the pelvis is in a neutral position. Neutral positioning of the pelvis is important in maintaining proper alignment of the hip joint.

Pelvic positioning. The image on the top demonstrates a neutral position of the pelvis. The image on the bottom demonstrates a slight anterior tilt of the pelvis. This position is a safe beginning posture for many movement patterns as this is the athletic stance for many sports specific drills. Additionally, many experts recommend a slight anterior pelvic tilt when attempting to maximizing running speed and agility[98].

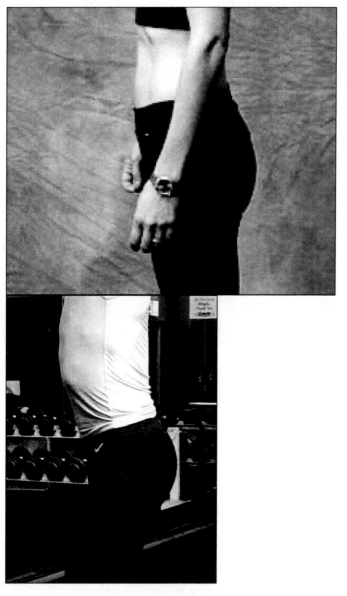

Neutral pelvis (top) and anterior pelvic tilt (bottom)

Force Couples Affecting The Hip

Several force couples are responsible for maintaining the proper positioning of the pelvis. **Force couples** are muscles that work together, usually pulling in opposite directions, to create rotation of a joint and maintain an optimal instantaneous axis of rotation (see table below). In simpler terms this refers to the muscles that work synergistically to provide equal and optimal forces around the joint during any movement. Listed below is a schematic representing the force couples affecting the lumbo-plevic-hip complex.

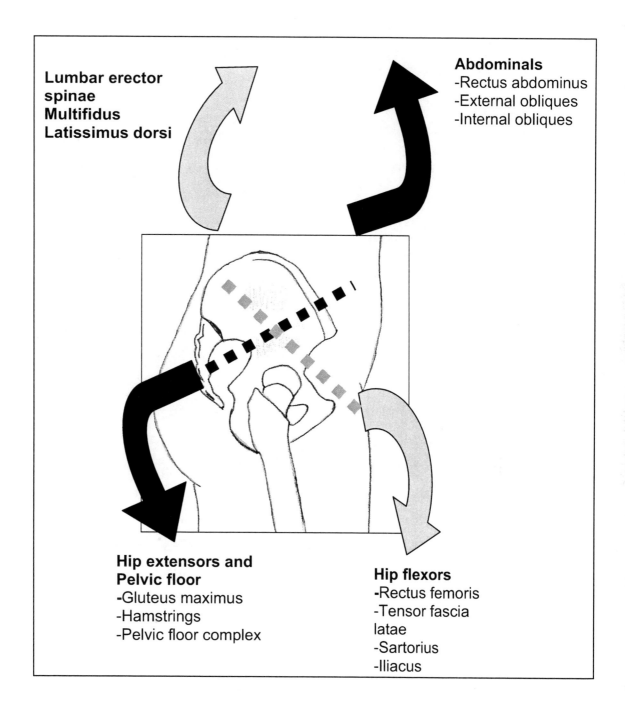

FORCE COUPLES	ACTIONS
Abdominals and gluteus maximus/ hamstrings	Posterior rotation (tilting) of the pelvis
Lumbar extensors and hip flexors	Anterior rotation (tilting) of the pelvis

Force couples of the lumbo-pelvic-hip complex

Alterations in the force couple relationships can have a dramatic impact on an individuals performance. An example of an altered force couple relationship resulting in a common postural dysfunction seen in many individuals is a posterior rotation of the pelvis secondary to a prolonged seated posture. This posture, common in many individuals due to the many hours spent in a seated posture in front of the computer and television and tends to create a lengthening of the lumbar erector spinae and hip flexors, specifically the psoas. There is a subsequent shortening of the deep hip rotators and abdominals, specifically the external obliques. This posture is often further patterned by specific exercise cueing such as "pull in the abdominals," "stand up tall" and "squeeze the glutes tight" in addition to exercises that encourage posterior rotation of the pelvis such as cueing the low back to remain flat or in contact with the ground during supine abdominal crunches as well as allowing the back to lose its normal lordosis while squatting. This is also a common postural fault in sports in which aesthetics are important, i.e. dancers and gymnasts, since it gives the illusion of creating an aesthetically appealing posture. However, it has very significant ramifications on function as Hodges and others have demonstrated optimal activation of the local system of the core (specifically the transversus abdominus) when the pelvis is in a neutral position.   Incidentally there was an increased activation of the transversus abdominus when the pelvis was positioned in a slight anterior tilt. Posterior tilting of the pelvis leads to altered recruitment strategies and decreased ability to control forces through the entire lumbo-pelvic-hip region and therefore decreased function of the kinetic chain. Additionally, a posterior tilted position of the pelvis tends to decrease the force production of the gluteus maximus secondary to the decrease in length-tension of the muscle. This tends to decrease the ability to generate extension force during any event that requires maximal hip extension most notably running and jumping. An even greater detriment to function is the decrease in force reduction, or the ability to control forces during the deceleration phase of a jump. This has routinely been observed to be a leading cause of lumbar disc injuries secondary to the compressive forces resulting from the flexed position of the lumbar spine. Another common injury pattern are knee injuries in female athletes since the individual can not appropriately decelerate the forces generated through the lower extremity often with direct correlation to injuries of the medial meniscus and anterior cruciate ligaments.

Altered length tension relationships have been linked to increases in knee injuries in female athletes. Altered length tension relationships are one cause of postural changes such as genu recarvatum (knee hyperextension) which has been reported to be one of the causative factors in female athletes suffering anterior cruciate injuries[99]. While more common in individuals demonstrating an anterior pelvic tilt, genu recarvatum may be observed in individuals demonstrating a posterior pelvic tilt as well.

The above studies require that the strength and conditioning specialist be cognizant of the dramatic ramifications that postural alterations play on functional flexibility especially as it relates to the youth athlete. In conclusion, it is important to teach and continually monitor for a neutral position of the spine and pelvis in order to maximize performance. Alterations in the pelvic position will alter the length-tension relationship of the force couples responsible for controlling pelvic position and potentially decrease performance and increase the likelihood of injuries.

Hip Range of Motion

Hip ranges of motion are located within the chart below along with the muscles producing those motions. It is important to recognize that these ranges are averages and variations will exist between individuals depending upon several factors including height, weight, muscle mass, gender and chosen athletic activity.

Hip	Movement	Range	Muscle responsible for movement
	Flexion	120-135°	Psoas major
			Iliacus
			Sartorius
			Pectineus
			Adductor longus/ brevis
			Adductor magnus (anterior fibers)
			Tensor fascia latae
			Gluteus medius (anterior fibers)

	Extension	10-30 °	Gluteus maximus
			Adductor magnus (posterior fibers)
			Gluteus medius (posterior fibers)
			Semitendinosus/ Semimembranosus
			Biceps femoris (long head)
	Abduction	40-45 °	Sartorius
			Tensor fascia latae
			Gluteus medius/ minimus
			Piriformis (when hip is flexed)
			Gluteus maximus (upper fibers)
	Adduction	20-30 °	Iliacus
			Psaos major
			Adductor complex
			Gluteus maximus (lower fibers)
	External rotation	40-45 °	Psoas major
			Iliacus
			Sartorius
			Obturator externus/ internus
			Gemmellus superior/ inferior
			Biceps femoris (long head)
			Piriformis
			Adductor complex
	Internal rotation	40-45 °	Tensor fascia latae
			Gluteus medius
			Semimembranosus/ semitendinosus

References

[1] Kisner, C. & Colby, L. (2002)

[2] Krivickas, L.S. (1999)

[3] Galley, P.M. & Foster A.L. (1987)

[4] Bryant, S. (1984)

[5] Alter, M. (2004)

[6] Williams, P.L., et al. (1995)

[7] Curwin, S.L. (1996)

[8] Culav, E.M., Clark, C.H. & Merilee, M.J. (1999)

[9] Von der Mark, K. (1981)

[10] Nimni, M.E. (1980)

[11] Simkin, PA. (1988)

[12] Cailliet, R. (1988)

[13] Widmann, F.K. (1978)

[14] Viidik, A. (1980)

[15] Ozkaya, N. & Nordin, M. (1999)

[16] Alexander, R.M. (1975)

[17] Bloom, W., Fawcett, D.W. & Raviola, E. (1994)

[18] Eldren, H.R. (1968)

[19] Zachazewski, J.E. (1990)

[20] Johns, R.J. & Wright, V. (1962)

[21] Garrett, W.E. (1990)

[22] Kannus, P. (2000)

[23] Lucas, G.L., Cooke, F.W. &. Friis, E.A. (1999)

[24] Huijing, P.A. (1999)

[25] Purslow, P.P. (1989)

[26] Cremar, M.A., Rosloneic, E.F. & Kang, A.H. (1998)

[27] Cohen, N.P., Foster, R.J. & Mow, V.C. (1998)

[28] Lieber, R. (2002)

[29] Williams, P.E. & Goldspink, G. (1976)

[30] Wang, K. & Ramirez-Mitchell, R. (1983)

[31] Wang, K., Rameriz-Mitchell, R. & Palter, D. (1984)

[32] Labeit, S. & Kolmereer, B. (1995)

[33] Trinick, J., Knight, P. & Whiting, A. (1984)

[34] Politou, A.S.M., Gautel, S., Improta, L., Vanelista, L. & Pastore, A. (1996)

[35] Wang, K., et al. (1993)

[36] Horowits, R., et al. (1986)

[37] Wang, K., McCarter, R., Wright, J., Beverly, J. & Ramirez-Mitchell R. (1991)

[38] Huxley, A.F. & Simmons, R,M. (1971)

[39] Huxley, A.F. (1957)

[40] Williams, P.L., Warwick, R., Dyson, M. & Mannister, L.H. (1989)

[41] Netter, F.H. (1987)

[42] Guyton, A. (1984)

[43] Moore, J.C. 1(984)

[44] Jami, L. (1992)

[45] Matthews, P. (1973)

[46] Garamvolgyi, N. (1971)

[47] Walshe, A.E., Wilson, G.J. & Murphy, A.J. (1996)

[48] Funatsu, T., Higuchi, H. & Ishiwata, S. (1990)

[49] Horowits, R. & Podolsky, R.J. (1987)

[50] Pollack, G.H. (1990)

[51] Gordon, A.M., Huxley, A.F. & Julian, F.J. (1966)

[52] Levangie, P. & Norkin, C. (2001)

[53] Saltin, B., et al. (1977)

[54] Bachrach, R.M. (1987)

[55] Feldman, D., Shrier, L., Rossignol, M. & Abenhaim, L. (1999)

[56] Doherty, T.J., et al. (1992)

[57] Tabary, J.C., Tabary, C., Tardieu, C., Tardieu, G. & Goldspink, G. (1972)

[58] Stevens J.E., Walter G.A., Okereke E., Scarborough M.T., Esterhai J.L., George S.Z., Kelley M.J., Tillman S.M., Gibbs J.D., Elliott M.A., Frimel T.N., Gibbs C.P. & Vandenborne K. (2004)

[59] F. A. Witzmann, Kim, D.H, & Fitts, R.H. (1982)

[60] Geboers, J.F., van Tuijl, J.H., Seelen, H.A. & Drost M.R. (2000)

[61] Bamman, M., Clarke, M., Feeback, D.L., et al. (1998)

[62] Duchateau, J. (1995)

[63] Ahtikoski, A.M., Koskinen, S.O.A., Virtanen, P., Kovanen, V. & Takala, T.E.S. (2001)

[64] Akeson, W.H., Amiel, D. & Woo, S. (1980)

[65] McDonough, A.L. (1981)

[66] Akeson, W.H., Amiel, D., Mechanics, G.L., Woo, S., Harwood, F.L. & Hammer, M.L. (1977)

[67] Akeson, W.H., Amiel, D. & LaViolette, D. (1967)

[68] Woo, S., Matthews, JV., Akeson, WH., Amiel, D., & Convery, R. (1975)

[69] Kubo, K., Akima, H., Ushiyama, J., Tabata, I., Fukuoka, H., Kanehisa, H. & Fukunaga, T. (2004)

[70] Kubo, K., Akima, H., Kouzaki, M., et al. (2000)

[71] Noyes, F.R. (1977)

[72] Anderson, J., Almeida-Silveira, & Perot, C. (1987)

[73] Holland, G. (1968)

[74] Siff, M.C. (1993)

[75] Iashvili, A. (1982)

[76] Mortimer, J.A. & Webster, D.D. (1983)

[77] Kubo, K., Kanehisa, H. & Fukunaga, T. (2002)

[78] Siff, M.C. (2000)

[79] Avela, J., Kyrolainen, H. & Komi, P.V. (1999)

[80] Vujnovich, A.L. & Dawson, N.J. (1994)

[81] Durant, R.H., Pendergras, R.A., Donner, J., Seymore, C. & Gaillard, G. (1991)

[82] Drabik, J. (1996)

[83] Drabik, J. 91996)

[84] Purvis, T. (2004)

[85] Purvis, T. (2004)

[86] Purvis, T. (2004)

[87] Sahrmann, S. (2002)

[88] Purvis, T. (2004)

[89] Purvis, T. (2004)

[90] Bigliani, L.U., Codd, T.P., Connor, P.M. & Levine, W.N. (1997)

[91] Meister, K., Day, T., Horodyski, M. & Wasik, M. (2005)

[92] Alter, M. (2004)

[93] Alter, M. (2004)

[94] Magee, D. (1997)

[95] Lee, D. (2004)

[96] Meister, K., Day, T., Horodyski, M. & Wasik, M. (2005)

[97] Alter, M. (2004)

[98] Kielbaso, J. 92005)

[99] Purvis, T. (2004)

7

Bioenergetics and the Developing Athlete: Can we increase metabolic capacity?

Dr. Kwame Brown

The purpose of this chapter is to provide an overall discussion of the factors affecting children's exercise performance during development. The main focus of this chapter is to explore the various means by which the body obtains energy, and how those processes are affected by developmental stage and training. Energy in a biological system is carried in small molecules known as ATP (Adenosine Tri-Phosphate). When these molecules are broken down, energy is released. ATP has been called the "energy currency" of the body. Every mechanism we will discuss below has as its primary goal the production of ATP.

The information given here should be used not in isolation, but in conjunction with the information in the other chapters of this text to make decisions as to the most effective conditioning methods to be used when training youth athletes. However, this chapter is by no means an exhaustive treatment of the concepts involved in bioenergetics and youth conditioning. Certainly, other factors also affect the developing athlete's ability to use energy. We will discuss briefly how those factors, such as differences in the cardiovascular system, the neuromuscular system and in ventilatory function will affect the various metabolic systems. The reader should also remain aware that there are two separate issues at hand: 1) the longitudinal change in metabolic efficiency and power due to growth and maturation, and 2) the effect of training on these factors. One should also recognize that when we talk about the different metabolic systems, these systems never operate in isolation, especially in children during short-burst activity. There is always an aerobic (presence of oxygen) component involved in anaerobic (absence of oxygen) activity, and vice versa. When we discuss the systems separately, we are only referring to the dominant system during an activity. For a much more detailed treatment of this subject and especially for a discussion of the research in this area and its merits, the reader is referred to Thomas W. Rowland's textbook, Children's Exercise Physiology [1] After reading this chapter, the reader should be able to identify the principal factors in the maturation of the biological energy systems, as well as some of the effects of training on these systems during development. Especially important is the effect of events during the pubertal period on the bioenergetic machinery. Also important to remember is that the existing knowledge base in this area is by no means complete and will hopefully continue to evolve. Therefore, the reader is encouraged to continue to consult the IYCA to further their own knowledge of this subject as new information becomes available.

Biological Energy Systems

In this section, we will discuss how the basic metabolic systems governing aerobic and anaerobic exercise differ during development as compared to adults. An overview will be given of the basic aerobic (oxygen-using) and anaerobic (non-oxygen using) systems. These systems are selected by the body based largely on intensity, with higher intensity activities necessitating use of the high energy production rate of the anaerobic systems, and lower intensity, longer duration activities requiring the higher yield of the aerobic systems. For more detail on these systems and how they relate to athletic conditioning, the reader is referred to the NSCA's (National Strength and Conditioning Association) textbook[2] as well as Voet and Voet's Biochemistry text[3].

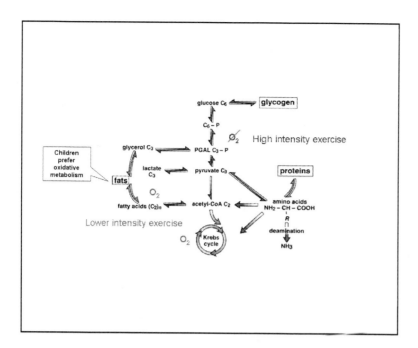

Figure 1: An overview of the relationship between anaerobic and aerobic metabolism and exercise intensity.

High intensity exercise occurs in the absence of oxygen and low intensity, steady state exercise uses oxygen, taking advantage of the slower but higher energy yield

Oxidative (aerobic): steady state

Overview

The term "aerobic" refers to the presence and use of oxygen in metabolic activity. Many people have misused this term to denote any kind of running or training outside of strength training. The aerobic systems are the preferred method of delivering energy to the contracting muscle as long as the intensity is sufficiently low and oxygen is present. The features of the oxidative system are: 1) fatty acids (basic units of fats) are the major source of energy (substrate), along with some carbohydrate and even protein and 2) energy yield is high and steady, but 3) the speed of energy production is slower than in anaerobic mechanisms (fast glycolysis and the phosphagen system, discussed below. The Krebs (citric acid) cycle and the electron transport chain represent the major metabolic machinery of the oxidative aerobic system. Substrates for the Krebs cycle can come from several different sources: blood glucose, glycogen from liver and muscle, as well as protein. Fatty acids are transformed into acetyl CoA before entering the Krebs cycle. Pyruvate from glycolysis, at low enough intensities, will be shuttled back through the Krebs cycle. Amino acids can enter the Krebs cycle in the mitochondria at several different points as oxaloacetate (5 Carbons), fumarate (4 Carbons) or pyruvate (3 Carbons).   The Krebs cycle results in the production of 6 NADH and 2 FADH2.   These molecules are fed into the electron transport chain, where they are used to facilitate the phosphorylation of ADP to ATP.

Yield

Slow glycolysis (during low intensity exercise in the presence of O2) results in the net yield of 36-38 ATP (2 ATP are consumed by glycolysis). The oxidation of fatty acids will net 100s of ATP molecules depending on length of the triglyceride chain.

Control

Intensity is the major determining factor in determining the preference of aerobic or anaerobic energy systems. The body needs enough time for the energy providing reactions (Krebs, electron transport) to occur – this is indicated by the relationship with the rate of pyruvate production[1]. If the rate of pyruvate production exceeds the rate of the oxidative mechanisms, this is defined as the anaerobic threshold, or the maximal rate of steady state activity[2]. The major limiting factor at steady state is the availability of substrate. The rate limiting step (or the step that will determine the speed and efficiency of energy production) in the Krebs cycle is the conversion of isocitrate to alpha-ketoglutarate by isocitrate dehydrogenase[3].   Also, if sufficient NADH and FADH2 are not readily available, the Krebs cycle will "wait" for these important hydrogen acceptors to become available[3]. Succinyl CoA (increased by the accumulation of GTP) will inhibit the formation of Citrate (oxaloacetate + acetyl CoA → citrate + CoA)[3]. The e- transport chain is, of course, inhibited by ATP (negative feedback) and stimulated by ADP (positive feedforward)[2,3].

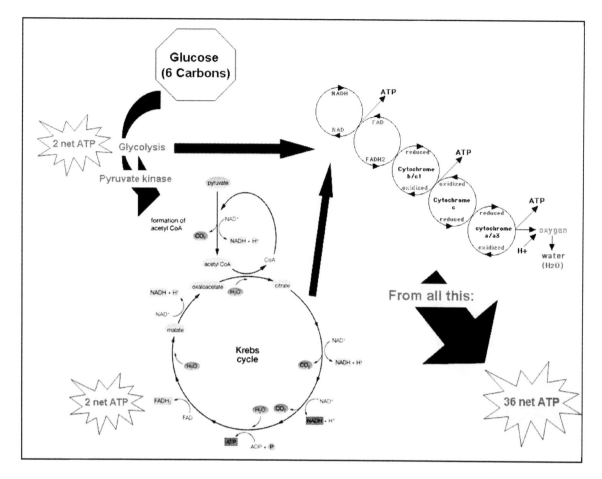

Figure 2: Aerobic metabolism. In the presence of oxygen, the ATP yield is much greater to serve the energy needs of the athlete over a longer period of time. The use of this energy system may persist at higher relative exercise intensities in prepubertal children than in adults.

Substrate Depletion and Recovery

During steady state exercise, depletion of available substrate (fats, carbohydrates) will occur at the level of the muscle and liver. It has been reported that the body of a prepubertal child may favor fatty acids as a substrate during exercise[4]. The implications of this information remain to be seen, but this may indicate a greater propensity toward fat loss in children during exercise as compared to adults. Additionally, children may preferentially use oxidative mechanisms during exercise.

Development and Aerobic Performance:

The oxidative metabolic machinery is of particular interest prior to puberty, as children at this developmental stage seem to preferentially use oxidation of fatty acids during moderate exercise[4]. Certainly, the performance of children in endurance activities will improve during development. We know that, all things being equal, an adolescent will run faster and farther than a prepubertal child. The question is: Through what mechanism? Is it the increase in muscle mass (which would mean, of course, more available sources of energy) allowing the developing athlete to perform more work? Is it the increase in efficiency of the internal machinery of the muscle? Is it the changes in the cardiovascular system? The answers to this question will be multiple and not easily elucidated. However, it is central to our understanding of how best to train a developing athlete to maximize performance, or to improve health in deconditioned or developmentally compromised children.

Aerobic power, typically measured as VO2 max (explained below), improves slightly during childhood, and then increases quite significantly in boys during puberty, while it plateaus as girls reach maturity.

There is an intimate relationship between the cardiac output (CO: the amount of oxygenated blood pumped out by the heart each minute), oxygen consumption by the body (VO2), and the difference in oxygen content between the arteries and veins, termed the arterial-venous difference (aO2 – vO2). This relationship is simplistically represented by the Fick equation: VO2 = CO (aO2 – vO2)[5]. One can easily see, then, that while the decision that the body makes to use oxidative mechanisms is largely dependent on the intensity of exercise, the efficiency and power of these mechanisms will be influenced by the components of the Fick equation, namely CO. CO is also related to heart rate and stroke volume (SV), which is the amount of blood pumped by the heart with each beat.

This brings us to a couple of differences between prepubertal children and adults that may affect oxygen delivery and therefore usage. Prepubertal and circumpubertal children have been reported to have a "hypokinetic" circulation, which suggests that there is less cardiac output relative to O2 uptake. However, Rowland refutes this suggestion, as well as other data that implicate lower cardiac function in children stating that "no maturational differences in cardiac functional reserve during exercise exist when variables are adjusted appropriately for body dimensions"[1]

VO2 Max (or Peak)

VO2 max is the way that maximal oxygen consumption, representative of the highest level of steady state exercise attainable, is measured in the laboratory. VO2max increases proportionally to body mass during puberty[6,7]. VO2 max has been reported to be lower in prepubertal children as compared to adults.

Stroke volume, or the amount of blood that the right ventricle of the heart can pump to the rest of the body with each beat, seems to be the major determinant of VO2max (or peak) in circumpubertal boys, while there doesn't appear to be much variation in the human population with regard to aO2 - vO2 (remember that the product of the arterial-venous difference and cardiac output = oxygen consumption)[6]. In other words, maximal oxygen usage appears to be heavily influenced by the level to which oxygenated blood can be delivered to the muscle. It seems that stroke volume during this period is basically catching up with the new O2 capacity brought on by increased muscle mass. Thus, it can be inferred that the changes seen at the onset of puberty (such as the initial increase in muscle mass) trigger the increase in physical capacity.

Training Effects on Endurance Capability

It was initially thought that VO2 max could not be improved in prepubertal children, but further analysis by multiple reviewers showed that many of the early studies addressing this question were poorly designed[8, 9, 10]. When studies are properly designed (relative to adult studies) with respect to subject selection (previously untrained), developmental stage, and training methods used (most effective appears to be at least three times a week at 85% VO2peak, there is an average increase in VO2max of about 5.8% (Rowland). Rowland postulates that children simply need longer program durations, as evidences by three studies with longer than usual training periods (fifteen weeks to eighteen months), which provided an increase of 10% - 19% improvement in VO2max[11, 12, 13]. Also, Obert et al. employed a thirteen week training program to elicit a 15% increase in ten to eleven year old boys and an 8% increase in girls of the same age[14]. A mixed training protocol was used in the Obert study. Interval training and continuous runs were performed over forty, one hour sessions at heart rates exceeding 90% of HRmax for the interval training and 80% HRmax for the continuous training sessions. It appears that intensity, more than length of program, plays a fairly large role in eliciting training effects in children. Studies that used lower training intensities for shorter durations produced more modest training effects[15, 16, 17].

Additionally, high intensity interval training (HIIT) has been found to be equal or superior to steady state training in eliciting changes in VO2 max in adults[18]. HIIT has also been shown to be effective in improving peak oxygen consumption in children[19, 20]. Mixed training protocols, where two days are spent performing continuous runs and the other two days are spent engaged in interval training have also been effective in improving maximal aerobic power[21].

Although several studies have shown long slow distance training to be effective in improving VO2 max , the other benefits of HIIT in addition to the increase in aerobic power warrant the use of interval training, both high and moderate intensity to improve movement skills and metabolic efficiency.

VO2 Max is not the Only Factor Affecting Aerobic Fitness

Despite the fact that VO2max can be improved in prepubertal children, this does not necessarily mean that this is something that trainers and coaches should focus on during training. Rowland states: "Increases in endurance performance as children grow are independent of VO2max and are instead linked to improvements in submaximal exercise economy". Children as they grow improve running economy such that they are able perform the same work at a lower percentage of VO2max. This probably is brought about by a combination of increased muscle mass (both skeletal and cardiac) and improvement in motor skills (efficient running pattern). Indeed, in elite adult runners, strength training has been shown to improve running economy and in turn endurance without a concomitant increase in VO2max[22]. Therefore, trainers and coaches should spend more time on improving running skill, neuromuscular coordination, and strength rather than simply reinforcing the same poor patterning over longer distances. More sport-specific conditioning should be reserved for adolescents who have proper movement mechanics.

Short Burst (Anaerobic) Activity

Anaerobic short-burst activity is defined as high intensity physical work performed over a period of less than three minutes[2]. The duration of the activity, practically speaking, is determined by the intensity of the action. Some actions require large amounts of force and require energy to be used very quickly at the level of the muscle, without time to liberate energy from the bloodstream (glucose), or glycogen stores in the muscle and liver, or fat stores. Energy for these kinds of activities, such as a vertical jump or short sprint, when performed at maximum is provided by the phosphagen system. When activity is still intense but not quite maximal, it can be sustained over a longer period of time. Events such as sprints between 100 and 800 meters begin to bring in energy from fast glycolysis, which is a bit slower than the phosphagen system, but still quicker than mobilizing energy from the body's storage (glycogen and fat).   When an individual increases the duration of the activity (concomitantly lowering the intensity), the body will begin to use systems like the oxidative mechanisms discussed above, mobilizing stored forms of energy in the presence of oxygen to provide greater energy supply over a longer period of time.

Phosphagen

Overview

The phosphagen system is set up to provide quick energy for short burst, intense activities (0-30 seconds). The rate of supply of ATP by this system is high, but overall yield is low compared to glycolysis and oxidative mechanisms. Creatine kinase is the synthetic enzyme for the phosphagen system.   There also exists within this system a more immediate source of energy through the myokinase reaction.

Control

An increase in ADP will increase creatine kinase activity (positive feedforward). Creatine kinase activity will stay up unless intensity lowers to allow time for glycolytic glycolysis. As ATP increases in the sarcoplasm (the inside of a muscle cell), this inhibits the activity of creatine kinase. This is a kind of "negative feedback", because the end product is signaling a halt to its own production.

Substrate Depletion and Recovery

The phosphagen system makes use of the phosphate donor creatine phosphate to make ATP from ADP, and hydrolyzes ATP (via the enzyme myosin ATPase) to free energy for the quick-burst muscle action. Many readers who have not been students of physiology will know the familiar creatine phosphate as a nutritional supplement taken by many athletes.

Special note: Creatine is a natural substance that the body makes naturally. While there have been few documented problems with children who have taken creatine, the IYCA does not recommend the use of nutritional supplements by developing children unless prescribed by a physician to treat a medical illness. You will learn below that prepubertal children have lower levels of creatine phosphate. While the next logical step may SEEM to be the supplementation of creatine in this population, this is not necessary or advisable as the long term effects are not known.

The Phosphagen System and Development

During sprints, prepubertal and pubertal boys seem to recover faster, but show lower power in cycling sprints[23]. This lower power production in children (corrected for body weight) has been previously explained by the fact that creatine phosphate levels have been shown to be lower in prepubertal children than adults[24]. However, this is not true at rest[4], and the lower power production is more likely due to the lack of an exercise-induced increase in the activity of creatine kinase, the enzyme that uses creatine phosphate to activate ADP to ATP[25] (Figure 3).

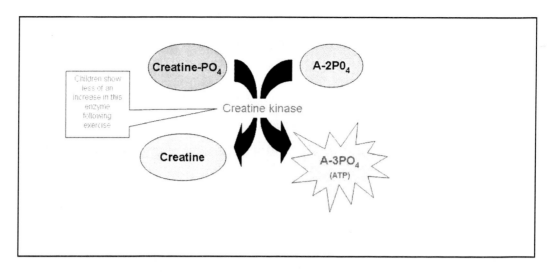

Figure 3: Phosphagen system in children. Children exhibit lower relative power during short burst activities, possibly due to less enzyme activity and a lower ability to rephosphorylate ADP to ATP.

Performance in both the bent arm hang and the vertical jump showed the biggest increase as boys approached peak height velocity[26] (the largest growth spurt).

It is largely unclear whether these changes can be linked to hormonal changes during puberty (testosterone and growth hormone), or whether the changes are simply due to the increase in body size and therefore muscle mass. It is likely that all of these factors play a role in the lower power output seen in children.

Glycolysis

Overview

The glycolytic systems provide energy for sustained bouts of high intensity exercise (6 seconds to 2-3 minutes), both in the absence of oxygen (fast glycolysis) and in the presence of oxygen (slow glycolysis)[2]. Since slow glycolysis basically involves shuttling of pyruvate, the end product of glycolysis, into the aforementioned Krebs cycle at moderate exercise intensities in the presence of oxygen[2,3], we will concentrate on fast (anaerobic) glycolysis in this section. Much more seems to be known about glycolysis in children as compared to the phosphagen system, probably because the processes involved and their factors are easier to measure.

Slow vs. Fast

During fast (anaerobic) glycolysis, pyruvate converted into Lactic acid (or lactate as it exists in the body)[2,3]. In slow (aerobic) glycolysis, pyruvate is transported into mitochondria, where it is fed into the Krebs (citric acid) cycle in the presence of O_2 [2,3].

Yield

During glycolysis one molecule of glucose will yield either two or three molecules of ATP, depending on which substrate the process begins with; glycogen (muscle and liver) or glucose (blood)[2].

Control

Glycolysis is inhibited by acidic conditions secondary to ischemia and the production of lactate and H+ ions. It is also possibly inhibited by increases in ATP, CrPO4, citrate and free fatty acids[27]. Primary control of glycolysis, though, is achieved via phosphorylation of glucose to hexokinase, another sugar with a slightly different structure. Transformation to this sugar makes the rest of the reactions involved in Glycolysis possible[3]. Another contributing factor to the control of glycolysis is the breakdown rate of glycogen (the stored form of glucose)[3]. The major rate-limiting step in glycolysis is the conversion of fructose-6-phosphate to fructose-1,6-bisphosphate by PFK (phosphofructokinase)[3]. Also, AMP produced by the phosphagen energy system will stimulate glycolysis via an increase in PFK activity. Finally, the presence of ammonia secondary to deamination of proteins will also increase PFK activity[3]. This is an important point, because the breakdown of proteins takes place when the body is depleted of energy during long bouts of exercise.

Development and the Anaerobic Systems

As exercise intensity increases, the lactate threshold (LT) is the point at which the body begins to rely on anaerobic mechanisms preferentially. As the intensity increases, we approach the onset of blood lactate accumulation (OBLA), which denotes the point at which lactate is being produced at such a rate that the body's mechanisms for buffering and clearing this waste product are overwhelmed[2]. It has been shown that with training, the intensity at which LT occurs can be raised[28]. There are some differences in youth athletes, especially during the prepubertal period with respect to LT and OBLA, which will be discussed below.

It has been observed that there is a lower peak [La] in prepubertal children (anaerobic glycolysis) after maximal and supramaximal exercise[29]. The kinetics (simply put, the speed) of lactate build up also differ in children in that there is a shorter time to peak in prepubertal children as compared to adults. In children as well as adults the decrease in [La] after intense exercise is augmented by active vs. passive recovery[30]. In other words, active recovery seems to speed along the clearance of lactate from the blood. However, there is a problem in interpreting this result to arrive at a training decision, because it has recently been shown that lactate is not just a waste product as previously mentioned, but another energy source[31]

In children, lactate threshold (LT) occurs at a higher % of peak oxygen consumption than in non-athletic adults[32] (Figure 4). In fact, the lactate kinetics in children appear to behave more like that of athletically trained adults. This means that children may switch to anaerobic mechanisms at a higher relative intensity than non-athletic adults. This phenomenon, in turn, could simply be due to the fact that children are simply more active than non-athletic adults. It remains to be seen what the relationship is between sedentary and active children. Optimal recovery intensity for lactate clearance was about the same (40% VO2 peak)[30]. Since active recovery also compromises resynthesis of glycogen (substrate), the lowest intensity possible was recommended by authors.   After correcting for body mass, Gaul et al. found that performance in prepubertal children was decreased to about 67% - 79% of the performance of adult men. This was accompanied by lower [La], as seen in other studies[33]. This could be interpreted to mean that while children seem to switch to anaerobic mechanisms of energy production at a higher relative intensity than adults, the "power" of this energy production is lower.

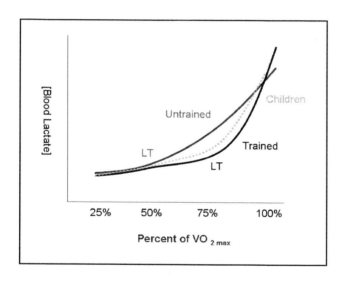

**Figure 4:
Anaerobic metabolism and development**

Lactate threshold, the point at which lactate begins to accumulate in the blood, is higher in children than in untrained adults.

Lactate production after maximal exercise increases by about 50% between age 6 and 14[1]. This suggests that there is an increase in the activity of glycolytic enzymes during growth and maturation. In support of this theory, glycolytic enzyme activity in children at age 4 is about 50% of that in 18 year old adolescents, including pyruvate kinase (PK), which functions in converting fructose 1,6-bisphosphate to pyruvate (Figure 5) during fast glycolysis[34].

This data suggests that children increase their glycolytic capacity during development, despite the fact that children engage preferentially in short-burst activities, and that this activity rate declines between the ages of 6 and 16[1]. Accordingly, children also exhibit diminished performance on tests of anaerobic power (as discussed above).

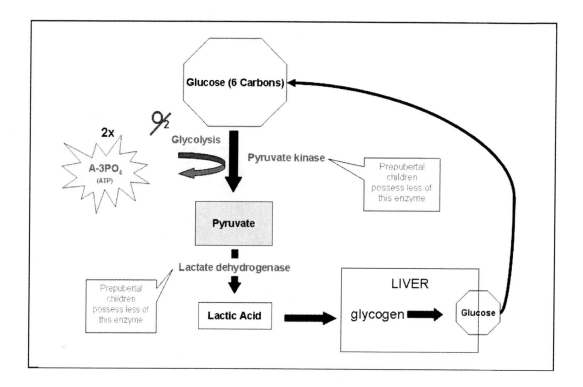

Figure 5: Anaerobic glycolysis in children. Anaerobic enzyme activities are lower in prepubertal children. This may impair the ability of the child to recycle energy through the liver and produce ATP. This may in turn serve to lower performance on tests of anaerobic capacity.

Training Effects on Short-Burst Activities and Anaerobic Metabolism

It has been shown in circumpubertal boys (age eleven to thirteen) that following high intensity training, a significant increase occurred in the activity of phosphofructokinase (PFK), which we know is the rate-limiting enzyme in glycolysis[35]. However, this seems to produce no obvious changes in the production of lactate after high intensity exercise[36].

Small increases in performance on tests of maximal anaerobic power have been observed in children after training. Depending on the test and method of training used, increases in maximal anaerobic power range from approximately 4% to 14%[37, 38, 39].

To be sure, level of neuromuscular coordination and muscular strength will factor greatly in determining the amount of improvement during training. Surely, prepubertal children who improve with regard to motor skills will make greater improvements in parameters like vertical jump height and sprint times than advanced athletes, given that they, quite simply, have more to learn. The motor skill factor will be of great consequence during the prepubertal years, as in the absence of the potential to increase muscle mass, neuromuscular coordination is likely the major factor in improving anaerobic power. No studies to this point have addressed the effects of teaching proper running and jumping mechanics to young children on the aforementioned parameters. This will likely be addressed by researchers in the years to come.

Special Populations

Many children suffering from such problems as breathing difficulties and obesity have been kept from performing physical activities for fear of medical complications. In many cases, the long-term adverse effects on overall health as well as exacerbation of the disorder in question resultant from inactivity lead the medical and scientific communities to conclude that for certain populations, exercise should be part of any medical prescription.

Asthma

Children with asthma and other airway obstructive diseases (such as cystic fibrosis) sometimes experience dyspnea and bronchospasm secondary to exercise-induced hyperventilation. These children may steer clear of exercise to avoid experiencing these unpleasant symptoms. However, this results in deconditioning of the musculoskeletal system as well as the metabolic machinery and cardiovascular system. This may in turn exacerbate the effects of the initial disease.

Children with mild to moderate asthma can still lead productive athletic lives. In fact, physical activity is encouraged, as it has been shown in some cases to reduce the number of hospitalizations, frequency of wheezing, time missed from school, and dependence on medication[40]. High intensity interval training has also been shown to be both well-tolerated and effective in improving both anaerobic and aerobic power in asthmatic children[41].

The practitioner should approach exercise programs with caution and progress children with asthma slowly. While they can achieve normalcy, asthma is a potentially dangerous condition and is compromised by deconditioning. This means that it is important for children with disorders like asthma must stay active. Although children with mild to moderate airway constriction can perform most sports, preferred sports (at least at first) are those which involved short bursts of activity, such as American football, baseball, sprinting, certain field events, and some gymnastics events. Make sure that children with asthma take whatever treatment they need, be it inhaler or oral medication prior to exercise.

Obesity

Obese children can certainly benefit from exercise and can lose weight rapidly, due to the propensity of the young body to burn fat more readily than adults during exercise[42]. Indeed, a variety of training methods have been shown to effect positive changes in the aerobic power and body composition of obese prepubertal children[43,44]. Care should be taken in these children. High impact exercise should probably be avoided due to the combination of increased body weight, deconditioning of the muscles and connective tissue, and the immaturity of the skeletal system.

Deconditioned non-obese children

There has been literally no research done on the aerobic and anaerobic function and responses to training in sedentary non-obese, otherwise healthy children. This is a growing epidemic in the United States. With the advent of sophisticated means of indoor entertainment, more and more children are engaging in less and less physical activity. Research needs to be conducted to ascertain the best methods for training this growing population.

Conclusions / Practical Applications

So, what does all this mean? Looking at the data in this area with a wide scope should lead the reader to the conclusion that the majority of training for prepubertal children should focus largely on the acquisition of basic movement skills (which will be discussed in other chapters). This can certainly be done in such a way that children are training at a high intensity in defined intervals. Many coaches, however, have made the mistake of assuming that making children run hard and often should be the priority, without regard to technique. We have all seen the coach that makes children run until they become nauseous. A more efficient use of training time may be achieved through interval training focusing on technique.

With regard to aerobic training, a perusal of the available evidence suggests that concludes that both interval training and long slow distance runs may be effective for prepubertal children in improving aerobic power. For LSD runs, the effective intensity would be above 85% HRmax, and the duration should be 45 minutes – 1 hour. However, children in this age group may have difficulty sustaining such a run, and in light of the myriad other more important parameters to improve in the developing athlete such as acquisition of basic skills, the practitioner's time may be better spent avoiding focusing on these kinds of runs. The IYCA recommends that technique intensive interval training of varying intensities and rest periods will be the "best medicine" in effecting changes in both aerobic and anaerobic power. Keep in mind that children may not be able to produce the same power as adults can, they do tend to recover quicker, so this should be taken into account when designing programs. Younger children (six to eleven) also tend to respond much more favorably to game-like situations, such as freeze-tag. Coaches can involve certain desired skills within games like this.

As the young athlete approaches late adolescence (usually fifteen to eighteen), and the need for sport-specific training arises, interval training is still the preferred method of training for anaerobic sports, as in adults. This method of training is the best way to improve variables involved in both aerobic and anaerobic efficiency / power. With young athletes who engage in aerobic sports, it may not be harmful to mix in some LSD training, but this should not constitute the majority of the training schedule. It is far more advantageous to improve the body's ability to recover from activity.

In short, while children are less capable than adults, especially during the prepubertal years, there is no reason that training cannot improve metabolic function. The practitioner can incorporate conditioning paradigms into training that focuses on the acquisition of basic movement skills, and progress toward sport-specific conditioning as the young athlete enters middle to late adolescence (fifteen to eighteen years old).

Below is a sample training program to effect changes in metabolic efficiency in beginning young athletes aged eleven to fourteen (volume may be increased as is age and skill appropriate):

Day	Training protocol	Work: rest ratio
1	2 x 25 meter skipping drills 2 x 25 meter sliding drills 2 x 25 meter double leg hurdle hops 2 x 25 meter agility ladder hop 2 x 10 meter side jumping through ladder	1:4
2	7 x 25 meter swim	1:3
3	4 x 50 meter runs	1:2
4	Active rest 2 days and repeat cycle	

References

[1] Rowland, T.W. (2005)

[2] Baechle, T., Earle, R. & Wathen, D. (eds.) (2002)

[3] Voet, D. & Voet J.G.(1995)

[4] Boisseau, N. & Delamarche, P. (2000)

[5] Guyton, A.C. & Hall, J.E. (1996)

[6] Paterson & Cunningham (1999)

[7] Williams, J.R., et al. (1992)

[8] LeMura, L.M. (1999)

[9] Baquet, G., et al. (2003)

[10] Payne, V. & Morrow, J. (1993)

[11] Williford H.N., et al. (1996)

[12] Yoshizawa, S., et al. (1997)

[13] Mobert, J.G., et al. (1997)

[14] Obert, P., et. al. (2003)

[15] Welsman, J.R., et al. (1997)

[16] Tolfrey, K. (1998)

[17] Williams C.A., et al. (2000)

[18] Laursen, P.B. & Jenkins, D.G. (2002)

[19] Counil, F.P., et al., (2003)

[20] Baquet, G., et al. (2002)

[21] Mahon, A.D. & Vaccaro, P. (1989)

[22] Paavolainen, L., et al. (1999)

[23] Duche P., Ratel S., et.al. (2002)

[24] Inbar, O. & Bar-Or, O. (1986)

[25] Duarte, J.A., et. al. (1999)

[26] Beunen, G. & Malina, R.M. (1998)

[27] Conley, M. (2000)

[28] Burke, J., et. al. (1994)

[29] Williams & Armstrong (1991)

[30] Dotan, R., Falk, B. & Raz, A. (2000)

[31] Brooks, G.A. (1988)

[32] Pfitzinger, P. & Freedson, P. (1997)

[33] Gaul, C.A., et. al., (1995)

[34] Berg, A., et al. (1986)

[35] Erickson, et al. (1973)

[36] Prado, L.S. (1997)

[37] Grodjinovsky, A., et al. (1980)

[38] Rotstein, A., et al. (1986)

[39] Sargeant, A.J., et al. (1985)

[40] Welsh, L., et al. (2005)

[41] Counil, F.P., et al. (2003)

[42] Dube, J. J., et al. (2002)

[43] LeMura, L.M. & Maziekas, M.T. (2002)

[44] DeStefano R.A. (2000)

8

Postural Development

Dr. Evan Osar

Success in any athletic arena requires a certain level of strength, flexibility and coordination that is specific to the given activity. Some activities may require a higher level of coordination (i.e. gymnastics), others require a higher level of strength (i.e. wrestling) and still others may require a higher level of specificity (i.e. a baseball pitcher). While overall there may not seem to be much similarity between these activities, there remains one constant through each of them; that constant being the body must move. Movement is critical to any task that is performed in athletics as well as throughout life. The higher the specificity, the higher the specificity of movement that is required. Therefore, sport specific activities require input from a variety of sources including the musculoskeletal, fasical and cardiovascular systems in order to produce the necessary movements. The coordination of these various sources of input must also be monitored and regulated, especially as movements become more specific, therefore putting these activities are under the control of the nervous system. Hence, the underlying goal of the youth strength and conditioning specialist becomes quite simply the optimization of movement abilities of the athlete.

There are many methods employed when attempting to improve athletic performance. Resistant programs focus on strength development, speed clinics target acceleration and deceleration techniques and flexibility programs are designed to enhance overall flexibility and range of motion (to name a few). The discussion of athletic enhancement as it pertains to movement, rarely includes the topic of posture. In fact, a quick review of many of the top books, manuals and courses addressing performance enhancement demonstrates it is a topic that is rarely if ever discussed in the realm of athletics and sports. However, when attempting to improve athletic performance, the positioning of musculo-skeletal-fascial system has a significant impact on movement and therefore the performance of the athlete. How does posture improve performance and how can the athletic performance of the athlete be enhanced through proper attention to the positioning of the body? The goal of this chapter is to answer this question by including a brief introduction to postural development, which will lead into the discussion of the components of optimal posture. This will lead into a discussion of some of the more common types of postural alterations and then specific techniques to improve posture will be included. While most of the information regarding posture comes from theoretical and clinical research on non-athletic populations, this chapter will attempt to bridge the gap between what is seen clinically and what coaches often observe on the field. Where applicable, references to some of the works regarding posture and movement are included, as the literature helps to support this approach to conditioning and athletic enhancement.

Postural Development

Posture develops as a result of adaptations of the musculoskeletal system to the stresses that are placed upon it. The first curve present in the spine at birth is a "C" shaped curve and is termed the **primary curve**. This curve eventually makes up the kyphotic curves of the thoracic spine and sacrum of an adult. The **secondary curves** develop as the child begins to move his/her body against gravity. Initially the weight of the head is heavy, which aids in the formation of the cervical lordosis. This curve develops at approximately three months of age. The lumbar curve develops at approximately six months of age as the child begins to sit up and crawl.

The center of gravity in a child is located around vertebral level T12. As the child develops, the center of gravity shifts to approximately level S2. As the child first begins to stand and walk, the feet are wide apart and the knees are in a varus position, in order to maintain balance. As the child grows, the legs become more valgus in position and then tend to straighten. The child's arches tend to be flat due to the large fat pads present, in addition to the underdeveloped intrinsic foot musculature. As the muscles develop and the fat pads diminish in size, the arches begin to appear. There is also an increased lumbar lordosis in children due to the weakness in the abdominal muscles, a relatively small pelvis and the weight of the abdominal organs. This posture should improve as a child grows and develops proper core strength.

As mentioned above, spinal curves are normal and necessary for proper development, weight bearing and shock absorption in the developing child. In contrast, spinal curvatures are abnormal curves resulting from either acquired or congenital causes. Often these curvatures are referred to as **scoliosis**.

Scoliosis is a curvature that usually results in the coronal plane (lateral direction) as opposed to the saggital plane nature of the lordotic and kyphotic curves. Acquired scolioses, scolioses that are typically developmental in nature, are often classified as structural or functional. Causes of structural scoliosis include genetics, spinal diseases such as poliomyelitis and muscular dystrophy or congenital causes such as a malformed vertebra (wedge vertebra or hemivertebra). Idiopathic scoliosis, suggesting there is no known cause, is the most common type of structural scoliosis. Although it can occur during the first few years of life, idiopathic scoliosis is most common during adolescence, usually occurring around puberty. Idiopathic scoliosis occurs most often in females and tends to have a familial tendency (present in more than one generation of a family. Functional scoliosis tends to be resultant of any number of causes such as postural alterations, leg length discrepancies or muscle imbalances and usually improves once the initiating factor is corrected). Research has found scoliosis in 80% of elite athletes involved in asymmetrical sports including throwing and racquet sports.

A simple test to determine between a structural and functional scoliosis is the Adam's test. To perform this test, stand behind the individual and observe the spine as he/she bends forward at the waist. The knees should remain straight throughout the test. As the individual bends forward, the functional scoliosis will improve while a structural scoliosis will remain curved or unchanged.

Since functional scoliosis tend to be caused by factors such as postural alterations secondary to muscle imbalances, the youth conditioning can have a significant place in the management of the athlete demonstrating this type of curvature. Management for any type of scoliosis needs to involve a team approach. In athletes where a curvature is suspected, be sure to have a qualified medical professional check in with your athlete on a regular basis, which could be every two, four, six or twelve months, depending on the severity and whether or not the curvatures are progressive. The youth conditioning coach will have the most frequent contact with the athlete, so it is imperative he/she check in with the athlete and the parents to make sure the curvature is not progressing. Monitor for increases in curvature, increasing pain or discomfort and limited ability to perform certain movement patterns. Depending on the age of the child, location of the curve, and sex of the athlete (females have a five times greater risk), early detection in some cases of progressive scoliosis may respond to conservative care (strengthening, stretching and postural awareness). While many athletes have had successful careers with a scoliosis, careful monitoring and early detection will help assure the athlete has the best chance at a long and productive career.

Additionally, increases in sagittal plane curvatures in the thoracic and lumbar spine of youth athletes has been associated with certain sports such as gymnastics and downhill skiing, necessitating the continual assessment of all young competitive athletes.

Components of Postural Control

While the body has often been studied as an isolated entity, simple observation of an athlete throwing a ball should dispel any notion of the body functioning in isolation. The complexity of this motion includes the initiation of motion from the lower extremity, rotation through the hips, pelvis and trunk and manifestation through the upper extremity. **Sensorimotor integration** is the process by which the central nervous system functions to constantly monitor and coordinate input from all of the different regions of the body in order to make the specific adjustments that are required to create efficient movements. Through analysis of each component, the nervous system is able to interpret the information received from the vestibular, ocular, proprioceptive, muscular, ligamentous and articular systems, in order to choose an optimal strategy in which to carry out a functional task.

Therefore, **optimal posture** is the coordinated activity of the neuromusculoskeletal system, which allows the ideal alignment of the kinetic chain while enabling optimal function and minimizing stresses across the entire system. This encourages proper neurological input to be received from the proprioceptive system, in addition to maintaining optimal length-tension relationships of the musculo-fasical system. The **length-tension** relationship is the point at which the actin and myosin filaments of the muscle fibers are optimally aligned and at which length provides the maximal strength in contraction. Whether the muscles are too short (secondary to over-activity or adaptive shortening) or too long (secondary to inhibition or adaptive lengthening) they can not generate maximum tension, in turn altering the force-couple relationship and therefore the compressive forces around the joint, leading to decreased performance and possibly injury.

Force couples are muscles that work together, usually pulling in opposite directions, to create rotation of a joint and maintain an optimal instantaneous axis of rotation (see table below). In simpler terms, this refers to the muscles that work synergistically to provide equal and optimal forces around the joint during any movement. For example, in the scapulo-thoracic (scapula and thorax) articulation, the upper and lower trapezius functions to upwardly rotate the scapula. Conversely, the pectoralis minor and levator scapula function to create downward rotation of the scapula. Collectively, these muscles function to maintain the tension around the scapula in order to provide the upper extremity a stable platform that is required when producing any movements of the upper limbs. Often there exists an imbalance of this force couple where there is shortening and over-activity of the pectoralis minor and levator scapula, which biases the shoulder toward downward rotation and inhibition of the upper trapezius. Since upward rotation is required during any overhead motion, impingement syndromes of the shoulder are a common complaint in throwing athletes presenting with a downward rotation of the scapula.

Another example of an altered force couple relationship resulting in a common postural dysfunction seen in many young athletes is a posterior rotation of the pelvis secondary to a prolonged seated posture. This posture, common in many adolescents and teens due to the many hours spent in school and in front of the computer and television, tends to create a lengthening of the lumbar erector spinae and hip flexors, specifically the psoas. There is a subsequent shortening of the deep hip rotators and abdominals, specifically the external obliques. This posture is often further patterned by specific exercise cueing such as "pull in the abdominals," "stand up tall" and "squeeze the glutes tight," in addition to exercises that encourage posterior rotation of the pelvis, such as cueing the low back to remain flat or in contact with the ground during supine abdominal crunches as well as allowing the back to lose its normal lordosis while squatting. This is also a common postural fault in sports in which aesthetics are important, i.e. dancers and gymnasts, since it gives the illusion of creating an aesthetically appealing posture. However, it has very significant ramifications on function as Hodges and others have demonstrated increased activation of the local system of the core (specifically the transversus abdominus) when the pelvis is in a neutral position and increased activation when in a slightly anterior tilted position. Posterior tilting of the pelvis leads to altered recruitment strategies and decreased ability to control forces through the entire lumbo-pelvic-hip region, therefore decreasing function of the kinetic chain. Additionally, a posterior tilted position of the pelvis tends to decrease the force production of the gluteus maximus secondary to the decrease in length-tension of the muscle. This tends to decrease the ability to generate extension force during any event that requires maximal hip extension, most notably running and jumping. An even greater detriment to function is the decrease in force reduction, or the ability to control forces during the deceleration phase of a jump. This has routinely been observed to be a leading cause of knee injuries in the female athlete since the individual can not appropriately decelerate the forces generated through the lower extremity, often with direct correlation to injuries of the medial meniscus and anterior cruciate ligaments.

FORCE COUPLES	ACTIONS
Upper and lower trapezius	Upward rotation of the scapula
Pectoralis minor and levator scapula	Downward rotation of the scapula
Lumbar ererctor spinae and hip flexors	Anterior rotation of the pelvis
Abdominals and gluteus maximus	Posterior rotation of the pelvis

Table 1. Force Couples

The above examples of downward rotation of the scapula and posterior rotation of the pelvis clearly demonstrate the necessity behind postural assessment of the youth athlete prior to and during any conditioning program. Typically, postural alterations do not improve without direct intervention, including proper postural cueing and often worsen as the athlete patterns or engrains the movement into his/her system. This cause and effect relationship is often a direct contributor of decreased performance and pain. While it is impossible to draw conclusive correlations between posture and performance since many athletes have succeeded despite postural alterations, the preceding case scenarios make convincing arguments that there is a definite correlative nature between posture and optimum function.

Any time the athlete performs an activity from a position that is less than ideal, there is a decrease in the efficiency of the movement and an increase in stress to certain regions of the system. For example, take the athlete with forward head and shoulder positioning. In response to verbal cues from coaches or parents, the athlete will attempt to stand up straight and correct the postural alterations. In compensation, the individual will often extend the upper thoracic spine, (appears as a lifting of the sternum) which appears on visual inspection, to correct the neck and shoulder positions. In reality, the lordotic curve in the neck is decreased and the shoulder position did not change.

While this may not seem to be a significant finding as the athletes overall posture appears to improve, this position will tend to "lock" (close pack position) the spine and limit motion, in particular, flexion and rotation. Flexion and rotation is required when performing many athletic events, including throwing a ball and swinging a tennis racquet. This will create a compensation through the lower back or shoulders, many times leading to decreased performance and eventually pain and dysfunction. Another effect of this posture is when the thorax is "locked" down; respiration is significantly restricted as normal ribcage excursion is limited. Ribcage excursion is required to allow the lungs to properly expand. With decreased ribcage excursion, the amount of oxygen intake is decreased leading to altered breathing patterns and over-activity of the accessory respiratory muscle, including the sternocleidomastoid, scalenes and pectoralis minor. This further limits the ability to perform athletic events secondary to respiratory substitution and decreased oxygenation of tissues. The over activity of the accessory breathing muscles further encourages the forward head posture and shoulder position, leading to even further compensatory changes throughout the thorax. Clinically, chronic fatigue and myofascial pain syndromes have been noted from long term presentation of this type of posture that has occurred secondary to the continued periods of overall decreased tissue oxygenation.

The above scenario exemplifies the effects of compensatory postural changes and **cumulative injury cycles** that result in response to altered length-tension relationships, force couples and arthrokinematics (joint mechanics). Ineffective load transfer often leads to biomechanical dysfunction manifesting as increased compressive loads on the spine and skeletal structures; an increase in tensile loads on the soft tissue structures, a resultant decrease in daily; occupational and/or athletic performance and, commonly, pain. This cycle tends to repeat in predictable patterns, while perpetuating the dysfunction ultimately leading to pain, biomechanical alterations and decreased performance.

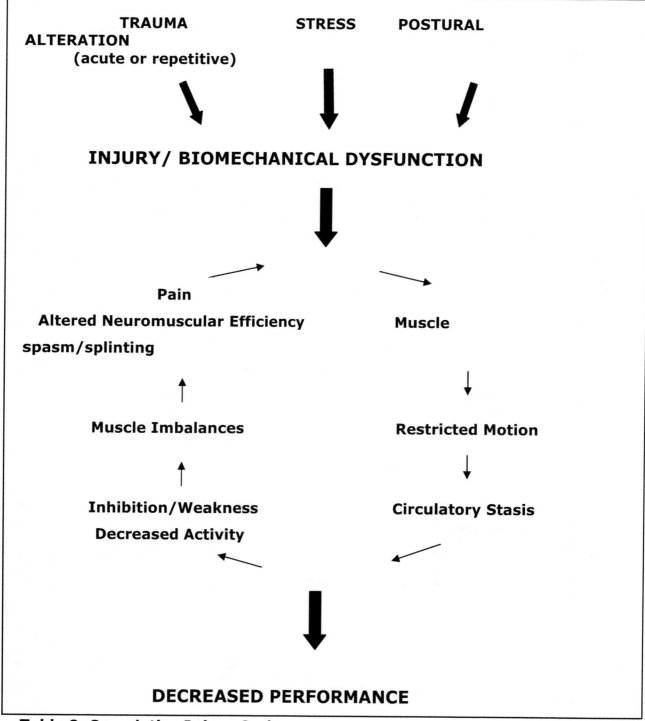

Table 2. Cumulative Injury Cycle

The Integrated Model of Function

The success an individual has in achieving proper posture and then perform activities of daily living such as walking, carrying a backpack or athletic events such as running, kicking a ball or performing an overhead pressing motion has to do with the efficiency of the kinetic chain in transferring loads through the body. Optimal function requires the ability to effectively transfer loads through the system. The successful completion of tasks such as these requires a strong structural base, adequate muscle force controlling the base, the necessary neural input to control the system and the proper emotional and physiological components to support the system. The Integrated Model of Function was initially developed by Vleeming and Lee to describe the interactions between the control system (nervous system), passive system (articulations and ligaments), active system (myofascial), physiological (nutrition) and psychological (emotions) in the control of the lumbo-pelvic-hip (LPH) complex.

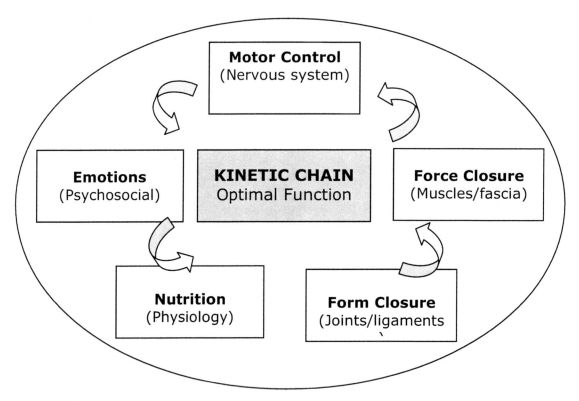

Figure 1. The Integrated Model of Function

Form Closure

Form closure relates to the actual shape of the bones, joints, articular (joint) surfaces and passive structures (ligaments and joint capsules) and their role in passive stabilization of the LPH complex. Certain joints have better form closure than others. For example, the sacroiliac joint has a high degree of form closure. The triangle shaped sacrum, which is thicker at the superior aspect than the inferior aspect, is supported in between the two ilia. Additionally, the articular surfaces on the sacrum and the ilia are non-uniform and contain projections that fit together snugly, increasing friction between the two surfaces. Finally, the sacrotuberous ligaments, in addition to the other strong ligaments of the sacroiliac joints, improve the stability of the pelvis.

Also, the hip joint contains good form closure due to its deep ball and socket articulation in addition to the ligaments that support the joint. Although it has less form closure than the pelvis and hips, the lumbar spine also contains good form closure. The thick vertebral bodies are able to withstand high levels of compression and are therefore a strong and stable platform in which to move upon. The facet joints (made up of the inferior articulating process of the superior vertebrae and the superior articulating process of the inferior vertebrae) support approximately 20% of the body's weight. Due to the sagittal plane orientation of the facets, they are able to provide a moderate amount of stability against transverse plane (rotation) forces. The intervetrebal discs, interspinous and intertransverse ligaments, anterior and posterior longitudinal ligaments and the iliolumbar ligament, as well as the joint capsules, contribute to the stability of the spine.

Force Control

Research has demonstrated that without musculofascial influence, the osseous-ligamentous skeleton would buckle under relatively small compressive forces. Therefore, adequate muscular input is required to optimize stability, s well as mobility of the spine. Optimum function requires the appropriate amount of compression across all joint surfaces. Either over-compression or under-compression of articular structures will influence the effectiveness of the system in achieving optimum performance.

Recently, there has been a push to understand the integrated function of the nervous, muscular, and skeletal systems. Works by Bogduk, Hodges, Hides, Richardson, McGill, Meyers, Vleeming and Lee few have begun to explain how the body functionally integrates these systems to provide both stability and motion in the body. The next section will take a traditional look at how muscles of the core act in isolation. A more integrated view will follow, which will begin to explain the rationale behind developing a more functional approach during rehabilitation and conditioning programs.

The Local and Global Muscle Systems

Muscles play a significant role in optimum performance of the kinetic chain, both in a role of stabilizers and as mobilizers. Due to this seemingly dichotic role, muscles have been categorized functionally by Bergmark, Comerford, Richardson et al as having either a local or a global function. The primary function of the local system is to provide inter-segmental stability to the articular structures. It has a "corset-like" role and thereby functions to reduce rotational and translational stresses to the lumbo-pelvic-hip complex, while preventing potentially damaging increases (hypomobility) or decreases (hypermobility) in joint motion. An additional important characteristic is the **feed forward** or anticipatory action of the local system. The local system fires in anticipation to movement in order to provide adequate joint stabilization.

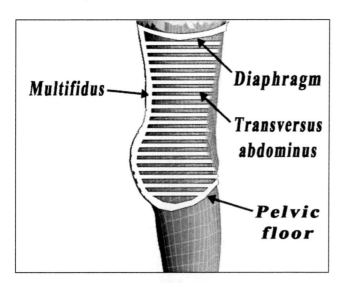

Image 1. Schematic representing the corset-like function of the local system of the core

The function of the global system is to provide gross stability to the head, spine, pelvis and extremities, in addition to providing general motion of the body. A more complete comparison follows in the following table.

Local system (stabilization)	Global system (movement)
■ Deeper, smaller muscles	■ Larger, more superficial muscles
■ Segmental control over 1-2 joint segments	■ Span many joint segments
■ Control intersegmental motion- rotational, translatory and shear forces	■ Produce gross motion
	■ Produce high force movements and stabilization
■ Anticipatory activity (feed forward mechanism)	■ Reaction to movement is direction specific
■ Reaction to movement is non-direction specific	■ Rapid fatigability
■ High resistance to fatigue	
Response to stress, trauma or fatigue	**Response to stress, trauma or fatigue**
■ Inhibition	■ Increased activity - hypertonicity or spasm
■ Timing delays	
Training guidelines	**Training guidelines**
■ Respond best to low loads and levels of effort	■ Respond best to higher loads and levels of effort
■ Increased frequency with low duration	■ Decreased frequency and duration

Table 3. Comparison of the Local and Global Systems

The table below categorizes the muscles of the lumbo-pelvic-hip complex based upon their function as part of either the local or global system. While they are categorized by function, it is important to realize some of the muscles may function as part of both systems since some of the fibers belong to each of the categories. For example, the deep fibers of the lumbar-erector spinae have been categorized as part of the local system, while the superficial fibers of the same muscle are categorized as part of the global system. Although the research has focused primarily on the muscles of the lumbo-pelvic-hip, there is clinical evidence that this muscle classification functions across the rest of the kinetic chain in a similar fashion.

Local system of the lumbo-pelvic-hip complex	Global system of the lumbo-pelvic-hip complex
Diaphragm	Rectus abdominus
Transversus abdominus	External and internal obliques
Pelvic floor	Superficial fibers of erector spinae
Multifidus	
Lower fibers of the internal obliques	Lateral fibers of quadratus lumborum
Deep fibers of psoas	Iliacus
Deep fibers of erector spinae	Superficial fibers of psoas
Medial fibers of quadratus lumborum	Rectus femoris
	Adductors
	Gluteals
	Hamstrings
	Piriformis

Table 4. Comparison of the Local and Global Muscles of the Lumbo-Pelvic-Hip Core

As mentioned previously, the global system functions in movement and general stabilization. Due to the broad musculo-tendinous attachments and distance from the axis of rotation, the muscles of the global system are better suited for large movements and gross stabilization. While traditionally studied in isolation, work by Vleeming, Myers and others have demonstrated a communication or fascial interconnection between muscles. These fascial connections join muscles in anatomical linkages or chains capable of transmitting forces to distal locations using bones and joints as levers along the path. These chains have significant roles in function and may contain muscles belonging to more than one chain, suggesting the varying roles of muscles. Four of these chains that have been identified as having a significant effect on the lumbo-pelvic-hip complex include the anterior oblique, deep longitudinal, lateral and posterior oblique chains are reviewed below.

CHAIN	COMPONENTS	FUNCTION
Anterior oblique chain	External obliques, abdominal fascia, contralateral internal obliques and adductor complex	Accleration and deceleration of the kinetic chain in the transverse plane
Deep longitudinal chain	Peroneii, long head of biceps femoris, sacrotuberous ligament, thoracolumbar fascia and erector spinae	Stabilization of the sacroiliac joint and transfer of energy from the lower extremity to the pelvis and spine

Table 5. Anterior oblique and deep longitudinal chains

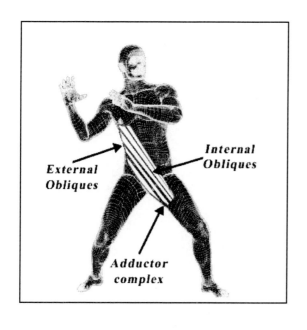

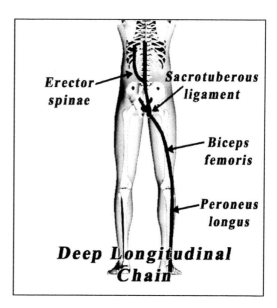

Image 2. The anterior oblique chain

Image 3. The deep longitudinal chain

CHAIN	COMPONENTS	FUNCTION
Lateral chain	Gluteus medius/minimus, tensor fascia latae, adductor complex and contralateral quadratus lumborum	Frontal plane stabilization and stabilization during unilateral stance
Posterior oblique chain	Gluteus maximus, thoracolumbar fascia and contralateral latissimus dorsi	Stabilization of the sacroiliac joint and transfer of energy between the lower and upper extremities

Table 6. Lateral and posterior oblique chains

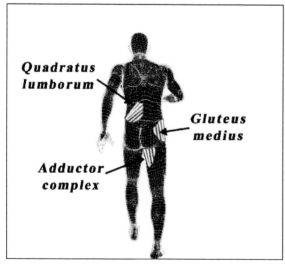

Image 4. The lateral chain

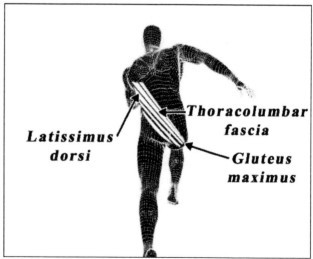

Image 5. The posterior oblique chain

While muscles have been identified as having either a global or local function, they function interdependently in order to provide multi-planar stabilization and dynamic movement patterns. It is this interconnection that necessitates multi-planar training and conditioning in a proprioceptively rich environment over isolated, uni-planar movements that often occur during traditional machine training. More on this topic will be discussed in other sections of this manual.

Motor Control

Although one of the most important concepts of proper stabilization of the kinetic chain, motor control is perhaps the most misunderstood components in the training and conditioning of the youth athlete. Most individuals in the training and conditioning field understand and implement the component of strength in the control of the kinetic chain. In fact, there are no shortages of books, courses, and seminars addressing this aspect. However, it is important to note strength alone is not necessarily the component that is lacking in athletes with musculoskeletal or postural dysfunction. The preferential recruitment of the appropriate muscles, the actual timing, muscle force and duration, are all equally important factors in controlling forces through the kinetic chain and the lack there of will inevitably lead to dysfunction in athletic performance. Referred to as **motor control,** this is the specific posture, stabilization and movement strategy chosen by the central nervous system in response to the accumulation of data it receives from the proprioceptive, vestibular and ocular systems. Motor control is highly adaptable and can be influenced by a variety of factors including previous experiences, injuries, emotional status and nutrition to name a few.

Until recently, the idea of adequate motor control was rarely addressed in the conditioning environment and, only slightly more frequently, in the rehabilitation arena. So why the recent emphasis on motor control? One reason that has been rarely discussed is the fact that there has not been an abundance of information regarding the timing, sequence or selection of firing patterns in relationship to optimum function. However, recent research has demonstrated timing delays the local and the global systems, which disrupts the load bearing capabilities of the system. Work by Hodges et.al. has demonstrated a timing delay in the transversus abdominus (TrA) in individuals with low back pain. Hodges demonstrated that in individuals with no low back pain, activation of the TrA preceded limb motion. However, in individuals with low back pain, limb motion preceded activation of the TrA. They also discovered the TrA became direction-specific (as opposed to working through any direction of trunk or pelvic motion) and contractions became phasic (contract and relax) in nature rather than tonically (constant low level of activation). A later study performed by Hodges et. al., additionally demonstrated a similar anticipatory reaction of the diaphragm to limb motion that aided in postural support and a phasic reaction in those individuals with movement and breathing dysfuctions. Other studies have demonstrated anticipatory actions in the pelvic floor and multifidus as well.

Several researches have noted atrophy in the local muscle system as well as one joint muscles following acute injury. For example, atrophy of the lumbar multifidii has been observed after even one episode of low back pain. Ballistic (plyometric) exercises and joint injury appear to create selective inhibition and muscle atrophy in the one joint muscles (stabilizers) of the knee and ankle joints.

Postural alterations have often been found clinically to be a compensation for decreased muscle function of the local system. These findings suggest improvements in performance can be achieved with proper muscular function and necessitates that appropriate motor learning be employed during all phases of a conditioning program. Likewise, improved motor control and specific training of the local system followed by integration with the global system, particularly in athletes that have been injured, will inevitably lead to improvements in athletic performance.

Nutrition

Increasing evidence has been emerging regarding the link between nutrition and neuromotor control. While it is not the goal of this section to discuss all the correlative aspects of this topic, a few of the more pertinent ones will be discussed.

Viscero-somatic (an organ's ability to refer to and/or cause pain in nerve, bone or soft tissue structures) causes of pain can be seen in multiple examples in the body such as the gall bladder's referral pattern into the right shoulder; the prostate referring into the low back; and heart problems manifesting as left sided jaw, chest and/or arm pain. While these are well known cause and effect relationships, few individuals, including specialists in gastro-intestinal disorders, recognize, let alone understand, or address the correlative effect of the diet on proper motor control of the kinetic chain.

While Eastern holistic healers and other natural health care professionals have long understood the importance of inflammatory reactions and disease processes in the body, it has only been a very recent phenomenon that Western medicine has even addressed this relationship. How does inflammation affect our motor control and therefore athletic performance?   Following is a basic explanation of this phenomenon.

Many of the common foods an average teenager consumes at nearly every meal are poisons to our system. Processed foods, preservatives, carbonated beverages, artificial colors, flavorings and sweeteners, many grain products (including but not limited to wheat, oat, rice and rye) are allergens and therefore irritate the linings of the esophagus, stomach, small and large intestines. Likewise, many athletes consume beverages, some even disguised as "sports enhancers," containing stimulates such as caffeine, which often contribute to inflammatory reactions in the body. The body's reaction to any toxic substance is to create an inflammatory reaction to heal the damaged cell walls. This is often why certain food or food products will irritate many individuals and why the antacid market will never be short of business.

While beneficial in short doses, there is a downside to having chronic inflammation perpetuate our system. Left untreated, chronic inflammation leads tofibrotic changes in the linings of the affected tissue. This reduces the extensibility of the wall, as well as mobility of the food or food particles that are traveling through the area. In his book "How to Eat, Move and Be Healthy," Paul Chek suggests that inflammation and/or pain of the GI track causes a reflexive inhibition or weakening of the local stabilizers of the anterior abdominal wall. In particular, the transversus abdominus is extremely susceptible to this inhibition and decreases the effectiveness of force closure and therefore stabilization across the lumbo-pelvic-hip complex. This phenomenon will have far reaching ramifications across the entire kinetic chain. Additional causes of visceral-somatic inhibition include constipation, irritable bowel syndrome and Crohn's disease.

Proper nutrition supports the entire neuromusculokeletal and cardiovascular systems. It provides the ground substances for tissue growth and repair, while enhancing physiological and endocrinological processes in the body, which may have the benefit of elevating the mood, improving concentration and the mind-body connection necessary for proper motor control and improved athletic performance.

Emotions

The psycho-somatic (an individuals thoughts and emotions manifesting as nerve, bone or soft tissue pain) cause of pain and dysfunction is well known and documented in the clinical setting, although it is often poorly understood. In fact, many specialists believe and therefore address thoughts and emotions as the cause of low back and pelvic pain, for example. While this may not be the entire story, there is no denying the dramatic effect thoughts and emotions can have on the neuromusculoskeletal system and therefore performance in sporting activities. Many student-athletes are under incredible levels of physical stress through two, per day workouts and eight hours of school work, followed by several hours of homework. There is an often ignored component of psychological stress that comes from a variety of sources, such as the pressure to perform well in scholastic tasks in addition to excelling in the athletic arena. While it is beyond the scope of this section to discuss all the components related to this topic, it is important to recognize this aspect when designing a conditioning program for the youth athlete. Most individuals have experienced times when of low energy, experienced mild depression and found it harder to hold their posture appropriately or to perform a certain exercise or sport activity that is usually easy to perform. The ability to perform these normal activities with greater of ease on good days is based upon our energy levels as well as our emotions, which affect and are affected by the nervous system. When the athlete is in a good place (i.e. proper rest, good relationships, productive and positive activities), his/her ability to perform complex motor tasks such as playing tennis or even less complex tasks such as performing activities of daily living, are painlessly increased. However, nervous system fatigue or overload (secondary to increased workout demands, too little sleep and/or increased stress) can have a dramatic effect on the neuromuscular abilities of the athlete. Similarly, individuals that have experienced severe trauma including physical, mental and especially sexual abuse, often have a decreased ability to exert the appropriate motor control to properly stabilize the LPH complex. These individuals will often demonstrate "guarded postures" including pulling the shoulders down and in, slumping through the trunk, posterior tilting of the pelvis and increased "gripping" through the deep hip rotators. While it is beyond the scope of this manual to discuss this subject in detail, it is essential that therapists and trainers recognize the importance that emotions play in the athlete's ability to control his/her body and be able to adjust the training and conditioning programs appropriately.

Conclusion

As discussed, several components are necessary in enabling the body to successfully achieve optimum posture and therefore perform a desired physical activity. Each component of the Integrated Model of Function, form closure, force closure, motor control, nutrition and emotions, impact the athlete's ability to effectively stabilize and transfer loads across the kinetic chain. The effectiveness of this approach will determine how successful an individual will be in performing his/her desired tasks. Each of these components will be expanded upon in other sections of this manual.

Postural Assessment

Postural assessments as performed by chiropractors, therapists and physical medicine specialists tend to be comprehensive in nature and can often seem overwhelming to the youth conditioning specialist who not only has the role of identifying but also correcting postural alterations in the youth athlete. He/she then has the task of incorporating corrective exercises into the training program to address the compensations and is most likely dealing with a group of athletes with a multitude of postural alterations. While it is negligent to ignore the posture of the youth athlete, it is also impossible to identify and correct all the various postural alterations in each individual especially when dealing with medium or larger groups of athletes.

The position at the IYCA is not to minimize the postural assessment but rather make it easily assimilated into the performance assessment of your athlete. While the initial screen may take up to five minutes per view when dealing with an athlete on an individual basis, it may take a total of five minutes when working with larger groups. The emphasis is on overall alignment and positioning rather than on specific intricate positioning of any region of the musculoskeletal system. It is important the youth conditioning specialist not lump or categorize all athletes with the same postural alteration without assessing them appropriately. The corrective exercises and cueing for an individual with a posterior tilt of the pelvis will be very different than that of an individual possessing an anterior rotation of the pelvis. Likewise, it is equally important to note an athlete experiencing an injury will always require a more detailed assessment.

While the initial screening may be performed statically, the youth conditioning specialist should continually monitor posture in all movement patterns and activities that the athlete is performing as posture is a dynamic entity.

Athletes demonstrating even mild postural alterations that do not respond to recommended postural cueing, should be referred out for further evaluation by a qualified chiropractor, physical therapist or sports medicine specialist to minimize the risks of potential altered biomechanics leading to injuries.

Postural Views

Posture is typically viewed from the front, back and both sides. The reason it is viewed from both sides is that alterations in the pelvis can occur side to side so both right and left sides should be evaluated. Similarly, shoulder position can vary between sides. Again, remember not to get inundated with minute details and look at the overall picture.

Listed below is an abbreviated list of landmarks that should be used to monitor when assessing posture. Visualizing straight lines and right angles makes the process of identifying postural alterations more efficient and manageable.

Lateral View

Imagine a plumb line hanging from the ceiling. This line should pass approximately through the center of the athlete's body bisecting the cervical spine, shoulder, lumbar spine, pelvis, knee and ankle. There should be a gentle anterior (lordotic) curve in the cervical and lumbar spine and a gentle backwards (kyphotic) curvature in the thoracic region. It is important to assess the pelvis for any anterior or posterior rotation. Traditionally, the landmarks used to assess for pelvic positioning were the anterior and posterior superior iliac spines. Using these landmarks, the majority of individuals would appear to have an anterior pelvic tilt. Using the anterior superior iliac spine (ASIS) and pubic symphysis is a more accurate method in assessing deviations of the pelvis. A straight line drawn between the ASIS and pubic symphysis should be aligned along the vertical axis or perpendicular to the floor (see image below). If the ASIS is forward in relation to the pubic symphysis, the pelvis is in an anterior tilt. If the pubic symphysis is in front of the ASIS, the pelvis is posteriorly tilted.

Anterior View

Imagine a plumb line hanging from the ceiling and bisecting the midline of the body. The line should bisect the head, neck, thorax (ribcage), pelvis and fall equidistance between the feet. Several horizontal lines should be visualized through the following landmarks: the eyes, across the shoulders, across the pelvis, through the midpoints of the patellae and medial malleoli. These lines should be parallel to each other.

Posterior View

Imagine a plumb line hanging from the ceiling and bisecting the midline of the body. The line should bisect the head, neck, spine, pelvis and fall equidistance between the feet. The scapulae should lie flat against the thorax and also be equidistant from the spine. The popliteal fossae (back of the knee) should face forward and the lower extremities should be equally vertical.

Anterior View

Head
Level and midline

Cervical spine
Straight
Symmetrical sloping of the trapezius
Symmetrical SCM and scalenes

Shoulders
Level
AC and SC joints level and symmetrical
Greater tubercle lateral and inferior to AC joint

Elbows
Elbow fossae point forward
Symmetrical valgus angle

Hands
Neutral (as if carrying a suitcase)
Fingers in slight flexion

Trunk
Sternum straight
Symmetrical rib alignment

Pelvis
Iliac crests level
ASIS level
Neutral (no rotation CW or CCW)

Femur
Great trochanters level and point slightly anterior

Knee
Patellae face forward
Symmetrical valgus angle (13-18 degrees)
Fibular heads level
Tibias vertical

Feet
Symmetrical toeing out (8-10 degrees)
Longitudinal arches normal and symmetrical
Medial and leteral malleoli level

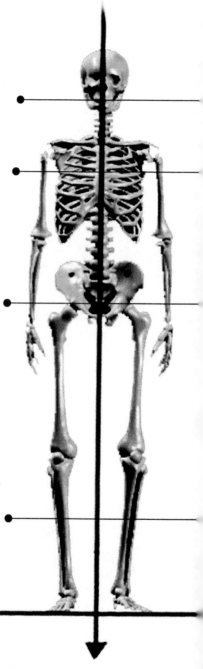

*In an upright position, the body's center of gravity is located midline, 1 cm. anterior to the secon sacral segment.

Posterior View

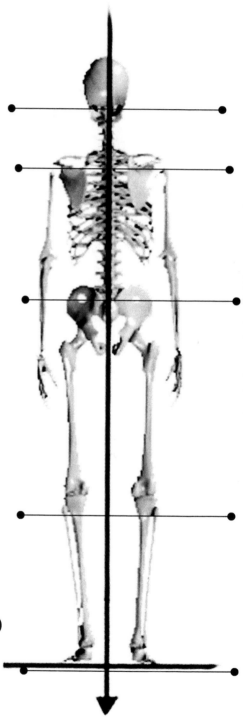

Head
　　Level and midline

Cervical spine
　　Straight

Shoulders
　　Level
　　Normal sloping and mass of trapezius

Scapula
　　Neutral (45 degrees upward rot.)
　　Flat against trunk
　　Equidistant (2-3") from spine

Thoracic spine
　　Straight

Lumbar spine
　　Straight

Pelvis
　　Iliac crests level
　　Greater trochanters level
　　Gluteal folds level

Knees
　　Popliteal fossae level and face posteriorly
　　Symmetrical valgus (13-18 degrees)
　　Fibular heads level

Feet
　　Symmetrical toeing out (8-10 degrees)
　　Achilles tendon and calcaneus neutral (straight)
　　Medial and leteral malleoli level

Lateral View

(observe from right and left sides)

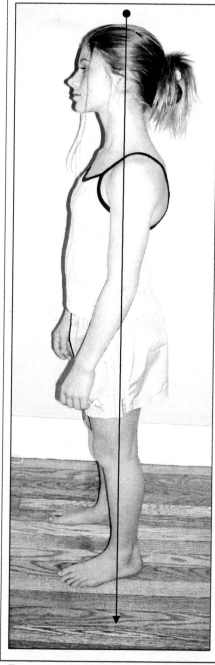

Head
> Ear in line with acromion process
> Neutral

Cervical spine
> Neutral (lordosis)

Shoulders
> Neutral

Elbow
> Symmetrical (slight flexion)

Thoracic Spine
> Neutral (kyphosis)

Lumbar Spine
> Neutral

Pelvis
> *ASIS and pubic symphysis on same vertical plane

Feet
> Longitudinal arches normal

*ASIS: Anterior superior iliac spine
-should be on same vertical plane as the pubic symphis

Image 6-8. Postural Views

Causes of Postural Alternations

Postural alterations can occur as a result of alterations in the timing, sequence and coordination leading to altered muscular recruitment patterns. Often postural corrections are difficult to correct since there are underlying causes to these muscle imbalances, including altered recruitment strategies. It is important to realize the nervous system controls and regulates muscle function. Often, postural alterations occur secondary to neurological inhibitions and substitution patterns. Shortness and/or tightness in one muscle will create a neurological inhibition of its functional antagonist. This reaction is known as **reciprocal inhibition**.

For example, shortness and tightness in the adductor complex (prime movers of hip adduction) can lead to inhibition of the gluteus medius (prime movers of hip abduction). Inhibition and weakness of the prime mover will create a compensatory increase in activity in the synergists. Chronic over-activity of the synergists will often cause the synergist muscles to become the dominant movers of the particular movement. The subsequent compensatory over-activation in which the synergists become the primary movers is known as **synergist dominance**. For example, the gluteus medius functions as the primary muscle of hip abduction and stabilizer of the pelvis during single leg stance. Additionally, it has a significant role in deceleration of pronation of the lower kinetic chain during the gait cycle. The gluteus medius is often found to be weak in the youth female athlete as a result of a variety of factors including prolonged sedentary posture, poor posture especially "hanging" on one hip while standing, an uncompensated Trendelenburg's gait (similar to the gait that is practiced by female models) and a weak core causing the individual to simply "hang" off their ligaments (see image below). In response to the weakened gluteus medius, there is an increase in the activity of the tensor fascia latae

(TFL) which takes over the role as the primary coronal plane stabilizer during single leg stance. The problem with this is the TFL is also a primary mover of internal rotation of the hip and has a significant response on the iliotibial band. If the TFL is allowed to function unopposed, it will pull the hip and lower extremity into internal rotation during single leg stance. Although internal rotation of the hip is required for normal biomechanics during single leg stance, increased activation of the TFL will accelerate both the speed and magnitude of these motions. These altered biomechanics are often a direct cause of a variety of injuries that plague the female athlete including anterior cruciate ligament injuries, iliotibial band syndromes and patellar tracking issues.

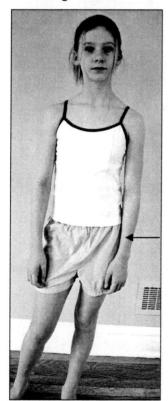

Note the increased weight bearing through the left hip (arrow) common in many females. Chronic adopting of this posture may lead to overstretching of the hip capsule and lengthening of the gluteus medius.

Image 9.

Activation of the TFL creates an internal rotation force around the hip joint, thereby causing a **reciprocal co-contraction** of the deep external rotators of the hip, particularly the pirifomis, obturators and quadratus femoris. While this functions to balance forces and increase joint stabilization, the ramifications include increased joint compression and compensatory hypermobility in the surrounding joints. Hypermobility of the sacroiliac joint is commonly observed clinically in individuals demonstrating an over-compression of either the hip or low back. Altered joint mechanics such as a hypermobility (excessive joint motion) or subluxation (joint fixation) causes a neurological inhibition of the surrounding muscles, typically the stabilizers (local system) of the joint. This is referred to as **arthrokinetic inhibition.** Joint dysfunction of the sacroiliac joint has been implicated in inhibition of the transversus abdominus, multifidus and pelvic floor muscles.

Additional causes of postural alterations include the conditioning level of the athlete and participation in different types of exercise. Athletes possessing weakness of the core musculature often develop postural alterations due to inefficient stabilization and compensatory strategies. Weakness of the core leads to altered length-tension relationships and altered joint mechanics. Many athletes will develop muscular imbalances secondary to improper resistance training programs or over-reliance on machine training. Certain exercises such as leg lifts for the abdominals and upright rows for the shoulders place the kinetic chain in less than optimal positions, work against the normal biomechanics of the body and create postural stress.

Janda reported pain as the single most important factor resulting in alterations in posture and compensatory changes of the musculoskeletal system. The nervous system will adopt an antalgic posture (position in order to minimize pain to injured tissue) in order to decrease stresses on soft tissue and articular structures. Antalgic postures will always lead to altered length tension relationships and compensatory patterns.

Regardless of the cause, postural alterations will ultimately create altered length tension relationships, force couple relationships, joint arthrokinematics leading to decreased neuromuscular efficiency, movement dysfunctions and ultimately pain. The next session will focus on three of the most common postural alterations the youth conditioning specialist will encounter in the youth athlete.

Common Postural Alterations in Youth Athletes

While it is impossible to discuss every possible presentation and characteristics of postural alterations, the following section will focus on the more common ones that will be encountered by the youth conditioning specialist.

Much of the literature has referenced the clinical works of Janda regarding common habitual postures. He observed that muscular patterns of healthy children with postural faults very closely resembled those seen in spastic children. Notably, there were patterns of hypertonicity (increased muscular activity) in postural muscles and hypotonicity (decreased muscular activity) with subsequent inhibition of the antagonist muscles. These muscles are categorized below.

MUSCLES PRONE TO HYPERTONICITY AND OVERACTIVITY	MUSCLES PRONE TO HYPOTONICITY AND INHIBITION
Gastrocnemius, soleus, adductors, rectus femoris, tensor fascia latae, iliopsoas, piriformis, lumbar erector spinae, quadratus lumborum, pectoralis major/minor, latissimus dorsi, teres major, upper trapezius, levator scapula, sternocleidomastoid, scalenes, masticatories, arm/forearm flexors	Peroneii, tibialis anterior, tibialis posterior, vastus medialis, gluteus maximus, medius, minimus, rectus abdominus, transverse abdominus, serratus anterior, rhomboids, middle and lower trapezius, longus capitis/coli, hyoids, arm/forearm extensors

Table 7. Muscle Comparison

It is interesting to note that work by Hodges, Richardson and Hides has noted dysfunction in the stabilization system, most notably, timing delays and inhibition, with a resultant over activity of the movement system. Interestingly, many of the muscles and substitution patterns Janda had noted clinically, are identical to findings by Hodges, Richardson, Hides and others. Most notably, there tends to be inhibition of the local system with any trauma, stress, fatigue or altered posture and then subsequent increase in activity in the global musculature. These findings are significant to strength and conditioning coaches as alterations in these patterns will most likely lead to pain and decreased efficiency during functional tasks. Improving function and performance will then include a multifaceted approach of posture restoration followed by appropriate neuromuscular recruitment of the stabilization and mobilization systems.

However, it is important to realize the neuromuscular system is an adaptable system and there are potential discrepancies that can occur when attempting to categorize every athlete into one type of posture. For example, Janda described the postural alterations occurring with dysfunction in the trunk, neck and upper extremity, which has been described above. While some athletes may display aspects of this posture, there are many common patterns that have developed in part due to cueing by well meaning coaches and parents. Expanding on this concept, Janda described predictable patterns of postural dysfunctions that occurred as a result of chronic muscle imbalances. They are termed the upper and lower crossed syndromes and are summarized below.

I. Upper Crossed Syndrome

Postural Alterations	Shortened/over-activate muscles	Weakened/iInhibited muscles
Forward head posture	Sternocleidomastoid Levator scapula Cerivical erector spinae	*Deep neck flexors
Increased thoracic kyphosis	Pectoralis major/minor	Thoracic erector spinae
Scapula- elevated, abducted, anterior tilted	Upper trapezius Levator scapula Pectoralis major/minor Latissimus dorsi	Middle and lower trapezius Serratus anterior Rhomboids
Shoulders- internal rotation	Pectoralis major Latissimus dorsi Teres major Anterior deltoid Subscapularis	Infraspinatus Teres minor Posterior deltoid

Table 8. Upper Crossed Syndrome

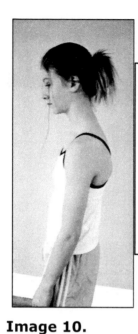

Forward head posture

Increased thoracic curvature and forward shoulder position

Image 10.

Common injuries resulting from the upper crossed syndrome include:
- Neck pain
- Headaches
- Rotator cuff impingement syndromes
- Bicipital tendonitis
- Thoracic outlet syndrome

Common movement pattern dysfunctions that will be noted include:
- Altered head and neck positioning in most movement patterns typically viewed as occipito-cervical (occiput and first cervical vertebrae) extension, neck extension and head protraction
- Altered scapular control viewed as winging, elevation and protraction in addition to poor eccentric control during pushing and pulling patterns

Table 9. Common Injuries and Movement Dysfunctions

II. Lower Crossed Syndrome

Postural Alterations	Shortened/overactive muscles	Weakened/inhibited muscles
Increased lumbar lordosis	Lumbar erector spinae	Abdominals
Anterior pelvic tilt	Hip flexors -Iliopsoas -Rectus femoris -Tensor fascia latae Lumbar erector spinae	Gluteals Hamstrings Abdominals

Table 10. Lower Crossed Syndrome

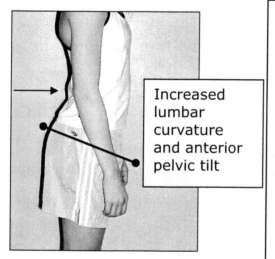

Increased lumbar curvature and anterior pelvic tilt

Image 11.

Common injuries resulting from the lower crossed syndrome include:
- Low back pain
- Sacroiliac joint and hip dysfunction
- Hamstring injuries
- Patellar tracking and iliotibial band syndromes

Common movement pattern dysfunctions that will be noted include:
- Altered lumbo-pelvic-hip positioning in most movement patterns typically viewed as protrusion of the abdominal region, hyperextension of the lumbar spine, decreased flexion of the lumbo-pelvic regions

Table 11. Common Injuries and Movement Dysfunctions

III. Inhibition/Dominance Syndrome

As adolescents and teenagers have become less active and the frequency of general movement in our youth rapidly decreases, additional common patterns have been observed. As a whole, today's youth tend to be more sedentary outside of the athletic arena and are likely to spend much of the day in a seated posture while at school, in front of a computer or watching television. The seated posture tends to put the pelvis in a posterior tilted position, the lower spine in a lengthened position, the upper spine in a shortened position, the scapula in a protracted position and the head in a forward position. This posture is further exacerbated by weakness of the core musculature and an over-emphasis on performing crunches and leg lift exercises for the abdominal region. The typical compensation for this muscle imbalance is to extend through the upper thoracic spine. This pattern is noted frequently in youth athletes and has been termed the inhibition/dominance syndrome. While it shares characteristics of the aforementioned syndromes, the difference lies in the inhibition and resultant weakness of the stabilization system and subsequent compensatory dominance of the movement system.

Postural Alterations	Shortened/over-active Muscles	Weakened/inhibited muscles
Forward head posture and increased upper cervical extension	Sternocleidomastoid Levator scapula Cervical erector spinae	*Deep neck flexors
Decreased upper thoracic curvature (thoracic lordosis)	Thoracic erector spinae	**Core stabilizers
Scapula- depressed, protracted, downward rotation, anterior tilted	Levator scapula Pectoralis major/minor Latissimus dorsi	Upper, middle, lower trapezius Serratus anterior
Increased thoraco-lumbar extension	Thoracic erector spinae	Core stabilizers
Lumbar kyphosis (lower lumbar flexion)	External/internal abdominal obliques Rectus abdominus	Core stabilizers Psoas Lumbar erector spinae
Posterior pelvic tilt	External/internal abdominal obliques Rectus abdominus Gluteus maximus Hamstrings	Core stabilizers Psoas Lumbar erector spinae
Hip external rotation	Deep external hip rotators -gemelli, obturators, quadratus femoris	Core stabilizers

*Deep Neck Flexors include the longus colli and longus capitis

**Core stabilizers include the transversus abdominus, diaphragm, multifidus and pelvic floor

Table 12. Inhibition/Dominance Syndrome

> **Common injuries resulting from the inhibition/dominance syndrome include:**
> - Neck pain and headaches
> - Rotator cuff impingement syndromes and bicipital tendonitis
> - Thoracic outlet syndrome
> - Low back pain
> - Sacroiliac and hip dysfunction
> - Anterior cruciate and medial collateral ligament tears
> - Patellar tracking and iliotibial band syndromes
> - Ankle sprains and plantar fascitis
> - Anterior and medial stress syndromes (shin splints of the tibialis anterior and posterior)
>
> **Common movement pattern dysfunctions that will be noted include:**
> - Poor ability to stabilize the thoraco-scapulo-humeral and lumbo-pelvic-hip complexes
> - Poor eccentric control during upper and lower kinetic chain movement patterns such as throwing, pushing, pulling, running and jumping
> - Repetitive movement patterns leading to overuse injuries of the spine, pelvis, lower and upper extremities

Table 13. Inhibition/Dominance Syndrome

Correcting Postural Abnormalities

One of the goals of the youth conditioning coach is to identify postural alterations in his/her athletes. For example, many athletes will display forward and rounded shoulders as described in the upper crossed syndrome. Coaches will often recognize this fault and cue the athlete to pull his/her shoulders and head back and the complying athlete will attempt to correct his/her posture. However, improper length in the muscles that allow this correction will make this correction nearly impossible to obtain without compensations. Also alterations in the lumbo-pelvic-hip complex can create compensatory changes through the thorax, scapula and neck. In the above scenario, there is often a myofascial restriction and/or shortness in the pectoralis minor and latissimus dorsi in the shoulders and the sternocleidomastoid and cervical erector spinae in the neck, making it difficult to assume proper positioning of the articular structures. Restoration of normal length in these tissues may not create lasting changes because the lower kinetic chain was not addressed.

The effect of one segment of the kinetic chain on a distant region cannot be ignored. Janda has described a direct reflexive relationship between the pelvis and neck regions, in which the position of the pelvis can influence the positioning of the eyes and therefore the entire neck and head complex. Likewise, a change in position of the head and neck will alter the position of the eyes and influence pelvic alignment. This relationship between the pelvis and the eyes has been referred to as the **oculopelvic and pelviocular reflexes**—reinforces the importance in ensuring and monitoring postural changes during any physical task the athlete is engaged in.

The youth conditioning specialist can have the greatest impact with the athlete demonstrating functional postural alterations. Since many of these postures manifest from poor habits, muscle imbalances and improper conditioning programs, attention to restoration of motor control, proper coordination throughout the kinetic chain and awareness of key areas have a tremendous effect in correcting postural alterations. Conditioning programs should be focused on restoration of length-tension relationships, force couple relationships, joint arthrokinematics and functional integration of the entire kinetic chain. Additional adjunctive modalities such as chiropractic manipulation for joint subluxation and massage therapy for restricted soft tissue structures may be effective in improving biomechanics and therefore simplifying the process of improving posture.

Cueing Improvements in Posture

Many of the readers recall prodding by parents or teachers to improve his/her posture. The most common instructions given were "stand up tall" or "put your shoulders back and lift your chest." Often this created a position that felt awkward and uncomfortable, which rarely caused any permanent postural corrections. Although our guardians and instructors were well meaning, the verbal cueing rarely worked and when it was effective, it often created a rigid posture that ultimately leads to other postural and movement dysfunctions.

Visualization is a technique that uses imagery and thought processes to coach the nervous system to change engrained motor patterns. In simpler terms, it is the mind-body connection where the mind finds the correct neuromuscular pathways in order to improve postural alteration. Visualization has long been used in other disciplines including yoga, Alexander and Feldenkrais techniques to improve posture with little or minimal manual therapy, or time intensive exercises. Visualization tends to stimulate the correct neuromotor response that enables the appropriate synergy of muscle activation combined with the occulomotor and vestibular reflexes, in order to regulate the postural change. Clinically, Diane Lee and Linda Joy Lee have demonstrated increased activation of the deeper, stabilization muscles with verbal cueing that includes phrases such as "feel," "hold," and "connect." In contrast, the movement system tends to be preferentially recruited by doing commands such as "move," "contract" and "pull in."

While imagery works well for verbal learners, it tends to be less effective for tactile learners. For these individuals, tactile feedback or facilitation tends to be more effective in producing the desired postural improvements. Using hand placement and tactile stimulation on the areas that require improvement can be extremely effective for those individuals who do not respond to the verbal cueing.

Certain visualization and tactile cues have been very effective in improving body awareness and hence the ability to restore posture. Listed in the table below is a summary of several common postural alterations and the verbal and tactile cues given to the athlete in order to activate the correct postural response by the neuromuscular system. The following list has been adapted from specific cueing as practiced by Linda Joy Lee.

Verbal cues for achieving a position of neutral spine

- ❖ From an upright position: "Imagine a wire connecting from the top of your head through the spine and gently lifting you up to the sky."

- ❖ From an upright position: "Imagine a wire connecting from the top of your head and suspending you from the sky."

- ❖ From an upright position: "Connect to your core and feel as if you are becoming taller and lighter."

Tactile cues

- ❖ Place one hand on top of the head and simulate a hook coming from the top of his/her head lifting towards the ceiling

Verbal cues for correcting an increased thoracic curvature (hyperkyphosis)

- ❖ From an upright position: Maintain a neutral lumbar spine position and "gently lift your sternum."

- ❖ From an upright position: "Imagine a hook from the top of your head gently lifting you up towards the sky."

Tactile cues

❖ Place one hand on upper sternum and one on the upper thoracic spine. Lift gently up in the front (superiorly) with the hand that is over the sternum and gently guide the spine down (inferiorly) with the hand that is on the back.

Cues for correcting a position of decreased thoracic curvature (hypokyphosis or thoracic lordosis)

❖ From a supine position: "Take a deep breath in, let it go and let the ribcage go heavy and soften into the floor."

❖ From an upright position: "Maintain a neutral lumbar spine position and "gently let your chest go heavy and soften through your mid-back."

❖ From an upright position: "Maintain a neutral lumbar spine position, take a deep breath in and "fill your mid-back with air as you soften the front of your rib cage."

Tactile cues

❖ Place one hand on upper sternum and one on the upper thoracic spine. Gently guide the sternum down (inferiorly) with the anterior hand and up (superiorly) with the hand that is over the spine.

Verbal cues for correcting a decrease in the lumbar lordosis (hypolordosis)

* From a supine position: "Soften your hips by relaxing your glutes; widen your sit bones allowing the pelvis to drop forward and the low back to come away from the floor."

* From a supine position: "Think of a wave coming in to shore as you gently allow the spine and pelvis to roll back (posterior tilt) and the low back flatten into the floor. Now imagine the wave moving away from the shore as you gently allow your pelvis to roll forward (anterior tilt) and the low back to gently move away from the floor."

* From an upright position: "Relax your hips and abdomen and think of a wire gently pulling your tailbone up towards the ceiling."

Tactile cues

* Place one hand in the lower lumbar spine and one hand on the lower abdomen. Gently guide the hand that is over the lumbar spine anteriorly while guiding the hand that is over the lower abdomen inferiorly towards the floor.

Cues for correcting an increase in the lumbar lordosis and anterior pelvic tilt (lower crossed syndrome)

* From a supine (lying face up) position: "Take a deep breath in and as you let it out slowly let your back and pelvis go heavy and fall into the floor."

* From an upright position: "Imagine a hook from the top of your head pulling up (along the vertical axis of the body) and one on your tailbone gently pulling down (along the vertical axis of the body). "Take a deep breath in and as you let it out imagine the

hooks gently lengthening out your spine making you longer."

Tactile cues

- ❖ Place one hand over the upper sacrum and pelvis and one hand on the lower abdomen. Gently guide the hand that is over the upper sacrum and pelvis posteriorly while guiding the hand that is over the lower abdomen superiorly gently moving up and in towards the spine.

Table 14. Visualization Cues

These cues are most effective when practiced prior to activity and should continue to be encouraged during the activity or sport specific skill the athlete is participating in. Daily attention to posture enables a "grooving" or neuromuscular conditioning and improves the likelihood the pattern becomes a habitual part of the athletes' movement patterns.

While proper cueing can have a positive effect on the ultimate posture adopted by an individual, improper cueing can likewise have a significant effect on recruitment strategies employed by the athlete. Listed below are a few common postural cues and resultant biomechanical alterations that tend to result as a response to that particular strategy. To demonstrate the varying effects between "doing" commands and visualization cues, see the images in the example at the top of the following page.

Common Postural Cues	Faulty Posture That May Result
❖ *"Pull your abs in and hold them tight."* ❖ *"Lock your abs in."* ❖ *"Brace your abdominal region."*	❖ Creates a fixation or "locking" of the thoracic cage due to the attachment of the abdominals over the lower 8 ribs. ❖ May create a posterior rotation of the pelvis due to the abdominals upward direction of pull on the pelvis.
❖ *"Lift your chest up and pull the shoulder blades down and back."* ❖ *"Extend the spine and squeeze the shoulder blades together."*	❖ Leads to extension of the upper thoracic spine and subsequent fixation of the thoracic cage ❖ Tends to create a depressed and retracted position of the scapula
❖ *"Squeeze your glutes (butt) and hold them tight."*	❖ Increases the compression in the posterior hip joint which may lead to altered hip mechanics ❖ May lead to posterior rotation of the pelvis due to the gluteal attachments to the pelvis and hips

Table 15. Postural Cues

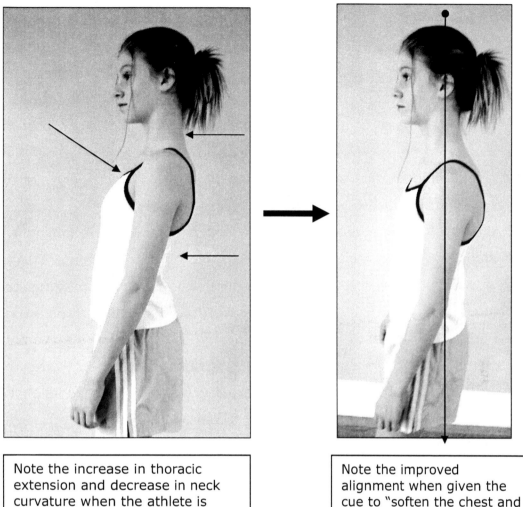

Note the increase in thoracic extension and decrease in neck curvature when the athlete is instructed to "stand up tall and pull shoulders back." There is no change in the shoulder position.

Image 12.

Note the improved alignment when given the cue to "soften the chest and imagine a wire gently pulling through the top of the head."

Image 13.

Conclusion

This chapter has attempted to define common postural alterations and introduce a paradigm that focuses on proper positioning of the kinetic chain as the basis of all movement patterns. It is imperative postural alterations be discovered and treated prior to initiating any strengthening or sports conditioning program. Any inefficiency in the neuromusculoskeletal system will cause a perpetuation (pattern overload) or substitution pattern (synergist dominance) enabling the dysfunction to persist. By recognizing and correcting deficiencies or dysfunction, the process of re-establishing normal motor patterns can begin. Then, by instituting a corrective program that incorporates a dynamic environment of multi-planar movements, integrated movement patterns and proprioceptively enriched activities, the youth conditioning specialist can condition the neuromuscular system to increase its ability to deal with gravity, ground reaction forces and external forces placed upon it.

References

1. Biel, A. (1997)

2. Bogduk, N. (1999)

3. Chek, P. (2003)

4. Chek, P. (2001)

5. Chek, P. (2004)

6. Chek, P. (2000)

7. Clark, M.A. (2001)

8. Clark, M.A. & Russell, A.M. (2002)

9. Evans, R.C. (1994)

10. Floyd, R.T. & Thompson, W.C. (1998)

11. Gross, J., Fetto, J. & Rosen, E. (1996)

12. Hodges, P.W., Richardson, C. & Hides, J. (2004)

13. Hodges, P.W. (2003)

14. Hodges, P.W. & Richards, C.A. (1996)

15. Janda, V. (1987)

16. Janda, V. (1988)

17. Janda, V. & Stara, V. (1987)

18. Janda, V. (1977)

19. Janda, V. (2000)

20. Kendall, F.P., McCreary, E.K. & Provance, P.G. (1993)

21. Lee, D. (2003)

22. Lee, D. (2003)

23. Lee, D. (1999)

24. Lee, D. (2003)

25. Lee, D. (2003)

26. Lee, L.J. (2004)

27. Lee, L.J. (2004)

28. Lee, L.J. (2004)

29. Liebenson, C. (1996)

30. McGill, S. (2004)

31. McGill, S. (2002)

32. Murphy, S., Buckle, P. & Stubbs, D. (2004)

33. Netter, F. (1989)

34. Osar, E. (2004)

35. Osar, E. (2002)

36. Primal 3D Interacive Series (2000)

37. Rachbauer, F., Sterzinger, W. & Eibl, G. (2004)

38. Sahrmann, S. (2002)

39. Stedman's Medical Dictionary (1990)

40. Sward, L. (2004)

41. Webster's Ninth New Collegiate Dictionary (1990)

42. Wojtys, E.M., Ashton-Miller, J.A., Huston, L.J. & Moga, P.J. (2004)

9

Endocrine Development and Implications
Dr. Cynthia Labella

The endocrine system is a collection of individual glands located in specific sites throughout the body. Each gland produces one or more hormones that travel through the bloodstream to reach the site of action at their target organs. Hormones are the chemical signals that control organ function and coordinate physiologic processes. The amount of hormones released and the timing of hormone release is carefully controlled. The glands respond to signals from other hormones and peptides, the central nervous system, environmental light, sleep, stress, nutrient levels, and exercise.

The endocrine system has both direct and indirect effects on athletic development during childhood and adolescence. Examples of the direct effects of hormones include control of metabolism and regulation of electrolyte balance. Indirect effects include the hormonal control of growth and maturation, and determination of gender differences (both of which influence athletic development). This chapter will describe the direct and indirect effects of the endocrine system-athletic development during childhood and adolescence, and discuss how exercise in turn influences hormonal function in the growing child and adolescent.

Growth Hormone

Growth hormone (GH) is produced by the pituitary gland, which is located at the base of the brain. GH regulates growth and development during childhood and adolescence by stimulating the production of the insulin-like growth factor (IGF), which acts directly on muscle and bone to stimulate growth of these tissues. IGF also mobilizes fatty acids from adipose tissue (fat) in order to provide the fuel required for growth.

GH levels progressively increase from birth throughout childhood, and gradually reach a stable level between twelve and eighteen years of age. GH levels are highest during the adolescent growth spurt. This surge in GH is triggered by the rising levels of estrogen and testosterone during puberty. By late adolescence GH production begins to decline and continues to fall steadily throughout adult life.

Growth Hormone and Exercise

Physical activity triggers an increase in GH; this acts directly on muscle cells to promote protein synthesis both during and after exercise[1]—the greater the exercise intensity, the greater the rise in GH. In adolescent athletes, the rise in GH in response to exercise becomes greater with each successive stage of puberty[2]. This is due to the rising levels of estrogen and testosterone that have a powerful stimulatory effect on GH release. What this means is, there will be a larger increase in muscle *size* in an adolescent who is in the later stages of puberty than one in the earlier stages when both are given the same resistance-exercise-training program. However, muscle size is only one of the factors that determine muscle strength. Resistance training also enhances neuromuscular connections and firing patterns. This seems to occur to the same degree in children as in adults. Neuromuscular facilitation is the mechanism by which pre-adolescents become stronger in response to resistance training.

Since GH stimulates an increase in both muscle size and muscle metabolic efficiency, it is probably involved in the progressive increase in anaerobic capacity that occurs during puberty. This means children and young adolescents can be expected to fatigue sooner during maximal effort strength, power, or speed drills than older adolescents.

Thyroid Hormone

Thyroid hormone (TH) is produced by the thyroid gland; this is located in the front of the neck, just beneath the larynx, or voice box. The main role of TH is to regulate metabolism. To accomplish this task, TH acts on several of the body's organs and systems: (1) TH stimulates production of metabolic enzymes in muscle cells; this increases oxygen uptake and energy expenditure; (2) TH increases absorption of carbohydrates from the gastrointestinal tract; (3) TH regulates the mobilization of fatty acids from adipose tissue; (3) TH increases the force of heart muscle contractions and regulates blood pressure

TH plays an important role in muscle development during the fetal period by regulating the growth and differentiation of muscle into slow-twitch and fast-twitch fibers.   TH is also essential for normal growth and development throughout childhood and adolescence, but the details are not completely understood. During puberty, TH levels do not change significantly. It is likely the function of TH during the pubertal growth spurt is to regulate GH levels or facilitate the actions of GH.

Thyroid Hormone and Exercise

TH is probably involved in the physiologic adaptations that lead to improvements in both aerobic and anaerobic capacity after training. While the details are not completely understood, TH's role may be to increase production of muscle-metabolic enzymes and to enhance nutrient and oxygen uptake by muscle.

Studies in adults have demonstrated increases in resting metabolic rate and TH levels after several weeks of endurance training[3]. Similar studies investigating the TH response to exercise in children and adolescents are lacking.

Calcitonin

The thyroid gland also produces calcitonin, a hormone that helps to regulate calcium levels in the blood and bone. When blood calcium levels become elevated, calcitonin is released and stimulates the bones to absorb calcium from the blood.

Calcitonin and Exercise

In healthy adult athletes, neither strength nor endurance exercise appear to have any effect on calcitonin levels. Studies of the effects of exercise on calcitonin levels in children and adolescents are lacking.

Parathyroid Hormone

The parathyroid glands are adjacent to the thyroid gland and secrete parathyroid hormone (PTH); this helps to regulate the level of calcium and phosphate in the blood. When blood calcium levels become low, PTH is released and stimulates the bones to release calcium into the blood. PTH also acts on the kidneys to decrease the amount calcium released in the urine and on the gastrointestinal tract to increase absorption of calcium. PTH release is controlled solely by blood calcium levels, and is not directly influenced by other hormones or the nervous system. Normal nerve and muscle function depends on a tightly controlled blood calcium level.

PTH and Exercise

In adolescents, PTH levels increase after moderate aerobic and anaerobic exercise[4]. This is probably because exercising muscles extracts calcium from the blood in order to facilitate contraction.

Insulin

Insulin is produced in the islet cells of the pancreas; this is located in the abdomen, behind the upper part of the small intestine. Insulin is regarded as the "hormone of plenty" because it is released in response to a meal, and acts to promote the storage of excess carbohydrate, protein, and fat. Insulin stimulates transport of glucose from blood into muscle and liver cells to be stored as glycogen. Insulin is the principal hormone that regulates blood glucose. Insulin is released in response to a rise in blood glucose concentration, such as happens immediately after a meal. Insulin also stimulates transport of fatty acids from blood into adipose tissue to be stored as fat. One of the effects of GH is to enhance the actions of insulin, particularly the transport of amino acids into cells for use in manufacturing protein for growth. Insulin stimulates protein synthesis and inhibits protein breakdown. Insulin levels increase by about 30% during puberty.

Insulin and Exercise

During prolonged exercise, the hormonal adaptations for energy-substrate utilization are different in children than in adults. Children demonstrate a lower decrease in insulin and an increase in catecholamines and glucagon in response to exercise; this could be responsible for a less-effective regulation of glycemia with a risk of hypoglycemia. Therefore, an adequate carbohydrate intake is recommended[5]. Blood glucose levels and the catecholamine responses were lower in girls than in boys, whereas the insulin values remained higher[6].

Training reduces insulin levels. Physical activity is associated with increased-insulin sensitivity and decreased-insulin secretion in adults, adolescents, and children[7].

Glucagon

Also produced in the pancreas, glucagon acts on several tissues (the liver) to make energy (glucose) available during the intervals between meals. In the liver it causes breakdown of glycogen and promotes conversion of amino acids into glucose for use as an energy source. Glucagon levels do not change significantly with puberty.

Glucagon and Exercise

In adults, high-intensity exercise is associated with an increase in glucagons; this is probably stimulated by catecholamines[8]. Low to moderate levels of exercise in adolescents do not have a significant effect on glucagon or catecholamine secretion[9].

Prolactin

Prolactin is produced in the pituitary gland and is responsible for stimulating the increase in breast development that occurs during pregnancy and for breast milk production after delivery. Prolactin also stimulates maternal behavior. Males and non-pregnant females produce low levels of prolactin. In males the role of prolactin is unclear. Prolactin stimulates the action of GH and may be involved in the regulation of fluid and electrolyte balance in response to heat stress.

Children are more susceptible to heat illness than adults. One of the reasons for this difference is that children sweat less than adults, and sweating is the body's main devise used to cools itself. Heat tolerance improves with maturation, primarily due to an increase in sweat rate. There is preliminary evidence to show that prolactin may be involved in stimulating this increase in sweat rate that occurs with puberty.

Prolactin and Exercise

Exercise causes a rise in prolactin levels in both boys and girls. The increase in prolactin, in response to exercise, becomes more pronounced with each stage of growth and maturation[10]. In this way, prolactin may be responsible for improving children's ability to acclimatization to the heat as they progress through puberty. Intense exercise training can cause a decrease in prolactin levels in adolescents[11].

Adrenal Gland Hormones

The adrenal glands are located adjacent to the kidneys and produce four categories of hormones: catecholamines, glucocorticoids, mineralocorticoids, and androgens.

Catecholamines

The principal catecholamine is epinephrine; this is released in large quantities in response to stress or low blood glucose. Epinephrine increases heart rate, blood pressure, ventilation, blood glucose levels, and inhibits protein breakdown in muscle cells[12]. Catecholamine levels decrease significantly with advancing puberty and are generally higher in boys than in girls[13].

Catecholamines and Exercise

Exercise stimulates catecholamine release, and there do not appear to be any significant differences in the degree of this response among children, adolescents, and adults[14].

Glucocorticoids

Glucocorticoids regulate the metabolism of carbohydrate, fat, protein, and minerals; and ensure an appropriate response to stress. Glucocorticoids tap the body's storage sites for energy in times of need—such as fasting, illness, or stress. They act on the liver and muscle to mobilize glucose from glycogen stores, and act on adipose tissue to mobilize fatty acids. In muscle, glucocorticoids also inhibit protein synthesis and promote protein breakdown in order to mobilize amino acids for fuel. Glucocorticoids also play a role in the regulation of bone mineral metabolism, and modulate the immune system and inflammatory processes.

The main glucocorticoid is cortisol. Cortisol release follows a circadian (day-night) pattern, peaking at eight a.m. and falling to a low point in the late afternoon. Cortisol levels do not change significantly through childhood and adolescence.

Glucocorticoids and Exercise

Both strength training and endurance exercise stimulate cortisol release[15]. The magnitude of this response decreases as children progress through the stages of puberty[16]. This is likely due to the influence of rising levels of estrogen and testosterone. The precise role, if any, that glucocorticoids play in muscle development is yet to be determined.

Mineralocorticoids

Aldosterone is the main mineralocorticoid, and plays a central role in the maintenance of electrolyte balance and blood pressure. Aldosterone acts on the kidneys, gastrointestinal tract, sweat glands, and salivary glands to stimulate the absorption of sodium. Aldosterone levels do not change significantly with growth and maturation.

Mineralocorticoids and Exercise

Exercise causes a rise in aldosterone levels; the magnitude of this response is similar for children, adolescents and adults[17].

Androgens

Adrenal androgens are the byproducts of cortisol synthesis, and include dehydroepiandrosterone (DHEA), dehydroepiandrosterone-sulfate (DHEA-S), and androstenedione. Adrenal androgen levels begin to increase at or between the age of six and ten, continue to rise as puberty progresses, peak in young adulthood, then begin to decline after age thirty. DHEA, DHEA-S, and androstenedione are weak androgens. They must first be converted into testosterone at their target tissues in order to exert their effects. The physiologic effects of adrenal androgens are negligible in males. They are not required for sexual maturation or the growth spurt. In females, DHEA, DHEA-S, and androstenedione are the source of the testosterone that is required to stimulate the growth of pubic and axillary hair during puberty.

Adrenal Androgens and Exercise

Adolescent female athletes demonstrate increased levels of DHEA and DHEA-S after moderate intensity training[18].

Testosterone

The primary source of testosterone is the male testes. Small quantities of testosterone are produced in males and females by conversion of adrenal androgens. Testosterone levels increase markedly during puberty stimulating growth and development of the male genitalia and secondary sexual characteristics (pubic, facial and axillary hair growth, deepening of the voice), accelerating bone growth, and increasing muscle mass. Most of testosterone's growth effects on bone, muscle, and skin are indirect because it must first be converted to estrogen in order to exert any action. Testosterone also influences growth during puberty by enhancing GH secretion. One direct effect of testosterone is, it causes greater bone deposition on the outer surface of the bones during puberty, resulting in males having thicker and stronger bones than females.

Testosterone stimulates protein synthesis within muscle cells, causing muscle size to increase in both length and width.

Testosterone stimulates an increase in red blood cell mass; this contributes to the development of increased-aerobic capacity during puberty. Since red blood cells are responsible for carrying oxygen to exercising muscles, this increase in red blood cell mass translates directly into an increase in aerobic capacity. Adrenal androgens are too weak to have a similar effect in females; this is why females have a lower red blood cell mass and lower aerobic capacity than males.

Testosterone and Exercise

Testosterone is responsible for gender differences in muscle strength and aerobic capacity. During puberty, under the influence of testosterone, boys experience greater gains in muscle strength, aerobic capacity, and anaerobic capacity than girls.

There is indirect evidence that testosterone may increase sweat rate and regulate sweat-electrolyte composition, and therefore probably works in conjunction with prolactin to improve tolerance to exercise in the heat. In boys, sweat rate increases only after puberty has started, whereas in girls sweat rate is less dependent on pubertal stage. This difference is likely mediated by testosterone.

Studies investigating the influence of exercise or intense training on testosterone levels have not demonstrated any significant effects in prepubertal or pubertal boys[19]. While intense training can cause reduced estrogen levels in adolescent girls, there is no evidence that endurance training or strength training significantly alters the testosterone levels or delays puberty in boys.

Similar to prepubertal boys, perpubertal girls do not demonstrate changes in testosterone levels in response to intense training[20]. Adolescent female athletes, however appear to demonstrate a slight increase in testosterone levels in response to exercise training[21].

Estrogen

Estrogen is responsible for regulating several physiologic processes in both males and females. In females, the ovaries produce varying levels of estrogen throughout the course of the monthly menstrual cycle. In males, estrogen is produced by enzymes in the target tissues that convert testosterone and adrenal androgens into estrogen. In boys and girls, the effect of estrogen on the bones is the same. Estrogen increases bone-calcium content and bone density. Estrogen levels increase during puberty in both boys and girls. At low levels, estrogen acts on the growth plates to stimulate linear bone growth. At high levels estrogen stimulates closure of the growth plates. Thus, in the early stages of puberty, estrogen accelerates growth, and in the later phases of puberty, estrogen decelerates growth. In this way, estrogen regulates the timing of the growth spurt, and increases and stabilizes bone density and calcium content. In girls, estrogen also stimulates development of the breasts and female genitalia, induces changes in the uterine lining during the menstrual cycle, and increases fat mass.

Progesterone

Progesterone is produced by the ovaries during the latter half of the menstrual cycle. It stimulates the monthly changes that prepare the internal lining of the uterus for pregnancy, and plays a role in stimulating breast development.

Exercise and Estrogen and Progesterone

Intense exercise lowers estrogen and progesterone levels; this causes menstrual irregularities and a decrease in bone mineral density. The responses of the sex hormone concentrations to exercise become more pronounced in the later stages of sexual maturation.

The Menstrual Cycle

The menstrual cycle is defined as that period of time from the beginning of one menstrual flow to the beginning of the next menstrual flow. The average age at the first menstrual period (menarche) is 12.3 years of age, with a normal range of nine to seventeen years of age. The age at menarche depends on many factors, including race, socioeconomic status, heredity, nutrition and culture. Levels of estrogen and progesterone follow specific patterns of variation during the course of the monthly menstrual cycle.

The Menstrual Cycle and Exercise

Scientific research has been unable to prove any significant impact of different phases of the menstrual cycle on sports performance, although subtle effects on some measures of fitness have been demonstrated. For girls with very heavy menstrual flows, the monthly blood loss can be significant enough to cause anemia. This anemia lowers aerobic capacity, and can therefore compromise performance, especially in endurance events. A vegetarian athlete is at greater risk for anemia because her diet often does not contain enough iron to replace the monthly losses. The prevalence of iron-deficiency anemia is 20% in adolescent female runners. A number of recent studies investigating whether changes in female hormone levels during the menstrual cycle may explain why females have an increased incidence of ligament injuries in the knee have produced inconclusive results.

Exercise does effect the menstrual cycle. Regular light or moderate exercise can reduce cramping and reduce the symptoms of premenstrual syndrome, as well as lighten menstrual blood flow. Regular intense exercise can cause menstrual irregularities such as secondary amenorrhea (loss of periods for six consecutive months) and oligomenorrhea (fewer than nine periods per year). Previously, it was thought this was because the body-fat percentage fell below a threshold level necessary for normal menstruation. This theory has been proven wrong. The current theory is that intense exercise causes a chronic "energy drain," where energy intake (calories) is insufficient to meet energy demands (exercise). In an effort to conserve energy, the body adapts to this energy drain by "turning off" the ovaries; this causes a decrease in the levels of estrogen and progesterone, and menstrual irregularities. The drop in estrogen levels leads to a decrease in bone mineral density. Other contributing factors include low body fat, high training intensity, suboptimal nutrition (especially low dietary intake of fat), physical and emotional stress, and eating disorders.

Athletic girls typically start puberty and menstruation at a later age than their non-athletic peers. For non-athletes, the average age at menarche is 12.3-12.8 years of age. For athletes the average age is thirteen to fourteen years of age. Several studies have investigated this phenomenon, and the majority of evidence suggests this delay in menarche seen in athletes, is due to a natural selection process. Girls who are genetically programmed to start puberty at an older age maintain a pre-pubertal body shape (narrower hips, less body fat, smaller breasts) for a longer period of time. This gives them a physical advantage over the girls who are genetically programmed to start puberty at a younger age because the pre-pubertal body type enables them to be more successful in sports and therefore more likely to stay active in sports longer.

Similar to girls with secondary amenorrhea, girls with delayed menarche have decreased bone mineral density for their age due to low levels of estrogen. It is unclear whether these girls go through a "catch-up" period once their menstrual cycles begin, or if this period of time for gains in bone density is permanently lost. It is clear that girls with secondary amenorrhea, experience a significant and irreversible loss of bone mineral density due to low estrogen levels and amounts to 4-20% per year. In the short term, this loss of bone density puts them at risk for stress fractures, and in the long term, for premature osteoporosis. Although the mechanical stimulation of weight-bearing exercise and muscle tension has been shown to build bone density, this positive effect does not occur when estrogen levels are inadequate. Athletes with menstrual irregularities due to intense exercise, also demonstrate alterations in other hormone levels. TH, prolactin, and calcitonin levels are often depressed in these athletes[22], while cortisol levels are increased[23]. These hormonal changes may be responsible for the compromised athletic performance that is sometimes seen in these athletes.

Puberty

Puberty describes the transitional period between childhood and adulthood that is characterized by the appearance of secondary-sexual characteristics and the achievement of reproductive capacity. Puberty is also a time of rapid growth and changes in body composition. All of these changes are orchestrated by the endocrine system and many have a significant impact on athletic development.

The age when puberty begins and the rate of progression varies from each child and onset; it is determined by genetic factors and multiple hormones, particularly GH, TH, estrogen, and testosterone. On average, boys begin puberty at 11.6 years of age complete puberty in three years, while girls begin at 11.2 years of age and complete puberty in four years.

Prior to puberty there are no significant differences between girls and boys with respect to body composition, strength, endurance, motor skill development, or injury risk. Body composition changes significantly during puberty. The earliest changes are seen in muscle mass; this begins at six 6 years of age in girls and 9.5 years of age in boys. Due to the effects of testosterone, the peak velocity of muscle growth is much greater for boys than for girls. During puberty, boys experience a net gain in muscle mass percentage, from 80-85% of body weight before puberty, to 90% of body weight at the end of puberty. In contrast, despite growth of absolute-muscle mass, girls actually experience a net loss in muscle mass percentage during puberty because they have even greater gains in absolute-fat mass. For girls, muscle mass is 80% of body weight before puberty and drops to 75% of body weight by the end of puberty. Hormones that stimulate this process include GH (via IGF), insulin, and testosterone. The spurt in muscle strength lags behind the spurt in muscle mass by about one year. Muscles first grow in size; later the increase in strength occurs due to testosterone's effects on protein structure and muscle enzyme activity. Muscle strength does not increase appreciably after menarche for girls. Even thought the spurt in muscle strength begins late in puberty, muscle strength continues to increase in males, especially with training, reaching a maximum by twenty-five years of age. The gender differences in muscle size and strength are more pronounced in the upper body than in the legs.

With respect to body-fat percentage, boys experience a net decrease from 14.3% of body weight before puberty to 11.2% of body weight at the end of puberty, while girls experience a net increase from 15.7% of body weight before puberty to 26.7% of body weight after puberty.

With respect to height, pubertal growth begins earlier in girls than boys but the magnitude of height gained during puberty is 3cm to 5cm greater in boys than in girls. Boys reach peak height velocity approximately two years later than girls. The growth spurt lasts anywhere from twenty-four to thirty-six months, and is highly variable from adolescent to adolescent, ranging from 5-11cm per year for girls and 6-13cm per year for boys. Peak weight velocity coincides with peak height velocity in boys, while peak weight velocity occurs about six to nine months after peak height velocity in girls.

Hormones also influence changes in body proportion during the growth spurt. The shoulders become wider in boys and the pelvis becomes wider in girls. The upper body to lower body ratio changes markedly during the pubertal growth spurts because the extremities begin to grow sooner than the trunk, and ultimately elongate more than the trunk.

The changes in body composition and body proportions affect the growing adolescent's center of mass, balance, and coordination; all of which can influence motor skill development. The changes in body composition during puberty are very different for boys vs. girls with respect to how they influence sports performance. Because boys gain both height and muscle mass they effectively "grow into their sport." In contract, girls experience an increase in muscle mass that is not proportional to the increase in height, and a greater increase in fat mass. This combination can have a negative effect on athletic performance. Consequently, girls may become frustrated and discouraged as they effectively "grow out of their sport."

The heart and lungs grow during puberty, and the magnitude is the same for girls and boys. Maximal aerobic capacity increases with puberty, for girls until fourteen years of age, and for boys until about seventeen or eighteen years of age. A combination of factors contribute to produce this increase in aerobic capacity, all of which are regulated by hormones: (1) growth of lean muscle mass, (2) increase in red blood cell mass, (3) increase in pulmonary ventilation, (4) increase in cardiac output, (5) increase in muscle oxygen extraction and oxidative metabolism. The increase in aerobic capacity is greater for boys because of the influence of testosterone, which stimulates red blood cell production and increases in lean muscle mass. The capacity for anaerobic exercise increases more gradually than does aerobic capacity.

The changes in body composition and strength can influence the risk of certain types of sports injury. Because bones grow faster than muscle-tendon units, relative muscle tightness and flexibility imbalances are common during the age of peak height velocity—twelve years of age for girls and fourteen years of age for boys. This tightness increases the risk for overuse injuries at the growth centers and can even negatively impact sports performance.

References

[1] Healy, et al. (2003)

[2] McMurray, et al. (1995) , Buyukyazi, Barton & Garhammer (2003)

[3] Simsch, et al. (2002), McMurray, et al.(1995)

[4] Rong , et al.(1997), Thorsen, et al. (1997), Ljunghall, et al. (1988), Takata, et al. (1998)

[5] Fellman & Coudert (1994)

[6] Delamarche, et al. (1994)

[7] Raitakari, et al. (1994), Ku, et al. (2000)

[8] Naveri, Kuoppasalmi & Harkonen (1985)

[9] Sills & Cerny (1983), Lavoie, et al. (1983)

[10] Falk, Bar-Or & MacDougall (1991)

[11] Steinacker, et al. (2000)

[12] Fryburg, et al. (1995)

[13] Weise, Eisenhofer & Merke (2002)

[14] Rowland, et al. (1996)

[15] Duclos, et al. (1998), Stupnicki & Obminski (1992), McMurray, et al. (1995), Buyukyazi, Barton & Garhammer (2003)

[16] Pullinen, et al. (2002), Laaneots, et al. (1998)

[17] Falk, Bar-Or & MacDougall (1991)

[18] Aizawa, et al. (2003), Kraemer, et al. (2001)

[19] Tsolakis, Vagenas & Dessypris (2003)

[20] Jaffre, et al. (2002)

[21] Kraemer, et al. (2001)

[22] Okano (1995), Creatsas, et al.(1992)

[23] Laughlin & Yen (1996)

10

YOUNG ATHLETES AND NUTRITION

Dr. John Berardi

While this text focuses primarily on the movement aspects of young-athletic development and preparation, no discussion of physical preparation—for any athlete—is complete without a thorough treatment of nutritional intake and supplementation. Of the modifiable factors contributing to optimal-exercise performance, nutritional intake is one of the most easily manipulated and most immediately beneficial. It is important to recognize that while training adaptations can take weeks to realize, several acute nutritional manipulations (i.e. caffeine ingestion [1] [2] [3], carbohydrate supplementation during endurance exercise [4] [5], glucose-electrolyte beverages while training in hot environments [6] [7] [8], and creatine supplementation [910]) have a much more rapid, almost immediate, impact on competition performance.

Further, from a chronic perspective, simply eating and supplementing appropriately can lead to the optimal intake and absorption of important macronutrients (proteins, carbohydrates, and fats) and micronutrients (vitamins and minerals) that are essential to the processes of muscle-protein turnover, (the breakdown of old tissue and the rebuilding of new, more functionally-adapted tissue) [11] [12] [13] [14] [15] [16] [17] [18] [19] [20] [21] nervous system function and recovery [22] [23] [24], immune system function and recovery [25] [26] [27] [28], and musculo-skeletal system function and recovery [29] [30] [31] [32] [33] [34] [35] [36] [37] [38]. Simply put, no other athletic intervention can hold as much power over an athlete's training adaptations, body composition, recovery, and competition-day performance as nutritional intake can.

In the case of the young athlete, one other critical consideration emerges: optimal-physical maturation. While the coaches of adult athletes need only concern themselves with the demands placed upon the athlete's body by his or her training and lifestyle stressors, the coaches of young athletes must also be concerned the athlete's physical maturation. An important question arises: why don't coaches pay more attention to their athletes' nutritional intake?

Since coaches are often juggling the responsibilities of teaching appropriate movement patterns, emphasizing skill development, and improving energy system efficiency, it is no surprise that they find it difficult to also take the time to discuss nutritional intake. Further, while it is easy to oversee what the athlete does for one to two hours per day, during his/her training sessions, it is much more difficult to oversee what the athlete is doing during the other twenty-two to twenty-three hours of each day.

Finally, many coaches are just not comfortable enough with the intricacies of nutrient metabolism and biochemistry to dispense nutritional information to their athletes. Yet, in the end, most of these same coaches do understand how important targeted-nutritional practices are. They also realize that if they fail to learn or fail communicate this knowledge effectively to their athletes, they will not only place their athletes in a compromised training state, they will also compromise their own effectiveness as a coach. This is quite a difficult position to be in.

Fortunately, by developing a good system of teaching their athletes the basics of good nutrition, coaches can help enhance their own effectiveness even if they do not fully understand the subtleties of protein needs; nutrient timing; meal combinations; the metabolic actions of insulin; the interaction between exercise and metabolism; free radicals and antioxidant intake; acid base balance; and other, more complex, biochemical considerations. Indeed, the study of nutrition is complex. But the actual practice of sports nutrition can be made simple. It is just a matter of good resource allocation.

A well-trained sports nutritionist will use his or her resources to take complex-nutritional biochemistry into account and translate that information into simple, easy to follow strategies. Then, the coach can use his or her resources to communicate these strategies to his or her athletes. And further, to hold his or her athletes accountable for following these strategies. In the case of young athletes, the parents also play an integral role. Often it is the job of the coach to communicate with the athletes and their parents, and it is the job of the parents to hold the athlete accountable for following the recommendations.

In order to assist coaches in the understanding of nutritional requirements and in the practice of communicating this information to their young athletes (and their parents), the goal of this chapter is two fold. First, coaches will develop a basic understanding of how a complete dietary strategy can be devised. Secondly, coaches will learn how to develop strategies for making this information simple enough that their young athletes can both understand and implement it.

Nutritional Pressures

Most strength coaches and nutritionists will agree that without appropriate nutritional interventions, the typical athlete's diet is far from optimal. This should come as no surprise to anyone who is not trained in nutrition or exercise science, as an athlete's habits are influenced by the same social pressures that influence a sedentary population. Cultural heritage, family dietary habits, peer pressures, and media influence all play roles in all of our food choices and athletes are not excluded. Since the North American diet is typically rich in highly processed "convenience foods," and athletes of all ages tend to be more "on the go" than most of their sedentary counterparts, athletes often develop habits inconsistent with what is necessary to support their training and competitive demands. Often, a complete nutritional re-education is required.

Fortunately, one advantage coaches of young athletes have in reprogramming their nutritional habits is that very little reprogramming is required. Young athletes are still forming habits and therefore, are more open to nutritional suggestion when compared to their adult counterparts who have formed habits years prior and are simply following nutritional paths of least resistance. To this end, it is essential that the key influencers in the life of the young athlete, parents/guardians, are educated and encouraged to support their child's nutritional requirements and begin good habit development early on.

Of course, this prior discussion assumes that no attempt has been made by the young athlete or their influencers to discover a nutritional competitive advantage. Indeed, with the emphasis that is being placed on youth athletics (and the contracts that may be waiting for these young athletes once they develop), many athletes and influencers have sought out nutritional advice as their "secret weapon." Unfortunately, the advice they are likely to find usually resides at one of the extreme ends of the nutritional spectrum. They are likely to find, on the one hand, sports supplement manufacturers recommending a myriad of pills and powders that are supported more by marketing claims than by actual laboratory or clinical data. Often, in an attempt to create a perceived *need* for their product, these manufacturers will go as far as emphasizing their pills and powders as substitutes for an adequate nutritional intake. And, on the other hand, athletes and their influencers are likely to find dogmatic dietitians insisting that a high-carbohydrate-balanced diet is all they need. Of course, the concept of a balanced diet is not only nebulous, but subject to varied interpretation. Where does that leave the athlete: C? confused and performing sub optimally, whether his or her supplement shelf is full or completely empty. In an attempt to navigate this informational minefield, athletes and their influencers must seek out competent professionals trained in both exercise science and nutrition. To be sure, these individuals are hard to find. However, their services are often well worth the effort.

Nutritional Goals

An important question to ask whenever discussing nutritional intake: "what do I hope to accomplish with my nutrition recommendations?" It is even more important to come up with the right answer, usually a comprehensive answer. After all, a single-minded focus on "performance" or "weight loss" or "health" might actually produce a dangerous result. For example, it is possible to devise a nutrition program that is targeted at improving health, yet actually reduces athletic performance. Consider low carbohydrate diets; these diets tend to reduce blood sugar, which is generally regarded as "healthy," but also lead to low-muscle-glycogen concentrations, which can negatively impact certain forms of sports performance (especially intermittent and endurance activity). Not at all what an athlete is after, regardless of the drop in blood sugar, as it is possible to improve both health and sports performance with a different type of eating plan.

Of course, it is also possible to design a nutritional program targeted at improving body composition that actually reduces both health and athletic performance. Consider low calorie diets; these diets tend to reduce body mass, often desirable in athletes and non-athletes alike. But, while dropping body mass, these diets can also reduce bone density—certainly a negative health outcome, especially in female athletes—and can reduce muscle mass and strength, which, of course, will reduce sports performance markedly. So, while the athlete "dropped weight," the outcome was not ideal since this drop in body mass was accompanied by health and performance declines. Again, not an ideal outcome since weight loss can be accomplished, along with improvements in health and athletic performance, with a well-designed nutritional program.

Finally, it is also possible to design a nutrition program targeted at improving performance, but that actually reduces health and negatively affects body composition. For example, high carbohydrate diets that are full of simple sugars and devoid of fiber and micronutrients, can improve muscle glycogen, increasing muscle energy stores, but can also increase body fat and, over time, induce insulin resistance. This outcome is not desirable either, as muscle glycogen concentrations can be maximized without negatively affecting body composition and health.

So, again, when posing the question "what do I hope to accomplish with my nutrition recommendations?" it should now be clear that the goal should be to focus on improving three specific targets: improving health, improving body composition, and improving performance. It is only in the intersection of these three goals that the best nutritional plans are made. And it is surprising that many coaches fail to take all three into account when giving nutritional advice to their athletes.

Outcome-Based Monitoring

In order to evaluate whether a set of sports nutrition recommendations are accomplishing the intended goals of improving health, body composition, and sports performance, a set of criterion measures is essential. If a coach fails to monitor his or her athlete's health (via routine blood analysis performed by the athlete's physician), body composition (via body weight and body fat measurements) and sports performance (via laboratory, gym, and/or competition performance), how can he or she possibly know whether or not his or her dietary suggestions are having the desired impact? And, of course, more important than simply monitoring the impact of these suggestions is the altering of these recommendations based on the results of your criterion measures. Many an athlete has grown frustrated when a nutritionist or coach has suggested a specific nutrition prescription and has failed to alter his or her prescription even in the face of negative results. Allowing ineffective recommendations to persist is unacceptable. Regularly monitoring an athlete's outcomes is the only way to ensure success.

In figure 1 (below), one way of visualizing an outcome-based decision making strategy is presented. In this example body composition goals are outlined (although, of course, the same model can be used for all important outcomes including body composition, health, and performance). As discussed above, in order to evaluate a set of sports-nutrition recommendations, a criterion measure is needed. In the case of the example below, two criterions are presented: muscle gain and fat loss. In order to be effective as a coach, whenever implementing a set of recommendations (represented by the words "follow plan" below), it is important to regularly (every few weeks) evaluate whether or not the set objectives have been accomplished (represented by the words "reach goals?" below). If the answer to this question is "yes," then the course of action is simple: the athlete should continue to follow the prescribed plan. However, if the answer is "no," then the course of action is to figure out what exact goal the athlete is trying to achieve (in this case, muscle gain or fat loss) and adjust the plan accordingly. Once this is done, the athlete should repeat the "follow plan" process until the athlete's goals are achieved.

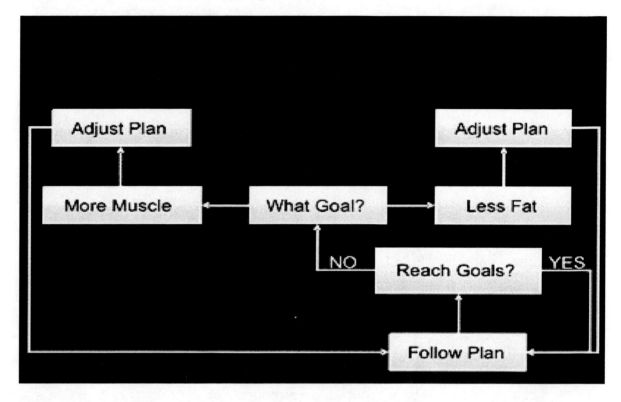

Figure 1 - Outcome-Based Decision Making For Body Composition Goals

While this outcome-based system may seem relatively simple, it is precisely the logical and systematic nature of this approach that makes it so effective. If coaches were to apply this simple, systematic approach to all aspects of their coaching, a tremendous amount of guess work would be eliminated from the coaching process and effective strategies for each athlete could be derived quickly and efficiently. Indeed, the short term application of systems such as this one might front load a portion of the work. But, in the end, putting systematic procedures in place will save much time.

The Basics of Good Nutrition

Until this point in the chapter, some of the nutritional pressures athletes face, as well as the nutritional goals and monitoring strategies important to ensuring athlete success, have been discussed. At this point, however, the basics of good nutrition should be introduced. While an exhaustive discussion of each aspect of nutritional prescription goes far beyond the scope of this chapter, the basics discussed here are sufficient to assist in the prevention of the typical energy, macronutrient, and micronutrient deficiencies seen in those athletes attempting to follow the typical North American diet while engaging in strenuous exercise or sport performance. It is important to note, however, that optimizing nutritional intake requires an individualized approach in which each athlete's daily energy expenditure, activity demands, body type, and unique physiology are taken into account. Such a plan is best designed by a sports nutrition professional, one trained in both exercise science and nutrition. Therefore seek the basics here, look to sports nutrition professionals for more individualized nutritional strategies.

Understanding Energy Balance

Energy balance, the relationship between energy ingested and energy expended is arguably the most important nutritional determinant of exercise performance, body composition, training adaptation, and optimal physiological functioning in athletes[39]. Unfortunately, this well-established message has been lost while many athletes and coaches search for the perfect macronutrient ratios; for the newest nutritional supplement that can boost energy production, fat loss, and muscle mass; and for the newest athlete-friendly diet. Despite this search for the "latest and greatest," the simple fact of the matter remains, to optimize health, body composition, and performance, energy balance is where one must start.

However, it is important to have a clear understanding of energy balance before one tries to apply it to practical ends.   This is emphasized as the classic model used to describe energy balance that most coaches and nutritionists carry around with them. These models are often incomplete and do not reflect the reality of body composition change or the most-current-scientific literature on the topic. With the simplistic view of energy balance during weight maintenance (seen in figure 2) as a starting point, erroneous conclusions may be drawn about how to design and monitor an athlete's eating plan.

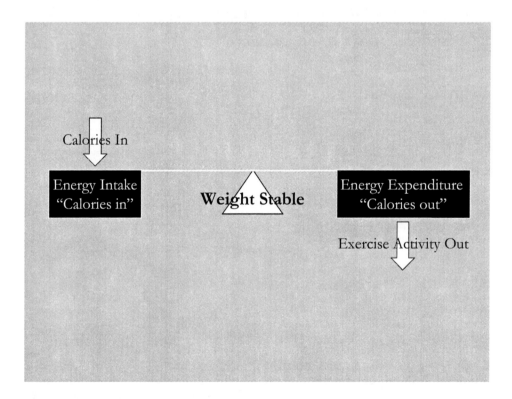

Figure 2 The Classic View of Energy Balance

In examining this model—a model commonly accepted both theoretically and operationally sound—we see that when an athlete's weight is stable, energy intake and expenditure must be "balanced," and we assume the athlete has achieved the right energy intake to meet his or her needs (and that no change is needed). Further, according to this model, when weight is gained, energy intake must exceed energy expenditure and it is assumed the athlete is eating too much (and should eat less). Finally, when energy expenditure exceeds energy intake, weight is lost and it is assumed that the athlete is eating too little (and should eat more). For the most part, this model is correct. However, this model does not take into account the true complexity of the energy balance equation (as seen in figure 3), the myriad of factors that will affect energy expenditure, and the relationships between work, heat, and storage (these relationships differentially affecting energy expenditure with different body types, different nutrient intakes, and different training status).

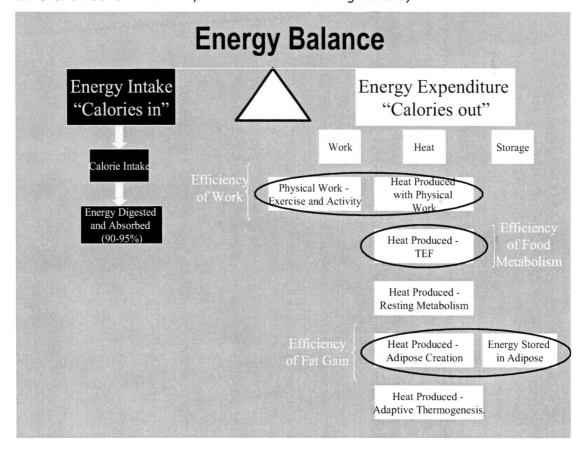

Figure 3. The myriad factors comprising energy balance [40]

Further, the classic model of energy balance also fails to take into account the relationships between energy expenditure and energy intake. With this model, energy intake and expenditure are assumed to be independent and therefore will affect body composition, simply increasing one side of the equation or decreasing the other side will achieve the desired effect. If only it were so simple. As several authors have written:

> "The regulatory systems (of the body) control both energy input and output so that for a given steady state, compensatory changes on the input side are made if expenditure is challenged, or on the output side (expenditure or efficiency) if intake is challenged...Realizing human obesity is caused by the interaction of an obesigenic environment with a large number of susceptibility genes, successful treatment will require uncoupling of these compensatory mechanisms[41]".

> "The critical issue in addressing the problem of alterations in body weight regulation is not intake or expenditure taken separately, but the adjustment of one to the other under ad libitum food intake conditions[42]".

In other words, energy input and output are interrelated—not independent as the classic energy balance equation suggests. As a result, when trying to manipulate body mass by decreasing energy intake, energy expenditure can be down regulated. Further more, when trying to manipulate body mass by increasing energy intake, energy expenditure can be up regulated. Take the example of an athlete trying to lose weight for competition by restricting energy intake. In doing so, not only will the athlete's metabolic rate eventually slow, preventing further weight loss, muscle mass will be compromised[43] and performance ability will suffer, as optimal athletic performance and health are related to total energy intake, metabolic rate, tissue turnover, and muscle mass[44] [45]. Furthermore, since the micronutrient content of the diet is often closely related to energy intake, decreases in energy ingestion may lead to micronutrient deficiencies. Only with a more complete understanding of how energy intake and expenditure influence each other (including how body type, macronutrient intake, nutritional supplements, and exercise activity impact this relationship), can optimal body health, body composition, and athletic performance be achieved. Take the following case study as an example:

Case Study #1

Elite Jr. National Level Endurance Athlete

History

Prior to seeking sports nutrition counseling, the athlete was 5'6", 165 lbs, and 23% body fat. As most elite participants in this athlete's sport were closer to 135 lbs and 12% body fat, this athlete needed to lose body mass and body fat to become more competitive. After being counseled to ingest a higher carbohydrate, energy restricted diet (see September 2002 data below for a summary of the nutritional prescription), this athlete lost a combination of fat and muscle mass, leaving the athlete 160lbs and 22% body fat.

Client Interaction

After early results were unpromising, this athlete sought additional consultation with a different sports-nutrition professional. After twelve weeks of following a modified set of recommendations (outlined below), the following results were achieved (body composition data recorded via calibrated-weigh scale and air-displacement plethysmography, energy intake data collected and analyzed as weighed diet records, and expenditure data estimated based on ACSM MET values):

September 2002:	December 2002:	Net result – 12 weeks:
5'6" ; 160lb ; 22% fat	5'6" ; 135lb ; 9% fat	25lbs lost
(125lb lean, 35lbs fat)	(123lb lean, 12lbs fat)	-23lb fat
		-2lbs lean
Exercise Expenditure:	**Exercise Expenditure:**	
~1200kcal/day	~1200kcal/day	
Energy Intake:	**Energy Intake:**	
~2500kcal/day	~4000kcal/day	
15% protein	35% protein	
65% carbohydrate	40% carbohydrate	
20% fat	25% fat	

Discussion

While surprising and (according to the conventional view of energy balance) improbable, this 25lb loss of body mass in the face of an increase in energy intake, may have occurred due to one or more the following reasons:

a) An increased protein intake and a resultant increase in energy expenditure (due to an increased TEF) and an increased protein turnover.

b) An upregulation of metabolic rate (both resting and exercise) due to an increase in energy intake

c) A dietary shift in food type; as this athlete began by eating a high proportion of carbohydrate from sugars and fat from saturated fats and ended eating mostly low glycemic, micronutrient and fiber-rich carbohydrate sources and a balanced-fat intake (rich in monounsaturated fats and polyunsaturated fats)

Table 1: Case study of female endurance athlete attempting to lose body mass and body fat

In considering the case study presented above, one of the most important factors playing into the athlete's inability to lose fat may have been the fact that her low energy intake was decreasing her energy expenditure, highlighting the important relationship between intake and output (depicted in figure 4 below).

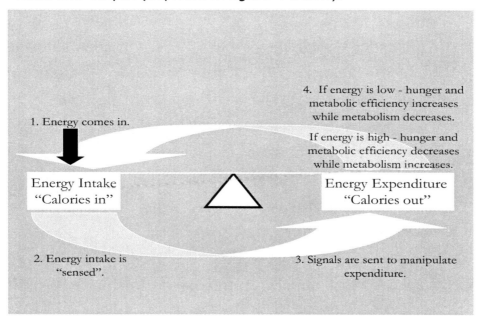

Figure 4: An Integrated Model of Energy Balance

In summary, the conventional-energy-balance equation may have limited predictive power in some athletes as a result of a number of factors including gender, body type, exercise activity, metabolic responsiveness to fluctuations in energy intake, and macronutrient intake. While the easy prescription is to tell athletes that in order to lose weight, they must eat less, and to gain weight they must eat more, this is not always the best prescription. As an initial strategy, it is most important for athletes to eat foods that are high in micronutrients; this is done in order to increase the ratio of micronutrients ingested to energy ingested. For example, an athlete who habitually eat sugary breakfast cereals (empty calories) in an attempt to increase the carbohydrate content of his or her diet, would benefit from exchanging these cereals for a combination of fruits, vegetables, and ancient grains (such as quinoa). Not only are these latter foods more micronutrient dense, they have more fiber and a lower glycemic index, both factors playing a role in improving health and body composition. With these foods, an athlete gets more bang for his or her nutritional buck.

In addition to improving the micronutrient to total energy ratio, for optimal adaptation and recovery, athletes must find ways to eat more energy while maintaining an optimal body composition and body mass for their specific activity. While it may seem counterintuitive to suggest an individual can lose fat mass while eating more food, taking advantage of appropriate food selection (choosing lower glycemic index carbohydrates, a higher percentage of the diet as protein, and a diet higher in mono- and poly-unsaturated fats) and nutrient timing (ingesting protein and carbohydrate supplements during and after exercise as well as ingesting a higher percentage of carbohydrate energy during the workout and post workout periods relative to the rest of the day) strategies can accomplish both goals [46 47 48 49 50 51 52 53 54 55 56].

Energy Balance in Young Athletes

When examining the energy needs of young athletes and adult athletes, one important difference comes to light. In children and adolescents, the energy costs associated with rest and a variety of activities (running, skiing, etc), are actually greater per kg of body mass vs. their adult counterparts[57]. Indeed, some data demonstrate the energy cost of physical activity (walking or running at any given speed, for example) per until body mass is as much as 15-25% higher in young athletes vs. adolescents and adults[58 59 60]. Of course, this does not necessarily mean *absolute*-energy requirements in active children are higher than in active adults. As seen in table 2 below, absolute-energy requirements *do* increase as children age and approach adulthood[61].

Years of Age	Energy Needs for Highly Physically Active Boys	Calorie Needs for Highly Physically Active Girls
8	2300-2400	2100-2200
9	2400-2500	2300-2400
10	2500-2600	2400-2500
11	2700-2800	2500-2600
12	2800-2900	2600-2700
13	3000-3100	2700-2800
14	3200-3300	2800-2900
15	3500-2600	2900-3000

Table 2: Estimated energy needs for physically active boys and girls age 8-15. These data are based on average height/weight statistics ("Center for National Health Statistics, 2000") and the Children's Energy Needs Calculator ("NCRC at the Baylor College of Medicine").

However, these data indicate that, when corrected for body mass and lean mass, children expend more energy per kg than adults do. Although the reasons for the increase in metabolic rate are not fully understood, it has been suggested that because of the high metabolic demands of organ tissues, the high ratio of organ mass to total body mass in children, contributes to a higher metabolic rate per kg of mass[62][63]. Further, during exercise, as children are unable to reduce antagonist co-contraction during movement, extra metabolic energy is required during physical activity, making children less economical than adults[64]. Finally, due to an increased stride frequency, children may expend more biomechanical energy during movement[65].

The practical implications of these findings suggest that per kg of body mass, children need to ingest more energy vs. their adult counterparts. Using adult equations to predict energy requirements for children would likely underestimate a child's needs, especially if that child is physically active. Table 2 above offers estimates of energy needs for children of different ages, however as discussed in the previous section above, actual energy needs will vary from child to child and from sport to sport. Only outcome-based decision making (described above) will help effectively determine a child's actual energy needs for optimal health, body composition, and sports performance.

Protein Intake

Proteins are composed of amino acids, which join together to form the peptide chains that we know as protein. Of the twenty amino acids, nine are indispensable or essential, meaning they cannot be made in the body and therefore must come from the diet. As a result of the essentiality of these amino acids, protein, unlike carbohydrate, must be present in the diet in certain amounts for survival.

The RDA (recommended dietary allowance) for dietary protein in sedentary individuals is 0.8g protein/kg body mass. While very few athletes are at risk for a true protein deficiency and most exceed the 0.8g protein/kg body mass recommendation of the RDA, some authors have suggested that athletes may need more protein than their sedentary counterparts (up to 2.0g protein/kg body mass). Whether or not this is true, and athletes actually *need* more protein (to prevent a negative nitrogen status and protein wasting), has been debated extensively and inconclusively[66] [67] [68] [69] [70] [71]. However, more important for sports nutrition, is the question of optimization. Of course, "optimal" is a loaded term; one that is difficult to define. In the context of this section, optimal will be defined as the protein intake that, when combined with sport-specific physical training, produces ideal body size and composition for that particular sport. Therefore, rather than focusing on the prevention of a protein deficiency, sports nutritionists should place their emphasis on optimization of an athlete's health, body composition and performance (the "intersection," discussed earlier). Using optimal health, body composition, and sports performance as a criterion, it should come as no surprise that since many athletes actually benefit from a relatively high dietary protein intake [72] [73] [74] [75] [76] [77] [78] [79] [80] [81] [82] [83] [84] [85] [86] (one that exceeds their calculated protein *needs*), athletes have often self-selected protein intakes that are higher than conventionally recommended.

When examining the question of protein needs, especially in the face of recommendations for athletes to eat more protein, many scientists and dietitians vehemently assert that higher protein diets (above the RDA) are not necessary for building muscle. With this assertion, the science agrees. Protein intakes above what the typical North American non-vegetarian eats, are unlikely to increase muscle mass directly. However, there may be additional benefits associated with an increased protein intake that make eating more protein important including:

1) **Increased Thermic Effect of Feeding**: While all macronutrients require metabolic processing for digestion, absorption, and storage or oxidation, the thermic effect of protein is roughly double that of carbohydrates and fat[87] [88] [89]. Therefore, eating a higher protein intake (relative to the RDA) may actually promote thermogenesis, a higher metabolic rate, and an increased muscle-fat ratio[90].

2) Increased Glucagon: Protein consumption increases plasma concentrations of the hormone glucagon[91] [92]. Glucagon is responsible for antagonizing the effects of insulin in adipose tissue, leading to greater fat mobilization[93] [94]. In addition, glucagon also decreases the amounts and activities of the enzymes responsible for making and storing fat in adipose and liver cells[95]. As a result, increased protein intakes may decrease daily fat balance, again leading to an increased muscle-fat ratio[96].

3) **Increased IGF-1**: Protein and amino-acid supplementation has been shown to increase the IGF-1 response to both exercise and feeding[97] [98] [99]. Since IGF-1 is an anabolic hormone that is related to muscle growth, another advantage associated with consuming more protein may be more muscle growth when overfeeding and/or muscle sparing when dieting.

4) Reduction in Cardiovascular Risk: Several studies have shown that increasing the percentage of protein in the diet (from 11% to 23%), while decreasing the percentage of carbohydrate (from 63% to 48%), lowers LDL cholesterol and triglyceride concentrations with concomitant increases in HDL cholesterol concentrations[100] [101].

5) Improved Weight-Loss Profile: Research by Don Layman and colleagues has demonstrated that reducing the carbohydrate ratio from 3.5:1 to 1.4:1, increases body fat loss, spares muscle mass, reduces triglyceride concentrations, improves satiety, and improves blood glucose management during hypocaloric diets [102] [103].

6) Increased Protein Turnover: As discussed in the introduction, all tissues of the body, including muscle, go through a regular program of turnover. Since the balance between protein breakdown and protein synthesis governs muscle protein turnover, increased protein turnover may best improve muscle adaptations to training. By increasing protein synthesis and protein breakdown, a diet high in both protein and energy intake may help break down muscle more rapidly, leading to a rapid rebuilding and adaptation to exercise training[104] [105].

7) Increased Provision of Auxiliary Nutrients: Although the benefits mentioned above have related specifically to protein and amino acids, it is important to recognize that we do not just eat protein and amino acids — we eat *food.* Therefore, high protein diets often provide auxiliary nutrients that could enhance performance and/or muscle growth. These nutrients include creatine, branched chain amino acids, conjugated linoleic acids, and/or additional nutrients that are important but remain to be discovered. This illustrates the need to get most of your protein from food, rather than supplements alone.

In the end, any discussion of protein intake that begins and ends with a conversation about whether protein builds big muscles, is incomplete. After all, with the powerful metabolic effects that protein promotes, protein intake needs to be examined for its ability to assist in body composition improvement—namely the improvement of the muscle-fat ratio.

When seeking to optimize an athlete's protein intake, a good rule of thumb is to design an athlete's diet from the foundation of 2.2g protein/kg body mass (1g protein/lb of body mass). Once the protein intake is fixed, add in carbohydrate and fat in order to meet total daily energy needs. However, this strategy should not be the end of the story. Truly, the best way to optimize an athlete's protein intake would be to experiment with a variety of levels of dietary protein (adjusting carbohydrate and fat energy to compensate for the increases or decreases in protein intake), assessing personal performance and body composition outcomes to determine which intake creates the best response. As with any training outcome, nutritional strategies should always be appraised using an outcome-based approach, in which the results of dietary changes are regularly assessed and future changes are made based on measurable outcomes. In addition to experimenting with overall protein intake, it is important to ensure that a large percentage of daily protein comes from complete protein sources (animal proteins). Even if an adequate total daily protein intake is ingested, if incomplete protein sources, protein sources that are missing one or more essential amino acid, make up the bulk of an athlete's dietary protein intake, the athlete may experience sub-optimal adaptation to training. Further more, if athletes consistently ingest animal protein (especially lean red meat), the B vitamin, zinc, and iron, deficiencies frequently seen (especially in female athletes) would occur much less frequently. Finally, although some individuals suggest that increased dietary protein intakes may be dangerous, these claims come as a result of several unproven claims about the dangers of high protein diets. In fact, there is no evidence that healthy individuals would experience any harm as a result of a high protein diet[106] [107] [108].

Protein Needs in Young Athletes

In adults, protein need is typically established as the amount of protein required to maintain nitrogen balance (i.e. to prevent protein loss/malnutrition) and, with an added safety margin, the RDA has been established as 0.8-1.0g/kg. In children, however, due to the energy and protein costs of growth and development, protein needs are defined as the amount of protein required to allow a *positive* nitrogen balance. Research has suggested that children from the ages of seven to ten require about 1.1-1.2g/kg, and children from the ages of eleven to fourteen require about 1g/kg[109]. However, there is little data in young athletes examining whether active children need more (although there is no reason to believe that young athletes would not require a higher intake, as do their athletic adult counterparts). As suggested prior, recommending nutrients in such a manner, as to only consider the prevention of deficiency (along with safety margin), short-changes the athlete in his or her quest for optimal health, body composition, and sports performance. As recommended above, a good rule of thumb is to design a young athlete's diet from the foundation of 2.2g protein/kg body mass (1g protein/lb of body mass). Once the protein intake is fixed, add in carbohydrate and fat in order to meet total daily energy needs. Evaluate the results of this intervention using an outcome-based decision-making strategy.

Carbohydrate Intake

Dietary carbohydrate intake has become a controversial topic with several authors challenging the high carbohydrate suggestions inherent in the US Food Guide Pyramid and the Canadian Food Guide, and recommending low carbohydrate diets. While (in sedentary individuals) a lower-carbohydrate intake has been shown to lead to weight loss, losses in body fat, a better preservation of muscle mass, and favorable changes in triglycerides and high-density-lipoprotein cholesterol[110], it is likely that extremely low-carbohydrate diets (i.e. ketogenic diets) will reduce an athlete's total energy intake, impair intense-exercise performance, reduce work capacity, suppress immune function, and increase perception of effort during normal exercise tasks[111][112][113][114][115][116][117]. These data lead to the suggestion that, while athletes could potentially benefit from a reduction in carbohydrate energy during rest periods and training periods of low volume/intensity, during periods of intense training or competition, athletes should follow a moderate- to high-carbohydrate diet. While some authors recommend as high as 70% of the diet come from carbohydrate, this amount of carbohydrate may be too high in all but high-volume endurance athletes. With a primary focus on carbohydrate intake, athletes are likely to displace dietary protein and fat and may have a more difficult time achieving an ideal-body composition for their sport (especially if a high percentage of this carbohydrate comes from high glycemic-index sources and protein intake is limited). Rather than suggesting a chronic-high-carbohydrate diet (as many dietitians do), a better-nutritional-counseling strategy might be to emphasize carbohydrate *type* and *timing,* rather than simply carbohydrate amount.

It is important to recognize that optimal sports performance can only be achieved when a number of factors converge. Not only does an athlete have to be well fueled for competition, but they have to be well fueled during training. They have to eat appropriately for recovery of every system, from muscular to neural to immune, and they have to be the right body size (and composition) for their sport. One danger associated with the current-sports-nutrition paradigm, relative to carbohydrate intake, is that with the single-minded purpose of increasing carbohydrate intake, other important goals can be ignored. There is no question that many studies have shown higher carbohydrate diets can lead to increased concentrations of muscle glycogen and delay fatigue [118] [119] [120]; can prevent exercise stress induced immunosuppression [121] [122] [123]; and, when combined with protein during the exercise and post exercise periods, stimulate an increase in muscle-protein synthesis and muscle-glycogen resynthesis [124] [125] [126] [127] [128] [129]. These physiological changes correlated well with improved performance in both intermittent and endurance events. Therefore it is understandable that the sports nutrition community has focused much of its energy on dietary carbohydrate intake.

But when carbohydrate intake (and muscle glycogen status) becomes the only consideration of the sports-nutrition professional, and the criterion measures discussed above (those that assess health, body composition, and sports performance) are ignored, the field of sports nutrition begins to suffer. This is what makes many nutritional recommendations paradoxical—dieticians may recommend a "balanced diet" that is high in carbohydrate and low in protein and fat. The question is raised, "where is the balance in that prescription?"

As athletes (both young and adult) often ingest the wrong types of carbohydrates at the wrong times, carbohydrate type and timing should be emphasized over carbohydrate amount. Athletes, rather than simply ingesting large amounts of empty-carbohydrate calories during the training day, should replace their high glycemic index, micronutrient devoid carbohydrate choices (foods like candy, many breakfast cereals, sodas, juices, breads, cereals, and pastas made from highly processed grains, etcetera that cause rapid increases in blood sugar with equally rapid subsequent reductions) with lower glycemic, micronutrient rich carbohydrate choices (foods like beans, ancient grains, unprocessed breads, pastas, and other grains, fruits, vegetables, etcetera that are digested more slowly and provide more continuous energy throughout the day). By substituting better carbohydrate choices, athletes will be better able to manage daily energy fluctuations, will ingest their daily recommendation of fiber (something many athletes fail to do), will be better able to lose fat while preserving muscle mass, and will prevent the development of magnesium and other micronutrient deficiencies common in athletic populations[130]. However, as will be discussed in the workout and post workout nutrition sections below, higher-glycemic carbohydrates can be ingested during and after exercise, in order to promote rapid-energy provision when it is most needed (during training and competition) and when the large-insulin response that accompanies high-glycemic-carbohydrate ingestion can lead to an improvement in muscle recovery.

In the end, athletes may be able to better manage body composition, while promoting equal recovery, when placing the majority of their carbohydrate energy during the workout and few hours post workout (when insulin sensitivity and glucose tolerance are highest) and fewer carbohydrates during the rest of the day (see workout nutrition section below).

Carbohydrate Intake and Young Athletes

There is currently no evidence to suggest that young athletes need more or less total carbohydrate than adult athletes on a kg basis. Although a few interesting studies have suggested that young athletes use relatively more fat (~70%) per kg and less endogenous carbohydrate(~23%) per kg during exercise than adult athletes[131] [132]. This reliance on aerobic metabolism may be one reason why children are often less successful in anaerobic activities than adults[133] [134]. However, when exogenous carbohydrate (i.e. liquid supplementation) is given during exercise, children oxidize a higher percentage of this carbohydrate vs. adults, while still oxidizing a large amount of endogenous fat[135]. The authors of this last study have speculated that since children have higher concentrations of intramuscular triglycerides[136] and an underdeveloped glycolytic capacity[137], greater oxidation of fat during periods of increased energy demands is a likely outcome. Further, the authors speculated that the increased oxidation of exogenous carbohydrate in children during exercise may be important in preserving endogenous fuels for physical development and maturation. To this end, liquid carbohydrate ingested during exercise may be beneficial from both a hydration perspective and a fuel utilization perspective.

Fat Intake

Despite years of anti-fat sentiment, especially among athletes, it has becoming clear that dietary fat is essential to the athlete's nutrition program. There are three main types of dietary fatty acids: saturated fatty acids, monounsaturated fatty acids, and polyunsaturated fatty acids (the often discussed omega 3 and omega 6 fats are both polyunsaturated fatty acids); each of these fats offers unique benefits. In the past, a simplistic view of fat was adopted, as coaches and athletes believed that fat made you fat. Reversing this belief structure will be difficult. However, it is critical to get this message out to athletes: Eating fat will not necessarily make you fat[138]. In fact, some fats (known as essential fatty acids) are absolutely necessary for survival. In addition, the right kinds of dietary fat can improve body composition by promoting fat loss [139] [140] [141] [142] [143]. Furthermore, certain fats can improve training hormonal status [144] [145], can increase the body's ability to store glycogen [146], can increase the body's ability to burn fat [147] [148] [149] [150], and can improve overall health by providing anti-inflammatory, anti-carcinogenic, anti-oxidant, and anti-thrombotic effects [151] [152]. With this list of benefits, it should be clear that fat avoidance is not only difficult, it is foolhardy. While the ADA recommends less than 30% of the diet of a sedentary individual should come from fat, research suggests that athletes should ingest approximately 30% of the diet as fat; as long as the individual proportions of fatty acids are distributed appropriately (i.e. fatty foods are selected appropriately). For optimal health and performance, a balanced approach toward fat consumption is warranted with approximately 33% of dietary fats coming from saturated sources (predominantly animal fats including red meat and dairy), approximately 33% coming from monounsaturated sources (many vegetable fats especially olive oil), and approximately 33% coming from polyunsaturated sources (predominantly vegetable fats especially flaxseed and fish oils). Of the polyunsaturated fats, approximately 50% should come from omega 6 fatty acids and approximately 50% should come from omega 3 fatty acids. It is important to realize that the distribution of fatty acids in the diet is as important as the absolute amount of fat, therefore athletes should pay attention to both.

One final note on fat should be offered: According to the "American Journal of Clinical Nutrition," over 30,000 deaths per year are attributed to the consumption of the one fat that can be labeled as universally bad: trans fat[153] [154]. Trans fats are man-made fats created when polyunsaturated vegetables oils (high in omega 6 fatty acids) are bombarded with hydrogen molecules. In so changing the structure of these fatty acids, natural essential fatty acids are destroyed and the new artificial fats become similar to saturated fats, yet cannot be metabolized properly.   This leads to inhibition of several-critical-enzymatic processes in the body, blood lipid abnormalities, and an increased risk of cardiovascular disease[155]. Unfortunately trans fats are found in far too many foods in the grocery aisles.   To reduce the amount of trans fats in the diet, one must eliminate foods that list hydrogenated or partially hydrogenated fats in the ingredients list.

Fat Intake and Young Athletes

Very little research has been done to examine whether young athletes have any special fat needs vs. adult athletes. Of course, as with adult athletes, young athletes are encouraged to avoid trans fats, as these fats can begin the onset of cardiovascular disease in both adults and in children.   Also, ensuring adequate intake of the essential fatty acids (with special attention to the omega 3 fatty acids) is especially important in the physical development of children[156]. Beyond these considerations, as with adult athletes, young athletes are encouraged to get approximately 30% of their daily energy from fat with each type of fat making up about 33% of total fat intake.

Vitamin and Mineral Intake

Suboptimal ingestion of certain vitamins and minerals may predispose both athletes and non-athletes to a number of diseases. For instance, suboptimal-folic acid levels, along with suboptimal levels of vitamins B(6) and B(12), are a risk factor for cardiovascular disease, neural tube defects, and colon and breast cancer; low levels of vitamin D contribute to osteopenia and fractures; and low levels of the antioxidant vitamins (vitamins A, E, and C) may increase risk for several chronic diseases[157]. Further, in the presence of low energy, protein, and vitamin D intake, low calcium intake may negatively influence estrogen levels and bone health. Although many athletes (both young and adult) do not achieve optimal vitamin and minerals intakes by diet alone, research has demonstrated the higher calorie, more nutrient dense diets that certain subsets of young athletes ingest (relative to their non-athlete counterparts), assist in achieving or coming close to their daily requirements[158] [159].

While current research does not suggest young athletes have increased vitamin needs, there is some evidence to suggest certain groups of young athletes may need to adjust their dietary intake to include more of the following vitamins: B1, B2, B6, E, and folate[160] [161]. Further, after intense exercise, the antioxidant status of young athletes appears to be compromised, indicating a need to emphasize additional antioxidant intake[162].

Likewise, current research does not suggest that young athletes have an increased need for dietary mineral intake, short of those minerals lost through sweat (sodium, potassium, calcium)[163] [164]. However, magnesium, calcium, zinc and iron are often identified as minerals young athletes may be deficient in; these deficiencies lead to impairments in bone development, decreased cognitive function, increased risk for stress fractures, and impaired muscle metabolism[165] [166] [167] [168].

As it is impossible to determine a particular athlete's vitamin and mineral needs by examining composite data from scientific studies (every athlete is different). Recent reviews have suggested it prudent for all adults to take vitamin and mineral supplements[169]. Unfortunately, little data are available to extend these recommendations to children. Although young athletes may demonstrate the same marginal intake of certain vitamins and minerals as adults, it is not known whether or not their responses to vitamin and mineral supplements are similar. Therefore, an adequate cost-benefit analysis should be done when recommending vitamin and mineral supplements to children.

At this point it is important to note it is likely that a well-planned dietary regimen would eliminate the need for vitamin and mineral supplementation. Therefore when posed with the question: to supplement or not to supplement; the only reasonable answer is: it depends. It depends on the current status of the diet and the willingness of the athlete to make improvements. If he or she is willing to make some changes in order to include foods with more of the B vitamins, more vitamin E, and more antioxidant vitamins, then it is unlikely he or she will need supplements. If he or she is unwilling to make these changes, vitamin supplements may be warranted.

Nutrition During Training and Competition

Fluid Needs and Hydration

During exercise, especially in hot climates, the evaporation of sweat is the primary means by which humans dissipate heat. This evaporative cooling, if excessive or prolonged, can lead to relatively large losses in body water. For example, the highest recorded sweat rate is 3.7L/hour (recorded by Olympic Champion Marathon runner Alberto Salazar). This sweat rate is equivalent to a loss of over 8 lbs an hour. Considering the fact that a dehydration of only 2% of body weight in adults (only about 3 lbs for the 147 lb Salazar), can lead to increased perceived exertion and central fatigue, a reduction in plasma volume, a decrease in sweat rate and cooling, a decrease in mental performance, a decrease in fine motor skills and precision, and a decrease in endurance and work capacity[170], preventing dehydration is critical for optimal performance during training and competition.

Voluntary dehydration, or dehydration occurring even when fluids are available in abundance, is of concern during both intermittent activities and prolonged activities in the heat for several reasons. First, our thirst mechanisms often underestimate our fluid needs during exercise and we simply fail to drink enough to replace fluid losses. Secondly, as water absorption from the gastrointestinal tract is limited a rate of 500ml - 1L per hour and the absorption of sports drinks (containing 6-8% carbohydrate) to a rate of 1 - 2L per hour, at the highest sweat rates in the most extreme conditions, it is difficult to actually replace all the fluid that is lost[171]. Further, electrolyte insufficiencies/imbalances can occur if fluid replacement practices do not include the addition of sodium and potassium, as these (and other) electrolytes are also lost during the evaporative cooling process. In particular, a severe fall in the concentration of sodium in body fluids (hyponatremia) can cause serious illness. Hyponatriemia can occur when sweat and urinary fluid losses are replaced with water alone, in the absence of sodium[172].

Interestingly, children may actually experience greater heat stress when exercising in hot environments, as a result of their higher production of metabolic heat during exercise, their greater ratio of body surface area to body mass, and their reduced sweating capacity[173] [174] [175]. Further more, in children, as little as a 1% loss of body mass (1lb for a 100lb child) during exercise can decrease endurance performance[176]. Therefore, voluntary dehydration is of particular concern to young athletes.

In order to prevent voluntary dehydration, a few things are clear. First, young athletes must drink during all athletic events, even when they are not thirsty. One good strategy is to drink every fifteen to twenty minutes during activity. Further more, in order to enhance both thirst and the rate of fluid absorption, the addition of both sodium chloride and carbohydrate, to a flavored (and chilled) beverage, may increase voluntary consumption in young athletes. In some studies, the use of such beverages has completely prevented voluntary dehydration[177].

Workout Nutrition

During and after training and competition, energy demands of the body are high [178] [179] [180] [181] [182] [183], fluid needs increase [184] [185] [186] [187] [188] [189], insulin sensitivity/glucose tolerance is dramatically improved [190] [191] [192] [193] [194] [195] [196], and skeletal muscle is primed for anabolism (as long as amino acids are provided) [197] [198] [199] [200] [201] [202] [203]. As a result, nutrition during and after exercise should focus on preventing dehydration (as discussed above), providing carbohydrate energy, stimulating glycogen resynthesis via a large insulin response, and stimulating increases in skeletal muscle-protein synthesis via a large insulin response coupled with an increase in amino acid availability.

As indicated, during the workout and post workout periods, insulin sensitivity/glucose tolerance is improved and, as a result, the efficiency of glycogen storage is highest at this time. This makes the workout and post workout periods the best times to ingest a large amount of carbohydrate (along with protein). In addition, since a large increase in insulin can facilitiate a greater-glycogen resynthesis and an increase in muscle-protein synthesis, higher-glycemic-index carbohydrates (i.e. sports drinks containing glucose or glucose polymers) and rapidly digesting proteins (i.e. liquid forms of protein such as milk proteins, rice proteins, etc) should be ingested during these times only. In providing a large amount of carbohydrate during this time, fewer carbohydrates can be ingested during the remainder of the day, while achieving better-body composition management and promoting maximal recovery. Indeed, one useful strategy is for athletes to ingest the majority of their carbohydrate energy (especially carbohydrate dense foods such as sugars, breads, whole grains) during and within the first few hours after exercise while ingesting fruits, vegetable, nuts, and legume carbohydrate sources throughout the remainder of the day. This strategy, in addition to delivering the majority of carbohydrate energy during periods of high glucose tolerance, emphasizes foods with a high micronutrient/macronutrient ratio during the remainder of the day.

As a starting point, athletes should begin by ingesting liquid carbohydrate protein supplements immediately prior to [204] or during exercise[205] [206], as well as immediately after exercise [207] [208] [209] [210] [211] [212] [213]. In order to facilitate fluid replacement, as well as rapid energy delivery, the two beverages should be diluted to 6 – 12% concentrations (80 – 120g of substrate per 1000ml water) and should provide approximately 0.8g carbohydrate/kg of body mass and 0.4g protein/kg body mass. Of course, as discussed earlier, experimentation with differing amounts of energy is important to determine the best composition for each individual athlete.

The Pre-Competition Meal

Unfortunately, when most coaches, athletes, and parents think of sports nutrition, they think only of the pre-competition meal. This is unfortunate because if an athlete (young or adult) waits until a pre-competition situation to decide to eat well, they have waited far too long. Good nutrition is training nutrition; it is about the food one eats day in and day out while preparing for competition day. Simply put, the adaptations that take place during training (and the food one eats during this time) are what lead to successful competition-day performances. One's only goal during a pre-competition meal is to not screw things up.

So, if the goal of pre-competition is to not screw things up, the question arises, what will screw things up? First, overeating within the few hours leading up to a competition will certainly screw things up. Some individuals have the notion that eating a lot before a competition will give them an abundance of energy for optimal performance, however this is an ineffective way to fuel the body. Large meals delay gastric emptying and therefore this feeding strategy will simply cause sensations of fullness, a diversion of blood flow from the muscles to the gut, and a feeling of discomfort during competition. Rather than eating a big meal immediately before the competition, one should eat normally for the days leading up to the competition and hydrate during the competition itself (if the competition is intermittent or prolonged). As young athletes oxidize exogenous carbohydrates better than adults, this strategy is particularly important in young athletes.

Secondly, by eating foods that are novel, disturb the gastrointestinal tract causing gas or the urge to defecate, or stomach cramping, will certainly screw things up. Rather than trying foods that one typically does not eat, in an attempt to boost performance or provide extra energy, a young athlete should stick with foods that he or she knows will not upset his or her stomach.

Finally, athletes often screw things up by attempting to "carb load" prior to competition; they do this by having large carbohydrate meals within a few hours of competition. This is an unwise strategy for several reasons. First, carbohydrate loading only is effective during prolonged exercise[214]. Secondly, carbohydrate loading is best accomplished on the days leading up to a competition, not on the competition day[215] [216]. Finally, eating a large meal of simple or rapidly digesting carbohydrates too close to a competition, can actually dull mental acuity and lead to rebound glycemia, a condition in which blood sugar falls low, leading to premature fatigue[217] [218].

In summary, the goal of the pre-competition meal should be to eat a comfortable amount of familiar foods within the few hours prior to exercise. This meal, rather than being ergogenic, should simply provide energy for competition without risking discomfort or fatigue.

Practical Nutrition Strategies

The Ten Habits

In an attempt to make the previous sections immediately applicable to young athletes, the following ten strategies were devised. As discussed in the introduction of this chapter, the science of sports nutrition can be complex, but the practical application of this science need not be. Achieving the goals of optimal health, body composition, and sports performance can be made simple by helping young athletes adhere to the following ten strategies. However, it is important to not confuse simple with simplistic. These strategies are in no way simplistic. They synthesize a complete body of literature to deliver, in ten simple steps, a system of nutritional intake that address concerns such as nutrient timing, protein needs, micronutrient needs, fat intake, acid base status, and more.

Habit #1 - Feed every two to three hours.

It is important to emphasize that every two to three hours a young athlete has the opportunity to feed his or her body energy to stimulate his or her metabolism, balance his or her blood sugar, and improve his or her health, body composition, and performance[219]. Rather than "snacks" and "meals," athletes should think in terms of feeding opportunities and ingest some energy (according to the habits below) every two to three hours.

Habit #2 - Ingest complete-lean protein with each feeding opportunity.

With all of the potential benefits of optimizing protein intake listed above, it is important to ingest some complete, lean protein with each feeding opportunity. If a young athlete is ingesting about 1g/lb of body mass and weighs 100lbs, they will be looking to get 100g/day. Over the course of five to six meals, that is about 20g per meal.

Habit #3 - Ingest vegetables with each feeding opportunity.

In addition to the rich micronutrient and phytochemical content of vegetables, vegetables also provide an alkaline load to the body. Because both proteins and grains present acid loads to the body, it is important to balance these acid loads with alkaline rich vegetables (and fruits)[220] [221]. A simple way to ensure one is getting enough is to ingest one to two servings with each meal.

Habit #4 – Eat veggies and fruits at any meal and "other" carbs mostly after exercise.

Another way of saying this is: ingest non-fruit and vegetable carbohydrates (including simple sugars and sports drinks, as well as starchy carbohydrates such as rice, pasta, potatoes, quinoa, etc) during and within the few hours after exercise. As carbohydrate tolerance is best during and after exercise, the majority of a young athlete's daily carbohydrate energy should come during these times. During the remainder of the day, carbohydrate sources that provide alkaline loads, more fiber, higher micronutrient/macronutrient ratio, a smaller insulin response, and better manage blood sugar should be ingested.

Habit #5 – Eat healthy fats daily.

About 30% of the young athlete's diet should come from fat. However, special care should be made to ensure that this intake is balanced between saturated, monounsaturated, and polyunsaturated fat. By balancing out the fat ratios in this way, health, body composition, and performance can be optimized.

And eating this way is fairly easy; by focusing on adding healthy fats into the diet (particularly monounsaturates and omega 3 fats), the saturated fats and omega 6 fatty acids, prevalent in the North American diet, can be balanced.

Types of Fat		Common Names (# of Carbon)	Prominent Sources
Saturated Fats		1) Myristic Acid (14) 2) Palmitic Acid (16) 3) Stearic Acid (18) 4) Arachidic Acid (20) 5) Lingoceric Acid (24)	1) Coconut and Palm oils 2) Animal fats 3) Animal fats 4) Peanut oil 5) Animal fats
Monounsaturated Fats		1) Palmitoleic Acid (16) 2) Oleic Acid (18)	1) Fish oil 2) Plants and animals
Polyunsaturated Fats	Omega 3 Fats	1) Alpha Linolenic Acid (18) 2) EPA (20) 3) DHA (22)	1) Plant fats – flaxseed 2) Fish oil 3) Fish and other animal
	Omega 6 Fats	1) Linoleic Acid (18) 2) Arachidonic Acid (20)	1) Corn, safflower, soy 2) Animal fat
Trans Fats		1) Hydrogenated Vegetable Oils	1) Processed vegetable fat

Table 3: Dietary Fat Types, Common Names, and Food Sources

Habit #6 – Most calorie-containing drinks (aside from workout nutrition) should be eliminated.

Fruit juice, soda, and other sugary beverages should be eliminated from the young athlete's diet. While many parents believe fruit juice is a healthy alternative to soda, fruit juices offer very little in the way of good nutrition and are certainly no substitute for fruits and vegetables. As the micronutrient/macronutrient ratios of sodas and fruit juices are abysmal, young athletes should be fed their calories and should drink water (or flavored water) as their habitual beverage.

Habit #7 – Eat whole foods instead of supplements whenever possible.

Most of a young athlete's intake should come from whole food sources. While there are certain times where liquid nutrition is useful (during and immediately after exercise as well as when traveling), a young athlete's dietary intake should be composed of whole, largely unprocessed foods.

Habit #8 – Plan to break the rules 10% of the time.

Emphasize to young athletes that their nutritional intake need not be perfect all the time. In fact, it is even important to have foods or feeding opportunities that do not necessarily follow the rules above—about 10% of the time. 100% nutritional discipline is never required for optimal progress. The difference, in results, between 90% adherence and 100% adherence is negligible. (Just be sure that it is clear what 10% of the time really means. For example, if a young athlete is eating five times per day for seven days of the week—that is thirty-five feeding opportunities—10% of thirty-five is about three to four feeding opportunities).

Habit #9 – Plan ahead and prepare meals in advance.

The hardest part about eating well is making sure that the eight rules above are followed consistently. Sometimes good nutrition is not about the food as much as it is about making sure the food is available when it is time to eat. Coaches and parents should come up with food preparation strategies in order to ensure that their young athletes can consistently get the nutrition they need, when they need it. As the old cliché says, "failing to plan is planning to fail."

Habit #10 – Eat as wide a variety of good foods as possible.

Most of us eat in a very habitual manner, ingesting similar breakfasts, lunches, and dinners. By establishing the habits above as the norm, it will eventually be easy to follow them. However, it is also important to balance out this daily habit with seasonal and healthy variety. 10% meals become great chances to feed young athletes a variety of non-habitual foods. Also, be sure to use a variety of protein sources, fruit and vegetable sources, etc.

Emphasize Food, Not Calories

While nutritionists often speak of calories, proteins, carbohydrates, and fats, one important lesson to remember is we do not eat calories, proteins, carbohydrates and fats; we eat food. One problem associated with the calorie and macronutrient focus, which is popular in the media today, is a big disconnect between knowledge and practice. What good is it to know that an athlete should eat a diet containing 30% fat when the athlete (or his or her parents) does not know which foods contain fats? How can an athlete observe the rules of nutrient timing if they do not know that breakfast cereals contain simple sugars?

Of course, some coaches and nutritionists adopt a stubborn view and refuse to help athletes who do not commit to learning all the relevant nutrition terminology. This may be the wrong approach. In some ways it is analogous to seek the counsel of a financial planner and have him or her assert that without an advanced knowledge of financial terms, they can not help. Sending an athlete out with the message "go study nutrition and when you learn all about it, then come back to me," is as ridiculous as an auto mechanic sending a customer with a broken down car out with the message "go learn all about the inner workings of your car, then come back to me." A good mechanic knows all about cars and can tell you exactly what needs to be done with yours when it breaks. Good coaches and nutritionists should know all about athlete calorie and macronutrient needs and should be able to translate those needs into foods their athletes can start eating to get immediate results.

Using the ten habits above, coaches can create food lists, such as the list provided in table 4 below, for each category of habits. This will help athletes better categorize which foods should be eaten and when.

Proteins	Carbohydrates			Fats		
Lean, Complete Proteins	Simple Sugars	Starchy Carbohydrates	Fruits and Vegetables	Saturated Fats	Mono-unsaturated Fats	Polyunsaturated Fats
Eaten With Each Feeding Opportunity	Only During and After Exercise (if at all)	Mostly After Exercise	With Each Meal	About 30% of Fat Intake	About 30% of Fat Intake	About 30% of Fat Intake

Lean meats (ground beef, chicken, turkey, etc.)	Soda	Bread	Spinach	Animal Fats (fat in eggs, dairy, meats, butter, etc.)	Olive Oil	Vegetable Fats
	Fruit Juice	Pasta	Carrots		Nuts	
	Table Sugar	Rice	Tomatoes		Avocado	Flax seeds/oil
Fish (salmon, tuna, etc.)		Potatoes	Broccoli		Etc.	Fish oil
	Sports Drinks	Oats	Cauliflower	Coconut Oil		Etc.
Eggs (Egg Whites)						
	Breakfast Cereal (some varieties)	Cereal Grains (wheat, rye, etc)	Apples	Palm Oil		
Low Fat Dairy (cottage cheese, yoghurt)			Oranges	Etc.		
	Etc.	Etc.	Avocados			
Milk Protein Supplements (Whey, Casein, Milk Protein Blends)			Berries			
			Etc.			
Etc.						

Table 4: Some examples of foods in each food category discussed in the ten habits. For more food their macronutrient and macronutrient composition, visit the USDA Nutrient Database online at http://www.nal.usda.gov/fnic/foodcomp/search/

Summary

New advances in sports nutrition knowledge have provided insight into the importance of nutritional intervention for athletes at all levels of competition. Since athletes are typically influenced by the same social pressures that non-athletes are, it is critical for strength and conditioning professionals to learn about proper-nutritional interventions in order to enhance the effectiveness of their efforts. Although individual approaches to nutrition are important and beyond the scope of this chapter, a few basic principles are universal to all athletes:

- First, athletes need to attempt to ingest as much energy as possible while achieving optimal body mass and composition for their sport.

- To do so, athletes should focus on ingesting approximately 1g protein/lb of body mass. Although this value is a bit higher than what most scientists agree is necessary for strength athletes (1.5 to 2.0 kg/bodyweight), it simplifies the calculations necessary to determine needs and the value can be adjusted based on established outcome measures.

- Dietary carbohydrate and fat energy should balance out the remaining portion of the diet with a higher proportion of carbohydrate than fat.

- It is also imperative that the primary sources of carbohydrates come from low glycemic index carbohydrates, to provide sufficient fiber and abundant nutrients. The intake of high glycemic index carbohydrates should be limited to during the workout and post-exercise periods.

- In addition, fat intake should be substantial (approximately 30% of total energy) with special attention to balancing saturated, monounsaturated, and polyunsaturated fats.

- Young athletes should take advantage of workout nutrition and fluid replacement strategies during and after exercise, namely the frequent ingestion of liquids, electrolytes, and energy.

- Young athletes should alter food selections in order to prevent deficiencies in the B, E, and antioxidant vitamins; as well as iron, calcium, magnesium, and zinc.

- Dietary recommendations should reflect one's current training modality and should be regularly adjusted to meet an athlete's changing needs.

- Rather than prescribing macronutrient or calorie loads to young athletes, a discussion of actual food is critical as young athletes are unlikely prepared to convert back and forth between calories, proteins, carbohydrates, fats, and foods.

- Seeking the assistance of a qualified Registered Dietitian, or a PhD or MD level sports nutritionist, who is knowledgeable in exercise physiology as well, is highly recommended. This will allow the athlete to achieve the desired goals in a healthful, but time efficient manner.

References

[1] Graham (2001)

[2] Graham (2001)

[3] Graham (1994)

[4] Ivy JL, Res PT, Sprague RC, et al. (2003)

[5] Jacobs, KA. &and Sherman, WM. (1999)

[6] Maughan, RJ. (1991)

[7] Noakes, TD. (1993)

[8] Wong, SH., Williams, C. &and Adams, N. (2000)

[9] Kreider, RB. (2003)

[10] Volek, JS. (2003)

[11] Biolo, G., Declan −Fleming, RY. and & Wolfe RR. (1995)

[12] Biolo, G., Maggi, SP., Williams, BD., et al. (1995)

[13] Biolo, G., Tipton, KD., Klein S, et al. (1997)

[14] Borsheim, E., Tipton, KD., Wolf, SE., et al. (2002)

[15] Chesley, A., MacDougall, JD., Tarnopolsky, MA., et al. (1992)

[16] Layman, DK. (2002)

[17] MacDougall, JD., Gibala, MJ., Tarnopolsky, MA., et al. (1995)

[18] Phillips SM, Tipton KD, Aarsland A, et al. (1997)

[19] Robinson SM, Jaccard C, Persaud C, et al. (1990)

[20] Tipton, KD., Borsheim, E., Wolf, SE., et al. (2003)

[21] Tipton KD, Rasmussen BB, Miller SL, et al. (2001)

[22] Blomstrand, E. (2001)

[23] Davis, JM., Alderson, NL. and& Welsh RS. (2000)

[24] Lieberman, HR. (2003)

[25] Bishop NC, Walsh NP, Haines DL, et al. (2001)

[26] Bishop NC, Walsh NP, Haines DL, et al. (2001)

[27] Mackinnon ,LT. (1997)

[28] Nieman, DC. (2001)

[29] Ivy JL, Goforth HW, Jr., Damon BM, et al. (2002)

[30] Jentjens, R. &and Jeukendrup, A. (2003)

[31] Layman, DK. (2002)

[32] Levenhagen DK, Gresham JD, Carlson MG, et al. (2001)

[33] Niles, ES, Lachowetz T, Garfi, J, et al. (2001)

[34] Petibois C, Cazorla G, Poortmans JR et al. (2002)

[35] Petibois C, Cazorla G, Poortmans JR et al. (2003)

[36] Rotman S, Slotboom J, Kreis R, et al. (2000)

[37] Snyder, AC. (1998)

[38] Wong, SH. &and Williams, C. (2000)

[39] Saris, WH. (2001)

[40] Berthoud, HR. (2002)

[41] Berthoud, HR. (2002)

[42] Jequier, E. (2002)

[43] Jequier, E. (2002)

[44] Burke, LM. (2001)

[45] Saris, WH. (2001)

[46] Bielinski, R., Schutz, Y. &and Jequier, E. (1985)

[47] Demling, RH. &and DeSanti, L. (2000)

[48] Doi T, Matsuo T, Sugawara M, et al. (2001)

[49] Esmarck B, Andersen JL, Olsen S, et al. (2001)

[50] Forslund AH, El Khoury AE, Olsson RM, et al. (1999)

[51] Layman DK, Boileau RA, Erickson DJ, et al. (2003)

[52] Levenhagen DK, Gresham JD, Carlson MG, et al. (2001)

[53] Robinson SM, Jaccard C, Persaud C, et al. (1990)

[54] Roy BD, Luttmer K, Bosman MJ, et al. (2002)

[55] Schutz, Y., Bray, G. &and Margen, S. (1987)

[56] Volek, JS. (2003)

[57] Harrell JS, McMurray RG, Baggett CD, Pennell ML, Pearce PF, Bangdiwala SI. (2005)

[58] Bar-Or, O. (2000)

[59] Astrand,, P-O. (1952)

[60] Daniels J, Oldridge N, Nagle F, While B. (1978)

[61] Bitar A, Vernet J, Coudert J, Vermorel M. (2000)

[62] Sun M, Gower BA, Bartolucci AA, Hunter GR, Figueroa-Colon R, Goran MI. (2001)

[63] Holliday, MA. (1971)

[64] Frost G, Dowling J, Dyson K, Bar-Or O. (1991)

[65] Unnithan, V,. & Eston R. (1990)

[66] Butterfield, GE. &and Calloway, DH. (1984)

[67] Lemon, PW. (1998)

[68] Lemon PW, Berardi JM and Noreen EE. (2002)

[69] Rennie, MJ. (2001)

[70] Rennie, MJ., Bohe, J. &and Wolfe, RR. (2002)

[71] Rennie, MJ. &and Tipton, KD. (2000)

[72] Biolo G, Tipton KD, Klein S, et al. (1997)

[73] Bos C, Benamouzig R, Bruhat A, et al. (2000)

[74] Bouthegourd JC, Roseau SM, Makarios-Lahham L, et al. (2002)

[75] Burke DG, Chilibeck PD, Davidson KS, et al. (2001)

[76] Campbell WW, Trappe TA, Wolfe RR, et al. (2001)

[77] Castaneda C, Gordon PL, Fielding RA, et al. (2000)

[78] Chandler RM, Byrne HK, Patterson JG et al. (1994)4

[79] Demling, RH. &and DeSanti, L. (2000)

[80] Forslund AH, El Khoury AE, Olsson RM, et al. (1999)

[81] Layman, DK. (2002)2

[82] Layman DK, Shiue H, Sather C, et al. (2003)

[83] Lemon PW, Berardi JM &and Noreen EE. (2002)

[84] Long SJ, Jeffcoat AR &and Millward DJ. (2000)

[85] Rowlands DS and Hopkins WG. (2002)

[86] Schutz Y, Bray G &and Margen S. (1987)

[87] Robinson DM, Jaccard C, Persaud C, Jackson AA, Jequire E, Shutz Y. (1990)

[88] Schultz Y, Bray G, Margen S. (1987)

[89] Thorne, A,. & Wahren, J. (1989)

[90] Forslund AH, El Khoury AE, Olsson RM, et al. (1999)

[91] Gutniack M, Grill V, Efendic S. (1986)

[92] Schmid R, Schusdziarra V, Schulte-Frohlinde E, Maier V, Classen M. (1989)

[93] Yamauchi, K. (1988)

[94] Carlson MG, Snead WL, Campbell PJ. (1993)

[95] Girard, J. (1994)

[96] Forslund AH, El Khoury AE, Olsson RM, et al. (1999)

[97] Castaneda C, Gordon PL, Fielding RA, Evans WJ, Crim MC. (2000)

[98] Carli G, Bonifazi M, Lodi L, Lupo C, Martelli G, Viti A. (1992)

[99] Kraemer WJ, Volek JS, Bush JA, Putukian M, Sebastianelli WJ. (1998)

[100] Wolfe, BM. (1995)

[101]Wolfe, BM., & Piche, LA. (1999)

[102] Layman DK, Boileau RA, Erickson DJ, Painter JE, Shiue H, Sather C, Christou DD. (2003)

[103] Layman DK, Shiue H, Sather C, Erickson DJ, Baum J. (2003)

[104] Roy BD, Fowles JR, Hill R, Tarnopolsky MA. (2000)

[105] Tarnopolsky MA, Atkinson SA, MacDougall JD, Chesley A, Phillips S, Schwarcz HP. (1992)

[106] Brandle, E., Sieberth, HG. and& Hautmann, RE. (1996)

[107] Poortmans, JR. &and Dellalieux, O. (2000)

[108] Skov AR, Toubro S, Bulow J, et al. (1999)

[109] Ziegler PJ, Khoo CS, Kris-Etherton PM, Jonnalagadda SS, Sherr B, Nelson JA. (1998)

[110] Westman EC, Mavropoulos J, Yancy WS, et al. (2003)

[111] Bishop NC, Blannin AK, Walsh NP, et al. (1999)

[112] Hawley, JA. (2002)

[113] Lambert, EV. &and Goedecke, JH. (2003)

[114] Lambert EV, Hawley JA, Goedecke J, et al. (1997)

[115] Maughan RJ, Greenhaff PL, Leiper JB, et al. (1997)

[116] Miller, SL. & and Wolfe, RR. (1999)

[117] Stepto NK, Carey AL, Staudacher HM, et al. (2002)

[118] Hawley JA, Schabort EJ, Noakes TD, et al. (1997)

[119] Rauch LH, Rodger I, Wilson GR, et al. (1995)

[120] Tarnopolsky MA, Atkinson SA, Phillips SM, et al. (1995)

[121] Bishop NC, Blannin AK, Walsh NP, et al. (1999)

[122] Bishop NC, Gleeson M, Nicholas CW, et al. (2002)

[123] Bishop NC, Walsh NP, Haines DL, et al. (2001)

[124] Blom PC, Hostmark AT, Vaage O, et al. (1987)

[125] Ivy JL, Goforth HW, Jr., Damon BM, et al. (2002)

[126] Kuo CH, Hunt DG, Ding Z, et al. (1999)

[127] Miller, SL. &and Wolfe, RR. (1999)

[128] Rasmussen BB, Tipton KD, Miller SL, et al. (2002)

[129] van Loon LJ, Kruijshoop M, Verhagen H, et al. (2000)

[130] Bohl CH and Volpe SL. Magnesium and exercise. (2002)

[131] Rowland TW, Auchinachie JA, Keenan TJ, Green GM. (1987)

[132] Mahon AD, Duncan GE, Howe CA, del Corral P. (1997)

[133] Hebestreit H, Meyer F, Htay-Htay, Heigenhauser GJ, Bar-Or O. (1996)

[134] Gaul CA, Docherty D, Cicchini R. (1995)

[135] Timmons BW, Bar-Or O, Riddell MC. (2003)

[136] Bell, RD, MacDougall JD, Billeter R, &and Howald H. (1980)

[137] Berg A, Kim SS, Keul J. (1986)

[138] Willett, WC. &and Leibel, RL. (2002)

[139] Beermann C, Jelinek J, Reinecker T, et al. (2003)

[140] Garcia-Lorda P, Megias R, I and Salas-Salvado J. (2003)

[141] Kriketos AD, Robertson RM, Sharp TA, et al. (2001)

[142] Parrish CC, Pathy DA, Parkes JG, et al. (1991)

[143] Terpstra, AH. (2004)

[144] Dorgan JF, Judd JT, Longcope C, et al. (1996)

[145] Reed MJ, Cheng RW, Simmonds M, et al. (1987)

[146] Delarue J, Couet C, Cohen R, et al. (1996)

[147] Delarue J, Couet C, Cohen R, et al. (1996)

[148] Garcia-Lorda P, Megias R, I and Salas-Salvado J. (2003)

[149] Lambert EV, Hawley JA, Goedecke J, et al. (1997)

[150] Terpstra, AH. (2004)

[151] Ford, F. (2002)

[152] Stark, AH. &and Madar, Z. (2002)

[153] Ascherio, A. &and Willett, WC. (1997)

[154] Shapiro, S. (1997)

[155] Ascherio, A. &and Willett, WC. (1997)

[156] Simopoulos, AP. (1989)

[157] Fletcher RH, Fairfield KM. (2002)

[158] Cupisti A, D'Alessandro C, Castrogiovanni S, Barale A, Morelli E. (2002)

[159] Rankinen T, Fogelholm M, Kujala U, Rauramaa R, Uusitupa M. (1995)

[160] Anyanwu EC, Ehiri JE, Kanu I. (2005)

[161] Guilland JC, Penaranda T, Gallet C, Boggio V, Fuchs F, Klepping J. (1989)

[162] Anyanwu, EC., Ehiri, JE., & Kanu, I. (2005)

[163] Fogelholm M, Ruokonen I, Laakso J, Vuorimaa T, Himberg J. (1993)

[164] McDonald, R., & Keen, C. (1988)

[165] Rowland, TX. (1996)

[166] Clarkson, PM., & Haymes, EM. (1995)

[167] Matovic, V., Fontana, D., Tominac, C., Goel, P., Chestnut, C.

[168] Bauer, S., Jakob, E., Berg, A.. &, Keul, J. (1994)

[169] Fletcher, RH. &, Fairfield, KM. (2002)

[170] Sawka, MN., & Pandolf, KB. (1990)

[171] American College of Sports Medicine. (1996)

[172] Meyer, F. &, Bar-Or O. (1994)

[173] American Academy of Pediatrics. (2000)

[174] Bar-Or, O. (1990)

[175] Meyer F, Bar-Or O, MacDougall D, Heigenhauswer GJF. (1992)

[176] Wilk, B., Yuxiu, H., & Bar-Or, O. (2002)

[177] Wilk, B., & Bar-Or O. (1996)

[178] Bielinski, R., Schutz, Y. and& Jequier, E. (1985)

[179] Carter, SL., Rennie, C. &and Tarnopolsky, MA. (2001)

[180] Forslund AH, El Khoury AE, Olsson RM, et al. (1999)

[181] Horton TJ, Pagliassotti MJ, Hobbs K, et al. (1998)

[182] Rowlands, DS &and Hopkins, WG. (2002)

[183] van Loon LJ, Greenhaff PL, Constantin-Teodosiu D, et al. (2001)

[184] Cheuvront SN, Carter R, III &and Sawka MN. (2003).

[185] Coyle, EF. (1999)

[186] Kay D and Marino FE. (2000)

[187] Maughan, RJ. (1991)

[188] Noakes, TD. (1993)

[189] Wong, SH., Williams, C. &and Adams, N. (2000)

[190] Casey A, Mann R, Banister K, et al. (2000)

[191] Fournier PA, Brau L, Ferreira LD, et al. (2002)

[192] Ivy, JL. (1998)

[193] Pascoe DD, Costill DL, Fink WJ, et al. (1993)

[194] Pascoe, DD. &and Gladden, LB. (1996)

[195] Price TB, Rothman DL, Taylor R, et al. (1994)

[196] Zachwieja JJ, Costill DL. &and Fink WJ. (1993)

[197] Borsheim E, Tipton KD, Wolf SE, et al. (2002)

[198] Levenhagen DK, Gresham JD, Carlson MG, et al. (2001)

[199] Rasmussen BB, Tipton KD, Miller SL, et al. (2000)

[200] Rennie MJ and Tipton KD. (2000)

[201] Tipton KD, Borsheim E, Wolf SE, et al. (2003)

[202] Tipton KD, Ferrando AA, Phillips SM, et al. (1999)

[203] Tipton KD, Rasmussen BB, Miller SL, et al. (2001)

[204] Tipton KD, Borsheim E, Wolf SE, et al. (2003)

[205] Ivy JL, Res PT, Sprague RC, et al. (2003)

[206] Noakes, TD. (1993)

[207] Ivy JL, Goforth HW, Jr., Damon BM, et al. (2002)

[208] Levenhagen DK, Gresham JD, Carlson MG, et al. (2001)

[209] Rasmussen BB, Tipton KD, Miller SL, et al. (2000)

[210] Tipton KD, Borsheim E, Wolf SE, et al. (2003)

[211] Tipton KD, Ferrando AA, Phillips SM, et al. (1999)

[212] van Loon LJ, Kruijshoop M, Verhagen H, et al. (2000)

[213] van Loon LJ, Saris WH, Kruijshoop M, et al. (2000)

[214] Hawley JA, Schabort EJ, Noakes TD, & Dennis SC. (1997)

[215] Kiens, B. (2001)

[216] Forgac, MT. (1979)

[217] Thomas, DE., Brotherhood, JR., Brand, JC. (1991)

[218] Spring B, Chiodo J, Harden M, Bourgeois MJ, Mason JD, & Lutherer L. (1989)

[219] Deutz, RC., Benardot, D., Martin, DE., & Cody, MM. (2000)

[220] Remer, T. (2001)

[221] Remer, T., Dimitriou, T., & Manz, F. (2003)

References

Ahtikoski, A.M., Koskinen, S.O.A., Virtanen, P., Kovanen, V. & Takala, T.E.S. (2001). Regulation of synthesis of fibrillar collagens in rat skeletal muscle during immobilization in shortened and lengthened positions. *Acta Physiologica Scandinavica, 172(2),* 131-140.

Aizawa, K., Akimoto, T., Inoue, H., Kimura, F., Joo, M., Murai, F. & Mesaki, N. Resting serum dehydroepiandrosterone sulfate level increases after 8-week resistance training among young females. Eur J Appl Physiol. 90(5-6):575-80, 2003.

Akeson, W.H., Amiel, D. & LaViolette, D. (1967). The connective tissue response to immobility: A study of the chondroitin 4- and 6-sulfate and dermatan sulfate changes in periarticular connective tissue of control and immobilized knees of dogs. *Clinical Orthopedics and Related Research, 51,* 183-197.

Akeson, W.H., Amiel, D. & Woo, S. (1980). Immobility effects on synovial joints: The pathomechanics of joints contracture. *Biorheology, 17(1/2),* 95-110.

Akeson, W.H., Amiel, D., Mechanics, G.L., Woo, S., Harwood, F.L. & Hammer, M.L. (1977). Collagen crosslinking alteration in joint contractures: Changes in reducible crosslinks in periartiuclare connective tissue collagen after nine weeks of immobilization. *Connective Tissue Research, 5(1),* 15-20).

Alexander, R.M. (1975). *Biomechanics.* London: Chapman and Hall.

Alter, M. (1996). *Science of Flexibility*. Champaign: Human Kinetics.

Alter, J. (2004) *Science of Flexibility* (3rd Ed.). Champaign, IL: Human Kinetics.

Anderson, J., Almeida-Silveira, & Perot, C. (1987). Reflex and muscular adaptations in rat soleus muscle after hindlimb suspension. *J Appl Physiol, 62,* 2168-2173, 8750-7587/87.

Anyanwu, EC., Ehiri, JE., & Kanu, I. (2005). Biochemical evaluation of antioxidant function after a controlled optimum physical exercise among adolescents. *Int J Adolesc Med Health, 17(1),* 57-66.

Armstrong, B.J. Kirby, & J.R. Welsman. (1997). London: Spon.

Asai, H, Aoki, J. (1996). Force development of dynamic and static contractions in children and adults. *Int J Sports Med., 17(3),* 170-4.

Ascherio, A., & Willett, WC. (1997). Health effects of trans fatty acids. *American Journal of Clinical Nutrition, 66,* 1006S-1010S.

Ascherio, A., & Willett, WC. (1997). Health effects of trans fatty acids. *American Journal of Clinical Nutrition, 66,* 1006S-1010S.

Assaiante, C. (1998). Development of Locomotor Balance Control in Healthy Children, Neuroscience and Biobehavioral reviews. *22 (4),* 527-532.

Astrand, P-O. (1952). Experimental studies of physical working capacity in relation to sex and age. Copenhagen: Munksgaard.

Avela, J., H. Kyrolainen, and PV. Komi. (1999). Alterd reflex sensitivity after repeated and prolonged passive muscle stretching. *Journal of Applied Physiology*, 86(4), 1283-1291.

Avlonitou, E. (1994). Somatometric variables for preadolescent swimmers. *J Sports Med Phys Fitness, 34(2),* 185-91.

Bachrach, R.M. 1987. Injuries to dancer's spine. *Dance Medicine*. Chicago: Pluribus Press.

Baechle, T., Earle, R., & Wathen, D. (2000). Resistance Training. *Essentials of Strength and Conditioning.* Champaign: Human Kinetics.

Baker, J., et al. (2000). The relationship between coaching behaviours and sport anxiety in athletes. *J. Sci. Med. Sport., 3,* 110-119.

Bale, P, Mayhew, JL, Piper, FC, Ball TE, Willman, MK. (1992). Biological and performance variables in relation to age in male and female adolescent athletes. *J Sports Med Phys Fitness, 32(2),* 142-8.

Bamman, MM., Clarke, MS., Feeback, DL., et al. (1998). Impact of resistance exercise during bed rest on skeletal muscle sarcopenia and myosin isofor distribution. *J Appl Physiol, 84,* 157–63.

Baquet, G., et al. (2002). Effects of high intensity intermittent training on peak VO2 in prepubertal children. *International journal of sports medicine, 23 (6),* 439-444.

Baquet, G., et al. (2003). Endurance training and aerobic fitness in young people. *Sports Med., 33(15),* 1127-1143.

Bar-Or, O., & Rowland, TW. (2004). *Pediatric Exercise Medicine: from physiologic principles to health care application. 1st Ed.* Champaign: Human Kinetics.

Bar-Or, O. (1990). Temperature regulation during exercise in children and adolescents. *Lamb DR, Gisolfi CV, eds. Perspectives in exercise science and sports medicine: fluid homeostasis during exercise*. Indianapolis: Benchmark Press, 1990.

Bar-Or, O. (2000). Nutrition for child and adolescent athletes. *GSSI Sports Science Exchange, 13(2).*

Basford, JR. (1985). Weightlifting, weight training and injuries. *Orthopedics, 8(8),* 1051-6.

Battinelli, T. (2000). Body Build and Body Build Indices. *Physique, Fitness, and Performance.* Boca Raton: CRC Press.

Bauer, S., Jakob, E., Berg, A., & Keul, J. (1994). Energy and nutritional intake in young weight lifters before and after nutritional counseling. *Schweiz Z Med Traumatol, (3)*, 35-42.

Beauchamp, M., et al. (2002). Pre-competition imagery, self-efficacy and performance in collegiate golfers. *J. Sports Sci., 20*, 697-705.

Beermann, C., Jelinek, J., Reinecker, T., et al. (2003). Short term effects of dietary medium-chain fatty acids and n-3 long-chain polyunsaturated fatty acids on the fat metabolism of healthy volunteers. *Lipids in Health and Disease, 2,*10.

Bell, RD., MacDougall, JD., Billeter, R., & Howald, H. (1980). Muscle fiber types and morphometric analysis of skeletal muscle in six-year-old children. *Med Sci Sports Exer., 12*, 28-31.

Benjamin, H, Glow, K. (2003). Strength Training for Children and Adolescents. *Phys Sports Med., 31(9)*. www.physsportsmed.com/issues/2003/0903/benjamin.htm.

Berg, A., et al. (1986). Skeletal muscle enzyme activities in healthy young subjects. *Int. J. Sports Med., 7*, 236-239.

Berg, A., Kim, SS., & Keul, J. (1986). Skeletal muscle enzyme activities in healthy young subjects. *Int J Sports Med., 7(4)*, 236-9.

Berthoud, HR. (2002). Multiple neural systems controlling food intake and body weight. *Neuroscience and Biobehavioral Reviews, 26*, 393-428.

Beunen, G. and Malina, R.M. (1998). Growth and physical performance relative to the timing of the adolescent spurt. *Exerc. Sport Sci Rev., 16*, 503-540.

Blair, A., et al. (1993). Imagery effects on the performance of skilled and novice soccer players. *J. Sports Sci., 11*, 95-101.

Bloomfield, J., Ackland, T.R., Elliott, B.C. (1994). Applied anatomy and biomechanics I sport. *Blackwell Scientific Publications* (pp. 263, 264).

Biel, Andrew. *Trail Guide to the Body*, Andrew Biel, Boulder, 1997.

Bielinski, R., Schutz, Y., & Jequier, E. (1985). Energy metabolism during the postexercise recovery in man. *American Journal of Clinical Nutrition, 42*, 69-82.

Biolo, G., Declan-Fleming, RY., & Wolfe, RR. (1995). Physiologic hyperinsulinemia stimulates protein synthesis and enhances transport of selected amino acids in human skeletal muscle. *Journal of Clinical Investigation, 95*, 811-819.

Biolo, G., Maggi, SP., Williams, BD., et al. (1995). Increased rates of muscle protein turnover and amino acid transport after resistance exercise in humans. *American Journal of Physiology, 268*, E514-E520.

Biolo, G., Tipton, KD., Klein, S., et al. (1997). An abundant supply of amino acids enhances the metabolic effect of exercise on muscle protein. *American Journal of Physiology, 273,* E122-E129.

Birrer, R, Levine, R. (1987). Performance Parameters in Children and Adolescent Athletes. *Sports Med., 4,* 211-27.

Bishop, NC., Blannin, AK., Walsh, NP., et al. (1999). Nutritional aspects of immunosuppression in athletes. *Sports Medicine, 28,* 151-176.

Bishop, NC., Gleeson, M., Nicholas, CW., et al. (2002). Influence of carbohydrate supplementation on plasma cytokine and neutrophil degranulation responses to high intensity intermittent exercise. *International Journal of Sports Nutrition and Exercise Metabolism 2002, 12,* 145-156.

Bishop, NC., Walsh, NP., Haines, DL., et al. (2001). Pre-exercise carbohydrate status and immune responses to prolonged cycling: II. Effect on plasma cytokine concentration. *International Journal of Sports Nutrition and Exercise Metabolism, 11,* 503-512.

Bitar, A., Vernet, J., Coudert, J., & Vermorel, M. (2000). Longitudinal changes in body composition, physical capacities and energy expenditure in boys and girls during the onset of puberty. *Eur J Nutr., 39(4),*157-63.

Blimkie, CJ. (1993). Resistance training during preadolescents: Issues and controversies. *Sports Med., 15(6),* 389-407.

Blom, PC., Hostmark, AT., Vaage, O., et al. (1987). Effect of different post-exercise sugar diets on the rate of muscle glycogen synthesis. *Medicine and Science in Sports and Exercise, 19,* 491-496.

Blomstrand, E. (2001). Amino acids and central fatigue. *Amino Acids, 20,* 25-34.

Bloom, W., Fawcett, D.W. & Raviola, E. (1994). *A textbook of histology.* 12th ed. New York: Chapman Hall.

Bogduk, Nikolai. (1999). *Clinical anatomy of the lumbar spine and sacrum.* London: Churchill Livingston.

Bohl, CH., & Volpe, SL. (2002). Magnesium and exercise. *Critical Review of Food Science and Nutrition, 42,* 533-563.

Boisseau, N., & Delamarche, P. (2000). Metabolic and Hormonal Responses to Exercise in Children and Adolescents. *Sports Medicine, 30 (6),* 405-422.

Bompa, T. (1994). *Theory and methodology of training.* Dubuque: Kendell Hunt.

Bompa, T. (2000). *Total training for young champions.* Champaign: Human Kinetics.

Bonjour, JQ, Theinzt, G, Bucks, B. (1991). Critical years and stages of puberty for spinal and femoral bone mass accumulation during adolescence. *J Clin Endocrinol Metab., 73,* 555-63.

Borsheim, E., Tipton, KD., Wolf, SE., et al. (2002). Essential amino acids and muscle protein recovery from resistance exercise. *American Journal of Physiology Endocrinology and Metabolism, 283,* E648-E657.

Bos, C., Benamouzig, R., Bruhat, A., et al. (2000). Short-term protein and energy supplementation activates nitrogen kinetics and accretion in poorly nourished elderly subjects. *American Journal of Clinical Nutrition, 71,* 1129-1137.

Bouthegourd, JC., Roseau, SM., Makarios-Lahham, L., et al. (2002). A preexercise alpha-lactalbumin-enriched whey protein meal preserves lipid oxidation and decreases adiposity in rats. *American Journal of Physiology Endocrinology and Metabolism, 283,* E565-E572.

Brady, TA, Cahill, BR, Bodnar, LM. (1982). Weight training-related injuries in the high school athlete. *Am J Sports Med., 10(1),* 1-5.

Brandle, E., Sieberth, HG., & Hautmann, RE. (1996). Effect of chronic dietary protein intake on the renal function in healthy subjects. *European Journal of Clinical Nutrition, 50,* 734-740.

Brooks, G.A. (1988). Lactate production during exercise: oxidizable substrate versus fatigue agent, *Sports Science Periodical on Research and Technology in Sport, 8 (1),* 1-11.

Brown, EW, Kimball, RG. (1983) Medical history associated with adolescent powerlifting. *Pediatrics, 72(5),* 636-44.

Brown, LE. (1998). Strength Testing in Children. *Strength and Conditioning, 20(5),* 75.

Brown, T., Vescovi, J. Is stepping back really counterproductive? *NSCA Journal, 26(1),* 42-44.

Bruns, W, Maffulli, N. (2000) Lower limb injuries in children in sports. *Clin Sports Med., 19(4),* 637-62.

Bryant, S. (1984). Flexibility and stretching. *The physician and the sports medicine, 12(2),* 171.

Burke, DG., Chilibeck, PD., Davidson, KS., et al. (2001). The effect of whey protein supplementation with and without creatine monohydrate combined with resistance training on lean tissue mass and muscle strength. *International Journal of Sports Nutrition and Exercise Metabolism, 11,* 349-364.

Burke, J., et. al. (1994). Comparison of effects of two interval-training programmes on lactate and ventilatory thresholds. *Brit. J. Sports Med., 28 (1),* 18-21

Burke, LM. (2001). Energy needs of athletes. *Canadian Journal of Applied Physiology, 26,* Suppl: S202-S219.

Burkhardt, E, Barton, B, Garhammer, J. (1990). Maximal impact and propulsion forces during jumping and explosive lifting exercises. *J Appl Sport Sci Res., 4(3),* 107.

Butterfield, GE., & Calloway, DH. (1984). Physical activity improves protein utilization in young men. *British Journal of Nutrition, 51,* 171-184.

Buyukyazi, G., Karamizrak, SO., & Islegen, C. (2003). Effects of continuous and interval running training on serum growth and cortisol hormones in junior male basketball players. *Acta Physiol Hung., 90(1),* 69-79.

Cailliet, R. (1988*). Soft Tissue Pain and Disability*. Philadelphia: FA Davis.

Caine, D., Howe, W., Ross, W. & Bergman, G. (1997). Does repetitive physical loading inhibit radial growth in female gymnasts? *Clin J Sports Med., 7(4),* 302-8.

Campbell, WW., Trappe, TA., Wolfe, RR., et al. (2001). The recommended dietary allowance for protein may not be adequate for older people to maintain skeletal muscle. *Journal of Gerontology Series A Biological Sciences and Medical Sciences, 56,* M373-M380.

Cantell, MH., Smyth, MM., Ahonen, TP. (1994). Clumsiness in adolescence: Educational, motor, and social outcomes of motor delay detected at 5 years. *Adapted Physical Activity Quarterly, 11(2),* 115–129.

Carli, G., Bonifazi, M., Lodi, L., Lupo, C., Martelli, G., & Viti, A. (1992). Changes in the exercise-induced hormone response to branched chain amino acid administration. *Eur J Appl Physiol Occup Physiol, 64(3),* 272-7.

Carlson, MG., Snead, WL., & Campbell, PJ. (1993). Regulation of free fatty acid metabolism by glucagon. *J Clin Endocrinol Metab, 77,* 11-15.

Carron, A., et al. (2002). Team cohesion and team success in sport. *J. Sports Sci., 20,*:119-26.

Carter, SL., Rennie, C., & Tarnopolsky, MA. (2001). Substrate utilization during endurance exercise in men and women after endurance training. *American Journal of Physiology Endocrinology and Metabolism, 280,* E898-E907.

Casey, A., Mann, R., Banister, K., et al. (2000). Effect of carbohydrate ingestion on glycogen resynthesis in human liver and skeletal muscle, measured by (13)C MRS. *American Journal of Physiology Endocrinology and Metabolism, 278,* E65-E75.

Castaneda, C., Gordon, PL., Fielding, RA., et al. (2000). Marginal protein intake results in reduced plasma IGF-I levels and skeletal muscle fiber atrophy in elderly women. Journal *of Nutrition in Health and Aging, 4,* 85-90.

Chandler, RM., Byrne, HK., Patterson, JG., et al. (1994). Dietary supplements affect the anabolic hormones after weight-training exercise. *Journal of Applied Physiology, 76,* 839-845.

Chek, P. (2003). *A Neurodevelopmental Approach to Conditioning, Vol I-II* [Cassette] California: Vista.

Chek, P. (2004). *How to Eat, Move and Be Healthy!* San Diego: Chek Institute.

Chek, P. (2000). *Movement That Matters.* California: Encinitas.

Chek, P. (2001 August). *Paul Chek on Exercise, Training and Rehab,* Course Handouts.

Cheng, JC, Maffulli, N, Leung, SS, Lee, WT, Chan, KM. (1999). Axial and peripheral bone mineral acquisition: a 3-year longitudinal study in Chinese adolescents. *Eur J Pediatr., 158(6),* 506-12.

Cheng-Ye Ji, Seiji Ohsawa. (1996). Changes in somatotype during growth in Chinese youth 7-18 years of age. *Am J Hum Bio., 8(3),* 347-359.

Chesley, A., MacDougall, J.D., Tarnopolsky, M.A., et al. (1992). Changes in human muscle protein synthesis after resistance exercise. *Journal of Applied Physiology, 73,* 1383-1388.

Cheuvront, SN., Carter, R. III, & Sawka, MN. (2003). Fluid balance and endurance exercise performance. *Current Sports Medicine Reports, 2,* 202-208.

Clark, J.E., Phillips, S.J., & Petersen, R. (1989) Developmental stability in jumping. *Developmental Psychology, 25,* 929-935.

Clark, JE. On becoming skillful: Patterns and constraints. *Research Quarterly, 66,* 173-183, 199.

Clark, M.A. & Russell, A.M. (2002). NASM OPT optimum performance training for the performance enhancement specialist. *National Academy of Sports Medicine, Course Manuel.*

Clark, M.A. (2001). Integrated training for the new millennium. *National Academy of Sports Medicine, Thousands Oaks.*

Clarkson, P.M., & Haymes, E.M. (1995). Exercise and mineral status of athletes, calcium, magnesium, phosphorus, and iron. *Med Sci Sports Exerc., 27,* 831.

Climatic heat stress and the exercising child and adolescent. (2000). *American Academy of Pediatrics. Pediatrics, 106.* 158.

Cohen, N.P., Foster, R.J. & Mow, VC. (1998). Composition and dynamics of articular cartilage: Structure, functional and maintaining healthy state. *J Othop Sport Phys Ther, 28,* 203.

Conley, M. (2000). Bioenergetics of exercise and training, essentials of strength training and conditioning. *National Strength and Conditioning Association.*

Conroy, B.P., Craemer, W.J., Maresh, C.M., Fleck, S.J., Stone, M.H., Fry, A.C., Miller, P.D. & Dalsky, G.P. (1993) Bone mineral density in elite junior Olympic weightlifters. *Med Sci Sports Exerc., 25(10),* 1103-9.

Cook, PC, Leit, ME. (1995) Issues in the pediatric athlete. *Orthop Clin North Am., 26(3),* 453-64.

Counil, F.P., et al., (2003). Training of aerobic and anaerobic fitness in children with asthma, J. *Pediatr., 142(2),* 179-84

Coyle, EF. (1992). Physiological determinants of endurance exercise performance. *Journal of Science and Medicine in Sport, 2,* 181-189.

Cratt, BJ. (1995). *Clumsy child syndrome: descriptions, evaluation, and remediation.* Newark: Gordon and Breach Publishing Group.

Creatsas,G., Salakos, N., Averkiou, M., Miras, K., & Aravantinos, D. (1992). Endocrinological profile of oligomenorrheic strenuously exercising adolescents. *Int J Gynaecol Obstet., 38(3),* 215-21.

Cremar, MA., Rosloneic, EF., & Kang, AH. (1998). The cartilage collagens: a review of their structure, organization and role in the pathogenesis of experimental arthritis in animals and in humans rheumatic disease. *J Mol Med, 76,* 275.

Culav, EM., Clark, CH., & Merilee, MJ. (1999). Connective tissues: Matrix composition and its relevance to physical therapy. *Phys Ther., 79,* 308.

Cupisti, A., D'Alessandro, C., Castrogiovanni, S., Barale, A., & Morelli, E. (2002). Nutrition knowledge and dietary composition in Italian adolescent female athletes and non-athletes. *Int J Sport Nutr Exerc Metab, 12,* 207.

Curwin, SL. (1996). Tendon injuries: Pathophysiology and treatment. *Athletic Injuries and Rehabilitation.* Philadelphia: WB Saunders.

Daniels, J., Oldridge, N., Nagle, F., & While, B. (1978). Differences and changes in VO_2 among young runners 10 to 18 years of age. *Med. Sci. Sports, 10,* 200-203.

Davis, JM., Alderson, NL., & Welsh, RS. (2000). Serotonin and central nervous system fatigue: nutritional considerations. *American Journal of Clinical Nutrition, 72,* 573S-578S.

Delamarche, P., Gratas-Delamarche, A., Monnier, M., Mayet, MH., Koubi, HE., & Favier, R. (1994). Glucoregulation and hormonal changes during prolonged exercise in boys and girls. *Eur J Appl Physiol., 68(1),* 3-8.

Delarue, J., Couet, C., Cohen, R., et al. (1996). Effects of fish oil on metabolic responses to oral fructose and glucose loads in healthy humans. *American Journal of Physiology, 270,* E353-E362.

Demling, RH., & DeSanti, L. (2000). Effect of a hypocaloric diet, increased protein intake and resistance training on lean mass gains and fat mass loss in overweight police officers. *Annals of Nutrition and Metabolism, 44,* 21-29.

DeStefano, R.A. (2000). Changes in body composition after a 12-wk aerobic exercise program in obese boys. *Pediatric Diabetes, 1(2),* 61-65.

Deutz, RC., Benardot, D., Martin, DE., & Cody, MM. (2000). Relationship between energy deficits and body composition in elite female gymnasts and runners. *Med Sci Sports Exerc., 32(3)*, 659-68.

Dishion, T., et al. (2005). Predicting early adolescent gang involvement from middle school adaptation. *J. Clin. Child Adolesc. Psychol., 34,* 62-73.

Doherty, TJ, et al. (1992). Effects of aging on the motor unit: a brief review. *Can J Appl Physiol, 18,* 331-358.

Dohoney, P, Chromiak, J, Lemire, D, Abadie, B, Kovacs, C. (2002) Prediction of one repetition maximum (1 RM) strength from a 4-6 RM and a 7-10 RM submaximal strength test in healthy young adult males. *J Ex Phys., 5(3),* 54-9.

Doi, T., Matsuo, T., Sugawara, M., et al. (2001). New approach for weight reduction by a combination of diet, light resistance exercise and the timing of ingesting a protein supplement. *Asia Pacific Journal of Clinical Nutrition, 10,* 226-232.

Dombovy, ML., Bonekat, HW., Williams, TJ., & Staats, BA. (1987). Exercise performance and ventilatory response in the menstrual cycle. *Med. Sci. Sports Exerc., 19,*111–7.

Donatelle, J.M. (1977). Growth of the corticospinal tract and the development of placing reactions in the postnatal rat. *J Comp Neurol., 175(2),* 207-31.

Dorgan, JF., Judd, JT., Longcope, C., et al. (1996). Effects of dietary fat and fiber on plasma and urine androgens and estrogens in men: a controlled feeding study. *American Journal of Clinical Nutrition, 64,* 850-855.

Dotan, R., Falk, B. & Raz, A. (2000). Intensity effect of active recovery from glycolytic exercise on decreasing blood lactate concentration in prepubertal children. Med. And Sci in Sports and Exerc (ACSM).

Dowshen, S (Reviewer). (2001). Strength Training and Your Child. *The Nemours Center for Children's Health Media.* http://kidshealth.org/parent/nutrition_fit/fitness/strength_training.html.

Drabik, J. (1996). *Children and Sports Training: How future champions should exercise to be healthy, fit, and happy.* Island Pond: Stadion Publishing Company.

Duarte, J.A., et. al. (1999). Exercise-induced signs of muscle overuse in children. *Int. J. Sports Med., 20 (2),*103-108.

Dube, J. J., Andreacci, J. L., Robertson, R. J., Goss, F. L., & Arslanian, S. (2002). Comparison of substrate utilization during treadmill exercise in children varying in body mass index. **Medicine and Science in Sports and Exercise, 34(5),** Supplement abstract 782.

Duchateau, J. (1995). Bed rest induces neural and contractile adaptations in triceps surae. *Med Sci Sports Exer., 27,*1581–9.

Duche, P., Ratel, S., et.al. (2002) Effect of age on the time course of cycling peak power during repeated sprints. *Medicine and Science in Sports and Exercise, 34 (5),* Supplement abstract 793.

Duclos, M., Corcuff, JB., Arsac, L., Moreau-Gaudry, F., Rashedi, M., Roger, P., Tabarin, A., & Manier, G. (1998). Corticotroph axis sensitivity after exercise in endurance-trained athletes. *Clin Endocrinol., 48(4),* 493-501.

Durant, R.H., Pendergras, R.A., Donner, J., Seymore, C. & Gaillard, G. (1991). Adolescents; attrition from school sponsored sports. *Am J Dis Child., 145(10),* 1119-23.

Dvorkin, LS. (1992). *Weightlifting and Age (Scientific and pedagogical fundamentals of a multi-year system of training junior weightlifters).* Livonia: Sportivny Press.

Eldren, H.R. (1968(. Physical properties of collagen fibers. *International Review of Connective Tissue Research, 4,* 248-283

Erickson, et al. (1973). Muscle metabolism and enzyme activities after training in boys 11-13 years old, *Acta. Physiol. Scand., 87,* 485-497.

Esmarck, B., Andersen, JL., Olsen, S., et al. (2001). Timing of postexercise protein intake is important for muscle hypertrophy with resistance training in elderly humans. *Journal of Physiology, 535,* 301-311.

Beachle, T., & Roger, W. (2002). *Essentials of strength training and conditioning.* (NSCA).

Evans, RC. (1994). *Illustrated Essentials In Orthopedic Physical Assessment.* Mosby: St. Louis.

Faigenbaum, AD., Kraemer, WJ., et. al. (1996). Youth Resistance Training: Position Statement Paper and Literature Review. *Strength Cond., 18(6),* 62-76.

Faigenbaum, AD., Loud, RL., O'Connell, J., Glover, S., O'Connell, J., Westcott, WL. (2001). Effects of different resistance training protocols on upper-body strength and endurance development in children. *J Strength Cond. Res., 15(4),* 459-65.

Faigenbaum, AD., Milliken, LA., Westcott, WL. (2003). Maximal Strength Testing in Healthy Children. J *Strength Cond. Res., 17(1),* 162-6.

Falk, B., Bar-Or, O., & MacDougall, JD. (1991). Aldosterone and prolactin response to exercise in the heat in circumpubertal boys. *J Appl Physiol., 71(5),* 1741-5, 1991.

Falk, B. Sadres, E, Constantini, N, Zigel, L, Lidor R, Eliakim, A. (2002). The association between adiposity and the response to resistance training among pre- and early-pubertal boys. *J Pediatr Endocrinol Metab., 15(5),* 97-606.

Fayt, C., et al. (1993). Children's and adults learning of a visuomanual coordination: role of ongoing visual feedback and of spatial errors as a function of age. *Perceptual and Motor Skills, 77 (2),* 659-69).

Feldman, D., Shrier, M., Rossignol, & Abenhaim, L. (1999). Adolescent growth is not associates with changes in flexibility. *Clinical Journal of Sport Medicine, 9(1),* 24-29.

Fellmann, N. & Coudert, J. (1994). Physiology of muscular exercise in children. *Arch Pediatr., 1(9),* 827-40.

Ferrel, C., et al. (2001). Coordination in childhood: modifications of visuomotor representations in 6-11 year old children. *Exp Brain Res., 138,* 313-321.

Fleck, SJ, Falkel, JE. (1986). Value of resistance training for the reduction of sports injuries. *Sports Med., 3(1),* 61-8.

Fletcher, RH., & Fairfield, KM. (2002). Vitamins for chronic disease prevention in adults: clinical applications. *Journal of the American Medical Association, 287(23),* 3127-3129.

Floyd, R.T., & Thompson, W.C. (1998). *Manuel of Structural Kinesiology,* 14th edition. Dubuque: WCB/McGraw-Hill.

Fogelholm, M., Ruokonen, I., Laakso, J., Vuorimaa, T., & Himberg, J. (1993). Lack of association between indices of vitamin B1, B2 and B6 status and exercise-induced blood lactate in young adults. *Int J Sport Nutr., 3,* 165.

Ford, F. (2002). Health benefits of omega-3s for the whole family. *Journal of Family Health Care, 12,* 91-93.

Forgac, MT. (1979). Carbohydrate loading—a review. *J Am Diet Assoc., 75(1),* 42-5.

Forslund, AH., El Khoury, AE., Olsson, RM., et al. (1996). Effect of protein intake and physical activity on 24-h pattern and rate of macronutrient utilization. *American Journal of Physiology, 276,* E964-E976.

Forslund, AH., El Khoury, AE., Olsson, RM., et al. (1999). Effect of protein intake and physical activity on 24-h pattern and rate of macronutrient utilization. *American Journal of Physiology, 276,* E964-E976.

Fournier, PA., Brau, L., Ferreira, LD., et al. (2002). Glycogen resynthesis in the absence of food ingestion during recovery from moderate or high intensity physical activity: novel insights from rat and human studies. *Comparative Biochemistry and Physiology. Part A, Molecular & Integrative Physiology, 133,* 755-763.

Francis, C., & Patterson, P. (1992). *The charlie francis training system.* Ottawa: TBLI Publications Inc.

Fronske, H., & Blakemore, C., (1997). The effect of critical cues on overhand throwing efficiency of elementary school children. *Physical Educator, 54 (2),* 88-95.

Frost, G., Dowling, J., Dyson, K., & Bar-Or, O. (1991). Cocontraction in three age groups of children during treadmill locomotion. *J Electromyog. Kinesiol, 7,* 179-186.

Frost, HM, Schonau, E. (2000). The "muscle-bone unit" in children and adolescents: a 2000 overview. *J Pediatr Endocrinol Metab., 13(6),* 571-90.

Fry, AC, Schilling, BK. (2002). Weightlifting Training and Hormonal Responses in Adolescent Males: Implications for Program Design. *Strength Cond., 24(5),* 7-12.

Fryburg, DA., Gelfand, RA., Jahn, LA., Oliveras, D., Sherwin, RS., Sacca, L., & Barrett, EJ. (1995). Effects of epinephrine on human muscle glucose and protein metabolism. *Am J Physiol., 268(1 Pt 1),* E55-9.

Fuchs, RK, Bauer, JJ, Snow, CM. (2001). Jumping Improves Hip and Lumbar Spine Bone Mass in Prepubescent Children: A Randomized Controlled Trial. *J Bone Miner Res., 16(1),* 148-56.

Funatsu, T., Higuchi, H., & Ishiwata, S. (1990). Elastic filaments in skeletal muscle revealed by selective removal of titin filaments with plasma gelsolin. *Journal of Cell Biology, 110(1),* 53-62.

Gallahue, D. (1989). Understanding motor development: Infants, children, adolescents. Indianapolis, Indiana: Benchmark Press.

Galley, P.M., & Foster, A.L. (1987) Human movement: An introductory text for physiotherapy students. Melborne: Churchill Livingstone.

Garamvolgyi, N. (1971). The functional morphology of muscle. *Contractile proteins and muscle.* New York: Marcel Dekker.

Garcia-Lorda, P., Megias, R. & Salas-Salvado, J. (2003). Nut consumption, body weight and insulin resistance. *European Journal of Clinical Nutrition, 57,* Suppl 1: S8-11.

Garrett, W.E. 1990. Muscle strain injuries: Clinical and basic aspects. *Medicine and Science in Sports and Exercises* 22(4), 436-443.

Gattone, M. (2002). Age and development of physical capacities. *Olympic Coach, 40(4),* 31-33.

Gaul, CA., Docherty, D., & Cicchini, R. (1995). Differences in anaerobic performance between boys and men. *Int J Sports Med.,16(7),* 451-5.

Gayle, G.W., & Pohlman, R.L.(1990). Comparative study of the dynamic, static, and rotary balance of deaf and hearing children. *Percept. Mot. Skills, 70 (3 Pt 1),* 883-8.

Geboers, JF., Van Tuijl, JH., Seelen, HA., & Drost, MR. (2000). Effect of immobilization on ankle dorsiflexion strength. *Scand J Rehabil Med., 32(2),* 66-71.

Gerhardt, & Schmolinsky. (1992). Track and field, the German textbook of athletics. Sports Book Publisher.

Golby, J., et al. (2003). A cognitive-behavioural analysis of mental toughness in national rugby league football teams. *Percept. Mot. Skills., 96,* 455-462.

Gibson, B. Performance Implications of Physical and Mental Growth of the Young Athlete. *Coaches Info Service: Sports Science Information for Coaches.* http://www.coachesinfo.com/category/tennis/203.

Girard, J. (1994). Regulation of lipogenic enzyme gene expression by nutrients and hormones. *FASEB J., 8(1),* 36-42.

Gordon, AM., Huxley, AF., & Julian, FJ. (1966). The variation in isometric tension with sarcomere length in vertebrate muscle fibers. *J Physiol., 184,* 170-192.

Graham, TE. (2001). Caffeine and exercise: metabolism, endurance and performance. *Sports Medicine, 31,* 785-807.

Graham, TE. (2001). Caffeine, coffee and ephedrine: impact on exercise performance and metabolism. *Canadian Journal of Applied Physiology, 26,* S103-S119.

Graham, TE., Rush, JW., & Van Soeren, MH. (1994). Caffeine and exercise: metabolism and performance. *Canadian Journal of Applied Physiology, 19,* 111-138.

Grodjinovsky, A., et al. (1980). Training effect on the anaerobic performance of children as measured by the Wingate anaerobic test. Baltimore: University Park Press.

Gross, J., Fetto, J. Rosen, E. (1996). *Musculoskeletal Examination.* Malden: Blackwell Science. Malden.

Guilland, JC., Penaranda, T., Gallet, C., Boggio, V., Fuchs, F., & Klepping, J. (1989). Vitamin status of young athletes including the effects of supplementation. *Med Sci Sports Exerc. 21(4),* 441-9.

Gumbs, VL, Segal, D, Halligan, JB, Lower, G. (1982). Bilateral distal radius and ulnar fractures in adolescent weight lifters. *Am J Sports Med., 10(6),* 375-9.

Gutniack, M., Grill, V., & Efendic, S. (1986). Effect of composition of mixed meals – low- vs. high-carbohydrate content on insulin glucagon, and somatostatin release in healthy humans and in patients with NIDDM. *Diabetes Care, 9(3),* 244-249.

Guy, JA, Micheli, LJ. (2001). Strength training for children and adolescents. *J Am Acad Orthop Surg., 9(1),* 29-36.

Guyton, A.C., & Hall, J.E. (1996). *Textbook of medical physiology* 9th Ed. Philadelphia: Saunders.

Hackney, AC., Muoio, D., & Meyer, WR. (2000). The effect of sex steroid hormones on substrate oxidation during prolonged submaximal exercise in women. *Jpn J Physiol., 50(5),* 489-94.

Halin, R., Germain, P., Bercier, S., Kapitaniak, B., & Buttelli, O. (2003). Neuromuscular response of young boys versus men during sustained maximal contraction. *Med Sci Sports Exerc., 35(6),* 1042-8.

Halin, R., Germain, P., Buttelli, O., & Kapitaniak, B. (2002). Differences in strength and surface electromyogram characteristics between pre-pubertal gymnasts and untrained boys during brief and maintained maximal isometric voluntary contractions. *Eur J Appl Physiol., 87(4-5),* 409-15.

Hall, J., Jones, NL., Toews, CL., & Sutton, JR. (1981). Effects of the menstrual cycle on blood lactate, O2 delivery, and performance during exercise. *J Appl Physiol., 51,*1493–9.

Halverson, L.E., & Roberton, M.A. (1979), The effects of instruction on overhand throwing development in children. *Psychology of Motor behavior and sport.* Champaign: Human Kinetics.

Halverson, L.E., Robertson, M.A., Safrit M.J., & Roberts, T.W. (1977) Effect of guided practice on overhand-throw ball velocities of kindergarten children. *Research Quarterly, 48,* 311-318.

Hansen, L, Bangsbo, J, Twisk, J, Klausen, K. (1999). Development of muscle strength in relation to training level and testosterone in young male soccer players. *J Appl Physiol., 87(3),* 1141-7.

Hardy L. (1992). Psychological stress, performance, and injury in sport. *Br. Med. Bull., 48,* 615-629.

Harrell, JS., McMurray, RG., Baggett, CD., Pennell, ML., Pearce, PF., & Bangdiwala, SI. (2005). Energy costs of physical activities in children and adolescents. *Med Sci Sports Exerc., 37(2),* 329-36.

Hartmann, J, Tunneman, H, (2000). *Fitness and Strength Training for All Sports: Theory, Methods, Programs.* Toronto: Sports Books Publishers.

Haskell, W. (2005). Personal interview.

Hatzitaki, V., et al. (2002). Perceptual-Motor contributions to static and dynamic balance control in children. *Journal of Motor Behavior, 34 (2),* 161-170.

Hawley, JA. (2002). Effect of increased fat availability on metabolism and exercise capacity. *Medicine and Science in Sports and Exercise, 34,* 1485-1491.

Hawley, JA., Schabort, EJ., Noakes, TD., & Dennis, SC. (1997). Carbohydrate-loading and exercise performance. *Sports Med., 24(2),*73-81.

Hawley, JA., Schabort, EJ., Noakes, TD., et al. (1997). Carbohydrate-loading and exercise performance. *An update. Sports Medicne, 24,* 73-81.

Haywood, & Getchell. (2001). *Life span motor development, 3rd Edition.* Champaign: Human Kinetics.

Healy, ML., Gibney, J., Russell-Jones, DL., Pentecost, C., Croos, P., Sonksen, PH., & Umpleby, AM. (2003). High dose growth hormone exerts an anabolic effect at rest and during exercise in endurance-trained athletes. *J Clin Endocrinol Metab., 88(11),* 5221-6.

Hebestreit, H., Meyer, F., Htay-Htay, Heigenhauser, GJ., & Bar-Or, O. (1996). Plasma metabolites, volume and electrolytes following 30-s high-intensity exercise in boys and men. *Eur J Appl Physiol Occup Physiol, 72(5-6),* 563-569.

Heinrich, CH, Going, SB, Pamenter, RW, Perry, CD, Boyden, TW, Lohman, TG. (1990). Bone mineral content of cyclically menstruating female resistance and endurance trained athletes. *Med Sci Sports Exerc., 22(5),* 558-63.

Henderson, S.E., & Sudgen, D.A.(1992). *Movement Assessment Battery for Children.* London: The Psychological Corporation, Harcourt Brace Jovanovich.

Hodges, P.W., Richards, C.A. *Inefficient Muscular Stabilization of the Lumbar Spine Associated with Low Back Pain*, Spine, 21 (22): 2640-2650, 1996.

Hodges, P.W. (2003). *The Science of Stability: Clinical Application to Assessment and Treatment of Segmental Spinal Stabilization for Low Back Pain*, Handouts.

Hodges, P., Richardson, C., & Hides, J. (2004). *Therapeutic Exercise for Lumbopelvic Stabilization 2nd Edition.* St. Louis: Churchill Livingston.

Hoiland, Erin.(2004) Brain Plasticity: What Is It? Learning and Memory. *Neuroscience for Kids.* www.faculty.washington.edu/chudler.plast.html.

Holland, G. (1968). The physiology of flexibility: A review of literature. *Kinesiology Review*: 49-62.

Holliday, MA. (1971). Metabolic rate and organ size during growth from infancy to maturity and during late gestation and early infancy. *Pediatrics, 47(1),* Suppl 2:169.

Hopper, DM. (1997). Somatotype in high performance female netball players may influence player position and the incidence of lower limb and back injuries. *Br J Sports Med., 31(3),* 197-9.

Horowits, R, et al. (1986). A physiological role for titin and nebulin in skeletal muscle. *Nature, 323,* 160-164.

Horowits, R., and R.J. Podolsky. 1987b. Thick filament movement and the effect of titin filaments in active skeletal muscle. (Abstract). Biophysical Journal 51(2, Pt. 2), 219a.

Horton, TJ., Pagliassotti, MJ., Hobbs, K., et al. (1998). Fuel metabolism in men and women during and after long-duration exercise. *Journal of Applied Physiology, 85,* 1823-1832.

Howland, DR., et al. (1995). Development of locomotor behavior in the spinal kitten. *Exp Neurol., 135(2),*108-22.

Huijing, P.A. (1999). Muscular force transmission: A unified, duel or multiple system? A review and some explorative experimental results. *Archives of Physiology and Biochemistry, 107(4),* 292-311.

Huxley, AF., & Simmons, RM. (1971). Proposed mechanism of force generation in striated muscle. *Nature, 233,* 533-538.

Huxley, AF. (1957). Muscle Stucture and theories of contractions. *Prog Biophs BIophys Chem, 7,* 225-318.

Iashvili, A. (1982). Active and passive flexibility in athletes specializing in different sports. *Teoriya i Praktika Fizischeskoi Kultury,7,* 51-52.

Inbar, O. &Bar-OR, O. (1986). Anaerobic characteristics of male children and adolescents. *Med Sci Sports Exerc., 18,* 264-269.

Intensive training and sports specialization in youth athletes. (2000). *American Academy of Pediatrics Committee on Sports Medicine and Fitness, 106(1),* 154-7

Ivy, JL., Res, PT., & Sprague RC., et al. (2003). Effect of a carbohydrate-protein supplement on endurance performance during exercise of varying intensity. *International Journal of Sports Nutrition and Exercise Metabolism, 13,* 382-395.

Ivy, JL. (1998). Glycogen resynthesis after exercise: effect of carbohydrate intake. *International Journal of Sports Medicine, 19,* Suppl 2: S142-S145.

Ivy, JL., Goforth, HW. Jr., Damon. BM., et al. (2002). Early postexercise muscle glycogen recovery is enhanced with a carbohydrate-protein supplement. *Journal of Applied Physiology, 93,* 1337-1344.

Ivy, JL., Res, PT., Sprague, RC., et al. (2003). Effect of a carbohydrate-protein supplement on endurance performance during exercise of varying intensity. *International Journal of Sports Nutrition and Exercise Metabolism, 13,* 382-395.

Jackson, DW., Jarrett, H., Bailey, D., Kausek, J., Swanson, J., & Powell, JW. (1978). Injury prediction in the young athlete: a preliminary report. *Am J Sports Med., 6(1),* 6-14.

Jacobs, KA., & Sherman, WM. (1999). The efficacy of carbohydrate supplementation and chronic high- carbohydrate diets for improving endurance performance. *International Journal of Sports Nutrition,* 92-115.

Jaffre, C., Lac, G., Benhamou, CL., & Courteix, D. (2002). Effects of chronic intensive training on androgenic and cortisol profiles in premenarchal female gymnasts. *Eur J Appl Physiol., 87(1),* 85-9.

Jami, L. (1992(. Golgi tendon organs in mammalian skeletal muscle: Functional properties of and central actions. *Physiological Reviews, 72(3),* 623-666.

Janda, V., & Stara, V. (1987). *Comparison of movement patterns in healthy and spastic children. Janda Compendium, Volulme 1.* Minneapolis: OPTP.

Janda, V. (1977). *Comparison of spastic syndromes of cerebral origin with the distribution of muscular tightness in postural defects. Janda Compendiulm, Volume 1.* Minneapolis: OPTP.

Janda, V. (1988). *Muscles and cervicogenic pain syndromes. Janda Compendium, Volume 2.* Minneapolis: OPTP.

Janda, V. (1987). *Muscles and motor control in low back pain: Assessment and management. Janda Compendium, Volume 2.* Minneapolis: OPTP.

Jentjens, R., & Jeukendrup, A. (2003). Determinants of post-exercise glycogen synthesis during short-term recovery. *Sports Medicine, 33,* 117-144.

Jequier, E. (2002). Leptin Signalling, Adiposity, and Energy Balance. *Ann N Y Acad Sci, 967,* 379-88.

Johns, R.J. & Wright, V. (1962). Relative importance of various tissues in joint stiffness. *Journal of Applied Physiology* 17(5), 824-828

Jones, B.H., Cowen, D.N. & Knapik, J.J. (1994). Exercise, training and injuries. *Sports Med., 18(3),*202-14.

Jones, L., Eksten, F. & Fleschler, A. (2001). *USA weightlifting coaching accreditation course: Sport performance coach manual.* Colorado Springs: USA Weightlifting.

Kubo, K., Akima, H., Ushiyama, J., Tabata, I., Fukuoka, H., Kanehisa, H., & Fukunaga, T. (2004). Effects of 20 days of bed rest on the viscoelastic properties of tendon structures in lower limb muscles. *Br J Sports Med., 38,* 324-330.

Kannus, P. (2000(. Structure of the tendon connective tissue. *Scandinavian Journal of Medicine and Science in Sports, 10(6),* 312-320.

Katzmarzyk, PT., Malina, RM., Song, TMK., Bouchard, C. (1998). Somatotype and indicators of metabolic fitness in youth. *Am J Human Bio., 10(3),* 341-50.

Kawakami, Y., Kanehisa, H., Ikegawa, S., & Fukunaga, T. (1993). Concentric and eccentric muscle strength before during and after fatigue in 13 year-old boys. *Eur J Appl Physiol Occup Physiol., 67(2),* 121-4.

Kay, D., & Marino, FE. (2000). Fluid ingestion and exercise hyperthermia: implications for performance, thermoregulation, metabolism and the development of fatigue. *Journal of Sports Science, 18,* 71-82.

Keen, M. (1992). Early development and attainment of normal mature gait. Journal of Prosthetics and Orthotics, *5(2),* 35-38.

Keilbaso, J. (2005). *Speed and agility revolution.* Plymoth: Crew Press.

Kendall, FP., McCreary, EK., Provance, PG. (1993). *Muscles Testing and Function*, 4th Edition. Baltimore: Williams and Wilkins.

Kentucky Youth Soccer Association (2005). *Coaches Handbook-Coaching Guidelines: What is the Role of a Coach.* http://www.kysoccer.org/coaches/handbook/coaching.guidelines/what.is.the.role.of.the.coach.html

Kidd, PS., McCoy, C., Steenbergen, L. (2000). Repetitive strain injuries in youth. *J Am Acad Nurse Pract., 12(10),* 413-26.

Kiens, B. (2001). Diet and training in the week before competition. *Can J Appl Physiol, 26,* S56-63.

Kilgore, L, et. al. (2001). USA weightlifting sports science committee position statement: Weight training and competition in youth populations. www.usaweightlifting.org.

Kirk, D., & MacPhail, A. (2000). *The game sense approach: rational, description and a brief overview of research.* Loughborough University: Institute of Youth Sport and partnership with Human Kinetics.

Kisner, C. & Colby, L.A. (2002). *Therapeutic exercise foundations and techniques.* 4th ed. Philadelphia: F.A. Davis.

Knapik, JJ., Bauman, CL., Jones, BH., Harris, JM., & Vaughan, L. (1991). Preseason strength and flexibility imbalances associated with athletic injuries in female collegiate athletes. *Am J Sports Med., 19 (1),* 76-81.

Komi, PV, Knuttgen, HG. (2003) Basic Considerations for Exercises. In: *Strength and Power in Sport* (2nd ed). (Komi, PV, Ed.). Malden: Blackwell Science LTD.

Kraemer, RR., Acevedo, EO., Synovitz, LB., Hebert, EP., Gimpel, T., & Castracane, VD. (2001). Leptin and steroid hormone responses to exercise in adolescent female runners over a 7-week season. *Eur J Appl Physiol., 86(1),* 85-91, 2001.

Kraemer, W, Fleck, S. (2005). *Strength Training for Young Athletes.* Champaign: Human Kinetics.

Kraemer, WJ. & Ratamess, N. (2005). Hormonal responses and adaptations to resistance exercise and training. *Sports Med., 35(4),* 339-61, 2005.

Kraemer, WJ., Volek, JS., Bush, JA., Putukian, M., & Sebastianelli, WJ. (1998). Hormonal responses to consecutive days of heavy-resistance exercise with or without nutritional supplementation. *J Appl Physiol, 85(4),* 1544-55.

Kreider, RB. (2003). Effects of creatine supplementation on performance and training adaptations. *Molecular and Cellular Biochemistry, 244,* 89-94.

Kriketos, AD., Robertson, RM., Sharp, TA., et al. (2001). Role of weight loss and polyunsaturated fatty acids in improving metabolic fitness in moderately obese, moderately hypertensive subjects. *Journal of Hypertension, 19,* 1745-1754.

Krivickas, L.S. (1999). Training flexibility. *Exercise in rehabilitation medicine.* Champaign: Human Kinetics.

Ku, CY., Gower, BA., Hunter, GR., & Goran, MI. (2000). Racial differences in insulin secretion and sensitivity in prepubertal children: role of physical fitness and physical activity. *Obes Res., 8(7),* 506-15.

Kubo, K., Akima, H., Kouzaki, M., et al. (2000). Changes in the elastic properties of tendon structures following 20 days bed-rest in humans. *Eur J Appl Physiol., 83,* 463–8.

Kubo, K., Kanehisa, H. & Fukunaga, T. (2002). Effects of resistance and stretching training programmes on the viscoelastic properties of human tendon structures in vivo. *Journal of Physiology, 538(1),* 219-226.

Kuo, CH., Hunt, DG., Ding, Z., et al. (1999). Effect of carbohydrate supplementation on postexercise GLUT-4 protein expression in skeletal muscle. *Journal of Applied Physiology, 87,* 2290-2295.

Kurilla, M. (2003). Rethinking the endo bias and introducing a new type: Mesendomorph. Retrieved on 2004 April 20 from http://www.bodybuilding.com/fun/kurilla4.htm.

Kurtz, T. (2001). *Science of Sports Training: How to plan and control for peak performance* (2nd ed.). Island Pond: Stadion Publishing Company.

Laaneots, L., Karelson, K., Smirnova, T., & Viru, A. (1998). Hormonal responses to exercise in girls during sexual maturation. *J Physiol Pharmacol., 49(1),* 121-33, 1998.

Labeit, S., & Kolmereer, B. (1995). Titins: Giant proteins in charge of muscle ultrastructure and elasticity. *Science, 270 (5234),* 293-296.

Lambert, EV., & Goedecke, JH. (2003). The role of dietary macronutrients in optimizing endurance performance. *Current Sports Medicne Reports, 2,* 194-201.

Lambert, EV., Hawley, JA., Goedecke, J., et al. (1997). Nutritional strategies for promoting fat utilization and delaying the onset of fatigue during prolonged exercise. *Journal of Sports Science 1997, 15,* 315-324.

Largo, R.H., et al. (2001). Neuromotor development from 5 to 18 years. Part I: timed performance. *Dev Med Child Neurol., 43,* 436-443.

Laughlin, GA., & Yen, SS. (1996). Nutritional and endocrine-metabolic aberrations in amenorrheic athletes. *J Clin Endocrinol Metab., 81(12),* 4301-9.

Laursen, P.B., & Jenkins, D.G.. (2002). The scientific basis for high-intensity interval training: optimising training programmes and maximising performance in highly trained endurance athletes. *Sports Med., 32(1),* 53-73.

Lavoie, JM., Cousineau, D., Peronnet, F., & Provencher, PJ. (1983). Metabolic and hormonal responses of elite swimmers during a regular training session. *Eur J Appl Physiol., 50(2),* 173-7.

Layman, DK. (2002). Role of leucine in protein metabolism during exercise and recovery. *Canadian Journal of Applied Physiology, 27,* 646-663.

Layman, DK., Boileau, RA., Erickson, DJ., Painter, JE., Shiue, H., Sather, C., & Christou, DD. (2003). A reduced ration of dietary carbohydrate to protein improves body composition and blood lipid profiles during weight loss in adult women. *J Nutr., 133.*

Lebrun, CM. (1994). The effect of phase of the menstrual cycle and the birth control pill on athletic performance. *Clin. Sports Med., 13,* 419–41.

Lee, D. (2003). *Integrating the lumbar spine, pelvis and hips,* Course handouts.

Lee, D.(1999). *The pelvic girdle,* 3rd Edition. London: Churchill Livingston.

Lee, D. (2003). *The pelvis: restoring function and relieving pain,* Course handouts.

Lee, D. (2003). *The thorax: an integrated approach,* 2nd Edition. British Columbia: Diane Lee Corporation.

Lee, D. (2003). *The thorax: restoring function and relieving pain,* Course handouts.

Lee, L. (2004). *The integrated lumbopelvic core & the functional lower limb: Restoring stability with mobility,* Course handouts.

Lemon, PW. (1998). Effects of exercise on dietary protein requirements. *International Journal of Sports Nutrition, 8,* 426-447.

Lemon, PW., Berardi, JM., & Noreen, EE. (2002). The role of protein and amino acid supplements in the athlete's diet: does type or timing of ingestion matter? *Current Sports Medicine Reports, 1,* 214-221.

LeMura, L.M., & Maziekas, M.T.(2002). Factors that alter body fat, body mass, and fat-free mass in pediatric obesity. *Med Sci Sports Exerc., 34 (3),* 487-96.

LeMura, L.M. (1999). Can exercise training improve maximal aerobic power (VO2 max) in children: a meta-analytic review. *J. Exerc. Physiol. Online, 2(3),* 1-22.

Levangie, P., & Norkin, C. (2001). Joint structure and function: A comprehensive analysis 3rd ed. Philadelphia: F.A. Davis Company.

Levenhagen, DK., Gresham, JD., Carlson, MG., et al. (2001). Postexercise nutrient intake timing in humans is critical to recovery of leg glucose and protein homeostasis. *American Journal of Physiology Endocrinology and Metabolism, 280,* E982-E993.

Liebenson, C. (1996). *Rehabilitation of the Spine.* Baltimore: Williams and Wilkins.

Lieber, R. (2002). *Skeletal muscle structure, function, and plasticity: The physiological basis of rehabilitation.* 2nd ed. Baltimore: Lippincott, Williams, and Wilkins.

Lieberman, HR. (2003). Nutrition, brain function and cognitive performance. *Appetite, 40,* 245-254.

Ljunghall, S., Joborn, H., Roxin, LE., Skarfors, ET., Wide, LE., & Lithell, HO. (1988). Increase in serum parathyroid hormone levels after prolonged physical exercise. *Med Sci Sports Exerc., 20(2),*122-5, 1988.

London, J.K., Jenkins, W. & Loudon, K.L. (1996). The relationship between static posture and ACL injury in female athletes. *J Orthop Sports Phys Ther., 24(2),*91-7.

Long, SJ., Jeffcoat, AR., & Millward, DJ. Effect of habitual dietary-protein intake on appetite and satiety. *Appetite, 35,* 79-88.

Lucas, G.L., Cookie, F.W. & Friis, E.A. (1999). *A primer on biomechanics.* New York: Springer Verlag.

MacDougall, JD., Gibala, MJ., Tarnopolsky, MA., et al. (1995). The time course for elevated muscle protein synthesis following heavy resistance exercise. *Canadian Journal of Applied Physiology, 20,* 480-486.

MacKelvie, KJ., Khan, KM., & McKay, HA. (2002). Is there a critical period for bone response to weight-bearing exercise in children and adolescents? A systematic review. *Br J Sports Med., 36,* 250-7.

Mackenzie, B. Coaching Styles. *Coach's' Training Bulletin.* http://www.brianmac.demon.co.uk/styles.htm

Mackinnon, LT. (1997). Immunity in athletes. *International Journal of Sports Medicine, 18,* Suppl 1: S62-S68.

MacPhil, A., & Kirk, D., & Tan, B. (2001). *Talen identification: selection and development.* Loughborough University: Institute of Youth Sport and partnership with Human Kinetics.

Madsen, N. & McLaughlin, T. (1984). Kinematic factors influencing performance and injury risk in the bench press exercise. *Med Sci Sports Exerc., 16(4),* 376-81.

Maffulli, N. & Pintore, E. (1990). Intensive training in young athletes. *Br J Sports Med., 24(4),* 237-9.

Mahon, A.D. & Vaccaro P. (1989). Ventilatory threshold and VO2max changes in children following endurance training. *Med Sci Sports Exerc., 21(4),* 425-31

Mahon, A.D., Duncan, G.E., Howe, C.A. & del Corral, P. (2001) Blood lactate and perceived exertion relative to ventilatory threshold: boys versus men. *Med Sci Sports Exerc, 29,*1332-1337.

Malina, R., Bouchard, C & Bar-Or, O. (2004). *Growth, Maturity, and Physical Activity* (2nd ed.). Champaign: Human Kinetics.

Malina, RM, Bielicki, T. (1996). Retrospective longitudinal growth study of boys and girls active in sport. *Acta Paediatr., 85(5),* 570-6.

Martens, R. & Seefeldt, V. (1979). Guidelines for children and sport, bill of rights for young athletes. *American Alliance for Health, Physical Eduacation, Recreation and Dance.* Article page on ed-web3.educ.msu.edu.ysi.bill.html.

Mathiowetz, V., Kashman N., Volland G., Weber K., Dowe M. & Rogers S. (1985). Grip and Pinch strength: Normative Data for adults. *Arch Phys Med Rehab., 66,* 69-72.

Matovic, V., Fontana, D., Tominac, C., Goel, P., & Chestnut, C. *Factors that influence peak bone mass in adolescent females.*

Matthews, P. (1973). The advances of the last decade of animal experimentation upon muscle spindles. *New Developments in Electromyography and Clinical Neurophysiology.*

Maughan, RJ. (1991). Fluid and electrolyte loss and replacement in exercise. *Journal of Sports Sciences, 9,* Spec No: 117-142.

Maughan, RJ., Greenhaff, PL., Leiper, JB., et al. (1997). Diet composition and the performance of high-intensity exercise. *Journal of Sports Science, 15,* 265-275.

McCaw, S.T. & Friday, J.J. (1994). A Comparison of Muscle Activity Between a Free Weight and Machine Bench Press. *J Strength Cond Res., 8(4),* 259-64.

McDonald, R., & Keen, C. (1988). Iron and magnesium nutrition and athletic performance. *Sports Med., 5,* 171.

McDonough, A.L. (1981(. Effects of immobilization and exercise on articular cartilage-A review of the literature. *The Journal of Orthopaedic and Sports Physical Therapy* 3(1, 2-5).

McGill, S. (2002). *Low back disorders: evidence based prevention and rehabilitation.* Champaign: Human Kinetics.

McGill, S. (2004). *Ultimate Back Fitness and Performance.* Champaign: Human Kinetics.

McGraw, MB. (1963). *The neuromuscular maturation of the human infant.* New York: Columbia University Press.

McMurray, RG., Eubank, TK., & Hackney, AC. (1995). Nocturnal hormonal responses to resistance exercise. *Eur J Appl Physiol., 72(1-2),* 121-6.

Medvedyev, AS. (1989). *A System of Multi-year Training in Weightlifting.* (A Charniga, trans.). Livonia, MI: Sportivny Press.

Mersch, F, Stoboy, H. (1989). Strength training and muscle hypertrophy in children. *Children and Exercise XIII.* Champaign: Human Kinetics.

Meyer, F., & Bar-Or, O. (1994). Fluid and electrolyte loss during exercise: the pediatric angle. *Sports Med., 18,* 4-9.

Meyer, F., Bar-Or, O., MacDougall, D., & Heigenhauswer, GJF. (1992). Sweat electrolye loss during exercise in the heat; effects of gender and maturation. *Med Sci Sports Exerc., 24,* 776.

Meyers, A., et al. (1996). Cognitive behavioral strategies in athletic performance enhancement. *Prog. Behav. Modif., 30,* 137-164.

Miller, SL., & Wolfe, RR. (1999). Physical exercise as a modulator of adaptation to low and high carbohydrate and low and high fat intakes. *European Journal of Clinical Nutrition, 53,* Suppl 1: S112-S119.

Mobert, J.G., et al. Cardiovascular adjustment to supine and seated postures: Effect of physical training. *Children and Exercise.*

Molner, GE. (1992). Pediatric rehabilitation, 2nd Ed. Williams and Wilkins.

Moore, J.C. 1984. The Golgi tendon organ: A review and update. *American Journal of Occupational Therapy* 38(4), 227-236.

Mortimer, J.A., & Webster, D.D. (1983). Dissociated changes of short- and long-latency myotatic responses prior to a brisk voluntary movement in normals, in karate experts, and in Parkinsonian patients. *Advances in Neurology, Vol. 39: Motor Control Mechanisms in Health and Disease.* New York: Raven.

Murphy, S., Buckle, P., & Stubbs, D. (2004). Classroom posture and self reported back and neck pain in schoolchildren. Retrieved 2005 August 1 from www.ncbi.hih.gov.

Murray, B. (2005). Understanding brain development and early learning. *Facsnet Biotechnology* published. http://www.facsnet.org/tools/sci_tech/biotek/eliot.php.

Myer, GD, Ford, KR, Palumbo, JP, Hewett, TE. (2005). Neurmuscular training improves performance and lower-extremity biomechanics in female athletes. *J Strength Cond Res., 19(1),* 51-60.

Nariyama, K, Hauspie, RC, Mino, T. (2001). Longitudinal growth of male Japanese junior high school athletes. *Am J Human Bio., 13(3),* 356-64.

Nau, KL, Katch, VL, Beekman, RH, Dick, M. (1990). Acute intra-arterial blood pressure response to bench press weight lifting in children. *Pediatr Exerc Sci., 2,* 37-45.

Naughton, G Farpour-Lambert, NJ, Carlson, J, Bradley, M, Van Praagh, E. (2000). Physiological issues surrounding the performance of adolescent athletes. *Sports Med., 30(5),* 309-25.

Naveri, H., Kuoppasalmi, K., & Harkonen, M. (1985). Plasma glucagon and catecholamines during exhaustive short-term exercise. *Eur J Appl Physiol., 53(4),* 308-11.

Netter, FH. (1987). *The ciba collection of medical illustrations, Vol 8.* Summit: Ciba-Geigy Corp.

Netter, F. (1989). *Atlas of human anatomy.* Summit: Ciba-Geigy Corporation.

Newcomer, K, Sinaki, M. (1996). Low back pain and its relationship to back strength and physical activity in children. *Acta Paediatr., 85(12),* 1433-9.

Newman, DG, Pearn, J, Barnes, A, Young, CM, Kehoe, M, Newman, J. (1984). Norms for hand grip strength. *Arch Dis Child., 59(5),* 453-9.

Nieman, DC. (2001). Exercise immunology: nutritional countermeasures. *Canadian Journal of Applied Physiology, :26,* Suppl: S45-S55.

Niles, ES., Lachowetz, T., Garfi,, J., et al. (2001). Carbohydrate-protein drink improves time to exhaustion after recovery from endurance exercise. *JEPonline, 4.*

Nimni, ME. (1980). The molecular organization of collagen and its role in determining the biophysical properties of connective tissues. *Biorheology, 17,* 51.

Noakes, TD. (1993). Fluid replacement during exercise. *Exercise and Sport Sciences Reviews, 21,* 297-330.

Nordstrom, P, Thorsen, K, Bergstrom, E, Lorentzon, R. (1996). High bone mass and altered relationships between bone mass, muscle strength, and body constitution in adolescent boys on a high level of physical activity. *Bone., 19(2),* 189-95.

Noyes, FR. (1977). Functional properties of knee ligaments and alterations induced by immobilization. *Clin Orthop Rel Res., 123,* 210–42.

Obert, P., et. al. (2003). Cardiovascular responses to endurance training in children: effect of gender, *European Journal of Clinical Investigation, 33,* 199–208.

Okano, H., Mizunuma, H., Soda, M., Matsui, H., Aoki, I., Honjo, S., & Ibuki, Y. (1995). Effects of exercise and amenorrhea on bone mineral density in teenage runners. *Endocr J., 42(2),* 271-6.

Orlick, T. (1975). Why eliminate kids? *Every Kid Can Win.* Chicago: Nelson-Hall.

Osar, E. (2005). *Complete hip and lower extremity conditioning, form and function.* Chicago: Form and Function.

Osar, E. (2004). *Complete core conditioning.* Chicago: Form and Function Publications.

Osar, E. (2002). *Form and Function*, 2nd edition. Chicago: Form and Function Publications.

Ozkaya, N. & Nordin, M. (1999). *Fundamentals of biomechanics equilibrium, motion, and deformation*. New York: Van Nostrand Reinhold.

Ozmun, JC, Mikesky, AE, Surburg, PR. (1994). Neuromuscular adaptations following prepubescent strength training. *Med Sci Sports Exerc., 26(4),* 510-4.

Paavolainen, L., et al. (1999).Explosive-strength training improves 5-km running time by improving running economy and muscle power, *J Appl Physiol* 86: 1527-1533.

Parrish, CC., Pathy, DA., Parkes, JG., et al. (1991). Dietary fish oils modify adipocyte structure and function. *Journal of Cellular Physiology, 148,* 493-502.

Pascoe, DD., & Gladden, LB. (1996). Muscle glycogen resynthesis after short term, high intensity exercise and resistance exercise. *Sports Medicine, 21,* 98-118.

Pascoe, DD., Costill, DL., Fink, WJ., et al. (1993). Glycogen resynthesis in skeletal muscle following resistive exercise. *Medicine and Science in Sports and Exercise, 25,* 349-354.

Paterson & Cunningham. (1999). The gas transporting system: Limits and modifications with age and training. *Can J Appl Physiol, 24(1),* 28-40.

Payne, V. (2002). *Human motor development: A lifespan approach* (5th Ed.). Boston, MA: McGraw-Hill.

Payne, V. & Morrow, J. (1993). The effect of physical training on prepubescent VO2 max: A meta-analysis. *Res Q., 64,* 305-313.

Peiper, A. (1963). *Cerebral function in infancy and childhood*. New York: Consultants Bureau.

Peltonen, JE, Taimela, S, Erkintalo, M, Salminen, JJ, Oksanen A, Kujala, UM. (1998). Back extensor and psoas muscle cross-sectional area, prior physical training, and trunk muscle strength—a longitudinal study in adolescent girls. *Eur J Appl Physiol Occup Physiol., 77(1),* 66-71.

Pennington, B. Doctors See a Big Rise in Injuries for Young Athletes. 2005 February 22, New York Times.

Petibois, C., Cazorla, G., Poortmans, JR., et al. (2002). Biochemical aspects of overtraining in endurance sports: a review. *Sports Medicine, 32,* 867-878.

Pfitzinger, P & Freedson, P. (1997). Blood lactate responses to exercise. In child: Part 2, lactate threshold. *Pediatr. Exerc. Sci., 9,* 299-307.

Phillips, SM., Tipton, KD., Aarsland, A., et al. (1997). Mixed muscle protein synthesis and breakdown after resistance exercise in humans. *American Journal of Physiology, 27,* E99-107.

Physical Education Digest. (1995) *Coaching; Block practice versus Distributed practice*. www.pedigest.com.

Pincus, D., & Friedman, A. (2004). Improving children's coping with everyday stress: transporting treatment interventions to the school setting. *Clin. Child Fam. Psychol. Rev., 7,* 223-240.

Politou, A.S.M., Gautel, S., Improta, L. Vanelista, L., & Pastore, A. (1996). The elastic I-band region of titin is assembled in a "modular" fashion by weakly interacting Ig-like domains. *Molecular Biology, 255 (4),* 604-616.

Pollack, G.H. (1990). *Muscles and molecules: Uncovering the principles of biological motion.* Seattle: Ebner & Sons.

Poortmans, JR., & Dellalieux, O. (2000). Do regular high protein diets have potential health risks on kidney function in athletes? *International Journal of Sports Nutrition and Exercise Metabolism, 10,* 28-38.

Position stand on exercise and fluid replacement. (1996). *American College of Sports Medicine. Med Sci Sports Exercise, 28,* i-vii.

Positive Coaching Alliance. (2005). The Positive Coach Mental Model. http://www.positivecoach.org/ConPics/Con4/pcmm_research.pdf

Prado, L.S. (1997). Lactate, ammonia, and catecholamine metabolism after anaerobic training. *Children and exercise XIX.* London: Spon.

Price, TB., Rothman, DL., Taylor, R., et al. (1994). Human muscle glycogen resynthesis after exercise: insulin-dependent and -independent phases. *Journal of Applied Physiology, 76,* 104-111.

Primal 3D Interacive Series. (2000). *Complete Human Anatomy.* London: Primal Pictures Ltd.

Pullinen, T., Mero, A., Huttunen, P., Pakarinen, A., & Komi, PV. (2002). Resistance exercise-induced hormonal responses in men, women, and pubescent boys. *Med Sci Sports Exerc., 34(5),* 806-13.

Purslow, P.P. (1989). Strain-induced reorientation of an intramuscular connective tissue network: Implications for passive muscle elasticity. *Journal of Biomechanics, 22(1),* 21-31.

Rachbauer, F., Sterzinger, W., & Eibl, G. (2004) Radiographic abnormalities in the thoracolumbar spine of young elite skiers. Retrieved from www.ncbi.hih.gov.

Raitakari, OT., Porkka, KV., & Viikari, JS. (1994). Relations of life-style with lipids, blood pressure, and insulin in adolescents and young adults: the Cardiovascular Risk in Young Finns Study. *Atherosclerosis, 111,* 237-46.

Ramsay, JA, Blimkie, CJ, Smith, K, Garner, S, MacDougall, JD, Sale, DG. (1994) Strength training effects in prepubescent boys. *Med Sci Sports Exerc., 22(5),* 6054-14.

Rankinen, T., Fogelholm, M., Kujala, U., Rauramaa, R., & Uusitupa, M. (1995). Dietary intake and nutritional status of athletic and nonathletic children in early puberty. *Int J Sport Nutr., 5,*136.

Rasmussen, BB., Tipton, KD., Miller, SL., et al. (2000). An oral essential amino acid-carbohydrate supplement enhances muscle protein anabolism after resistance exercise. *Journal of Applied Physiology, 88,* 386-392.

Ratel, S, Bedu, M, Hennegrave, A, Dore, E, Duche, P. (2002) Effects of age and recovery duration on peak power output during repeated cycling sprints. *Int J Sports Med., 23(6),* 397-402.

Rauch, LH., Rodger, I., Wilson, GR., et al. (1995). The effects of carbohydrate loading on muscle glycogen content and cycling performance. *International Journal of Sports Nutrition, 5,* 25-36.

Reading Master Learning Systems. *Learning Styles.* http://readingmaster.com/WebPages/Learning_Styles.htm

Redman, LM., & Weatherby, RP. (2004). Measuring performance during the menstrual cycle: a model using oral contraceptives. *Med Sci Sports Exerc., 36(1),*130-6.

Reed, MJ., Cheng, RW., Simmonds, M., et al. (1987). Dietary lipids: an additional regulator of plasma levels of sex hormone binding globulin. *Journal of Clinical Endocrinology and Metabolism, 64,* 1083-1085.

Remer, T. (2001). Influence of nutrition on acid-base balance—metabolic aspects. *Eur J Nutr., 40(5),* 214-20.

Remer, T., Dimitriou, T., & Manz, F. (2003). Dietary potential renal acid load and renal net acid excretion in healthy, free-living children and adolescents. *Am J Clin Nutr., 77(5),* 1255-60.

Rennie, MJ. (2001). Control of muscle protein synthesis as a result of contractile activity and amino acid availability: implications for protein requirements. *International Journal of Sports Nutrition and Exercise Metabolism, 11,* Suppl: S170-S176.

Rennie, MJ., & Tipton, KD. (2000). Protein and amino acid metabolism during and after exercise and the effects of nutrition. *Annual Review of Nutrition, 20,* 457-483.

Rennie, MJ., Bohe, J., & Wolfe, RR. (2002). Latency, duration and dose response relationships of amino acid effects on human muscle protein synthesis. *Journal of Nutrition, 132,* 3225S-3227S.

Riach, C.L., & J.L. Starkes. (1994). Velocity of centre of pressure excursions as an indicator of postural control systems in children. *Gait and Posture 2,*167-172.

Rians, CB., Weltman, A., Cahill, BR., Janney, CA., Tippett, SR., & Katch, FI. (1987). Strength training for prepubescent males: is it safe? *Am J Sports Med., 15(5),* 483-9.

Risser, WL. (1991). Weight-training injuries in children and adolescents. *Am Fam Physician., 44(6),* 2104-8.

Robert, C. & Corcos, D.(1988). Coaches guide to teaching sport skills. Champaign: Human Kinetics Books.

Robinson, S., Jaccard, C., Persaud, C., et al. (1990). Protein turnover and thermogenesis in response to high-protein and high-carbohydrate feeding in men. *American Journal of Clinical Nutrition, 52,* 72-80.

Rogers, J. (2000). USA track and field. *USA Track and Field Coaching Manual.* Champaign: Human Kinetics.

Rong, H., Berg, U., Torring, O., et al. (1997). Effect of acute endurance and strength exercise on circulating calcium-regulating hormones and bone markers in young healthy males. *Scand J Med Sci Sports, 7(3),*152-9.

Rosique, J, Rebato, E, Apraiz, AG, Pacheco, JL. (1994). Somatotype Related to Centripetal Fat Patterning of 8- to 19-year-old Basque Boys and Girls. *Am J Human Biol., 6,* 171-181.

Ross D. (2003). Speed training; the basics. *Master Track and Field.* Retrieved from Coach.org.

Ross, WD, Day, JA. (1972). Physique and performance of young skiers. *J Sports Med Phys Fitness., 12(1),* 30-7.

Rotman, S., Slotboom, J., Kreis, R., et al. (2000). Muscle glycogen recovery after exercise measured by 13C-magnetic resonance spectroscopy in humans: effect of nutritional solutions. *Magnetic Resonance Materials in Physics, Biology and Medicine, 11,* 114-121.

Rotstein, A., et al. (1986). Effects of training on anaerobic threshold, maximal aerobic power and anaerobic performance of preadolescent boys. *Int. J. Sports Med., 7,* 281-286.

Rowland, T.W. (2005). *Children's exercise physiology.* Champaign :Human Kinetics.

Rowland, TW., Maresh, CM., Charkoudian, N., Vanderburgh, PM., Castellani, JW., & Armstrong, LE. (1996). Plasma norepinephrine responses to cycle exercise in boys and men. *Int J Sports Med., 17(1),* 22-6, 1996.

Rowland, TW., Auchinachie, JA., Keenan, TJ., Green, GM. (1987). Physiologic responses to treadmill running in adult and prepubertal males. *Int J Sports Med, 8,* 292-297.

Rowland, TX. (1996). Iron deficiency in the adolescent athlete. In: Bar-Or B, ed. The child and adolescent athlete. *Oxford: Blackwell Science, 274.*

Rowlands, DS., & Hopkins, WG. (2002). Effect of high-fat, high-carbohydrate, and high-protein meals on metabolism and performance during endurance cycling. *International Journal of Sport Nutrition and Exercise Metabolism, 12,* 318-335.

Roy, BD., Luttmer, K., Bosman, MJ., et al. (2002). The influence of post-exercise macronutrient intake on energy balance and protein metabolism in active females participating in endurance training. *International Journal of Sports Nutrition and Exercise Metabolism, 12,* 172-188.

Ryan, N. (1989). Stress-coping strategies identified from school age children's perspective. *Res. Nurs. Health., 12,* 111-122.

Sahrmann, S. (2002). *Diagnosis and treatment of movement impairment syndromes.* St. Louis: Mosby.

Sale, D. (1991). Testing Strength and Power. *Physiological Testing of the High-Performance Athlete.* Champaign: Human Kinetics.

Salokun, SO. (1994). Minimizing injury rates in soccer through preselection of players by somatotypes. *J Sports Med Phys Fitness., 34,* 64-9.

Saltin, B et al. (1977). Fiber types and metabolic potentials of skeletal muscles in sedentary man and endurance runners. *Ann N Y Acad Sci., 301,* 3-29.

Sansone, R., & Sawyer, A. (2005). Weight loss pressure on a 5 year old wrestler. *Br. J. Sports Med., 39,* e2.

Sargeant, A.J., et al. (1985). Effects of supplementary physical activity on body composition, aerobic, and anaerobic power in 13-year old boys. Champaign: Human Kinetics.

Saris, WH. (2001). The concept of energy homeostasis for optimal health during training. *Canadian Journal of Applied Physiology, 26,* Suppl: S167-S175.

Sawka, MN., & Pandolf, KB. (1990). Effects of body water loss in physiological function and exercise performance. *Lamb DR, Gisolfi CV, eds. Perspectives in exercise science and sports medicine: fluid homeostasis during exercise.* Indianapolis: Benchmark Press.

Schmid, R., Schusdziarra, V., Schulte-Frohlinde, E., Maier, V., & Classen, M. (1989). Role of amino acids in stimulation of postprandial insulin, glucagon, and pancreatic polypeptide in humans. *Pancreas, 4,* 305-314.

Schutz, Y., Bray, G., & Margen, S. (1987). Postprandial thermogenesis at rest and during exercise in elderly men ingesting two levels of protein. *Journal of the American College of Nutrition, 6,* 497-506.

Seger, JY, Thorstensson, A. (1994). Muscle strength and myoelectric activity in prepubertal and adult males and females. *Eur J Appl Physiol Occup Physiol., 69(1),* 81-7.

Seger, JY, Thorstensson, A. (2000). Muscle strength and electromyogram in boys and girls followed through puberty. *Eur J Appl Physiol., 81(1-2),* 54-61.

Shapiro, S. (1997). Do trans fatty acids increase the risk of coronary artery disease? A critique of the epidemiologic evidence. *American Journal of Clinical Nutrition, 66,* 1011S-1017S.

Sharma, SS, Dixit, NK. (1985). Somatotype of athletes and their performance. *Int J Sports Med., 6(3),* 161-2.

Siff, M.C. (1993). Exercise and the soft tissues. Fitness *and Sports Review International, 28(1),* 32.

Siff, M. (2000). *Supertraining.* 5th ed. Denver: Supertraining International.

Siff, M. (2000). Biomechanical Foundations of Strength and Power Training. *Biomechanics in Sport: Performance Enhancement and Injury Prevention.* Malden: Blackwell Science.

Siff, M. (2003). *Supertraining* (6th ed.). Denver: Supertraining International.

Sills, I.N., & Cerny, F.J. (1983). Responses to continuous and intermittent exercise in healthy and insulin-dependent diabetic children. *Med Sci Sports Exerc., 15(6),* 450-4.

Simkin, PA. (1988). *Primer on the rheumatic diseases,* ed 9. Atlanta: Arthritis Foundation.

Simopoulos, AP. (1989). Summary of the NATO advanced research workshop on dietary omega 3 and omega 6 fatty acids: biological effects and nutritional essentiality. *J Nutr., 119(4),* 521-8.

Simsch, C., Lormes, W., Petersen, KG., Baur, S., Liu, Y., Hackney, AC., Lehmann, M., & Steinacker, JM. (2002). Training intensity influences leptin and thyroid hormones in highly trained rowers. *Int J Sports Med., 23(6),* 422-7.

Skov, AR., Toubro, S., Bulow, J., et al. (1999). Changes in renal function during weight loss induced by high vs low-protein low-fat diets in overweight subjects. *International Journal of Obesity and Related Metabolic Disorders, 23,* 1170-1177.

Smith, R., & Small, F. (1996). *Way to go coach.* Portola Valley: Warde Publishers, Inc.

Smyth, M.M., & Mason, U.C. (1998). Use of proprioception in normal and clumsy children. *Dev. Med. Child Neurol., 40 (10),* 672-81.

Snyder, AC. (1998). Overtraining and glycogen depletion hypothesis. *Medicine and Science in Sports and Exercise, 30,* 1146-1150.

Special Olympics Coaching Guide (2003). Principles of Coaching. http://www.specialolympics.org/Special+Olympics+Public+Website/English/Coach/Coaching_Guides/Principles+of+Coaching/Stages+of+Learning.htm

Spring, B., Chiodo, J., Harden, M., Bourgeois, MJ., Mason, JD., & Lutherer, L. (1989). Psychobiological effects of carbohydrates. *J Clin Psychiatry, 50,* Suppl:27-33.

Stanitski, CL. (1989) Common injuries in preadolescent and adolescent athletes. Recommendations for prevention. *Sports Med., 7(1),* 32-41.

Stark, AH., & Madar, Z. (2002). Olive oil as a functional food: epidemiology and nutritional approaches. *Nutrition Reviews, 60,* 170-176.

Stedman's Medical Dictionary, 25th Edition. (1990) Baltimore: Williams & Wilkins

Steinacker, JM., Lormes, W., Kellmann, M., Liu, Y., Reissnecker, S., Opitz-Gress, A., Baller, B., Gunther, K., Petersen, KG., Kallus, KW., Lehmann, M., & Altenburg, D. (2000). Training of junior rowers before world championships. Effects on performance, mood state and selected hormonal and metabolic responses. *J Sports Med Phys Fitness., 40(4),* 327-35.

Stepto, NK., Carey, AL., Staudacher, HM., et al. (2002). Effect of short-term fat adaptation on high-intensity training. *Medicine and Science in Sports and Exercise, 34,* 449-455.

Stevens, JE., Walter, GA., Okereke, E., Scarborough, MT., Esterhai, JL., George, SZ., Kelley, MJ., Tillman, SM., Gibbs, JD., Elliott, MA., Frimel, TN., Gibbs, CP., Vandenborne, K. (2004). Muscle adaptations with immobilization and rehabilitation after ankle fracture. *Med Sci Sports Exerc., 36(10),*1695-701.

Stone, MH. (1982) Considerations in Gaining A Strength-Power Training Effect (Machines vs. Free Weights). *NSCA Journal., 4(1),* 22-24.

Streepey, J.W. & Angulo-Kinzler, R.M. (2002). The role of task difficulty in the control of dynamic balance in children and adults. *Human Movement Science, 21,* 423-428.

Strength Training by Children and Adolescents. (2001). *American Academy of Pediatrics Committee on Sports Medicine and Fitness, 107(6),* 1470-2.

Stupnicki, R., & Obminski, Z. (1992). Glucocorticoid response to exercise as measured by serum and salivary cortisol. *Eur J Appl Physiol., 65(6),* 546-9.

Suler, J. (2002). Somatotypes. *Teaching Clinical Psychology.* Retrieved from http://www.rider.edu/~suler/somato.html.

Suman, OE, Spies, RJ, Celis, MM, Mlcak, RP, Herndon, DN. (2001). Effects of a 12-week resistance exercise program on skeletal muscle strength in children with burn injuries. *J Appl Physiol., 91,* 1168-75.

Sun, M., Gower, BA., Bartolucci, AA., Hunter, GR., Figueroa-Colon, R., & Goran, MI. (2001). A longitudinal study of resting energy expenditure relative to body composition during puberty in African American and white children. *Am J Clin Nutr., 73(2),* 308-15.

Sunnegardh, J, Bratteby, LE, Nordesjo, LO, Nordgren, B. (1988) Isometric and isokinetic muscle strength, anthropometry, and physical activity in 8 and 13 year old Swedish children. *Eur J Appl Physiol Occup Physiol., 58(3),* 291-7.

Sutherland, D., et. al. (1988). The *development of mature walking, Clinics in Devel. Med.* Philadelphia: Mackeith Press: Oxford Blackwell Scientific Pubs., Ltd.

Sward, L. (2004). *The thoracolumbar spine in young elite athletes. Current concepts on the effects of physical training.* Retrieved from www.ncbi.hih.gov.

Tabary, J.C., C. Tabary, C. Tardieu, G. Tardieu, and G. Goldspink. (1972). Physiological and structural changes in the cat's soleus muscle due to immobilization at different lengths by plaster casts. *Journal of Physiology, 224(1),* 231-244.

Takada, H., Washino, K., Nagashima, M., & Iwata, H. (1998). Response of parathyroid hormone to anaerobic exercise in adolescent female athletes. *Acta Paediatr Jpn., 40(1),* 73-7.

Tan, B., & MacPhail, A. (2001). *Physical education: cognitive development and academic performance.* Loughborough University: Institute of Youth Sport and partnership with Human Kinetics.

Tarnopolsky, MA., Atkinson, SA., Phillips, SM., et al. (1995). Carbohydrate loading and metabolism during exercise in men and women. *Journal of Applied Physiology, 78,* 1360-1368.

Terpstra, AH. (2004). Effect of conjugated linoleic acid on body composition and plasma lipids in humans: an overview of the literature. *American Journal of Clinical Nutrition, 79,* 352-361.

Terry, P., et al. (1998). The influence of game location on athletes' psychological states. *J Sci Med Sport., 1,* 29-37.

The American Heritage Dictionary. (1983). Dell Publishing Inc.

Thelen, E, Kelso JAS, & Fogel A. (1987). Self-organizing systems and infant motor development. *Developmental review, 7,* 37-65.

Thelen, E. (1982) Kicking, rocking and waving: Contextual analysis of rhythmical stereotypes in normal human infants. *Animal Behaviour, 1981, 29,* 3-11.

Thelen, E. (1995). Motor development: A new synthesis. *American Psychologist, 50,* 79-95,

Thomas, DE., Brotherhood, JR., & Brand, JC. (1991). Carbohydrate feeding before exercise: effect of glycemic index. *Int J Sports Med., 12(2),* 180-6.

Thompson, J. (2003). *The double-goal coach.* New York: Harper-Collins Publishers.

Thompson, J. (1995). *Positive coaching.* Palo Alto: Warde Publishers, Inc.

Thomsen, K., Riis, B., Krabbe, S., & Christiansen, C. (1986). Testosterone regulates the haemoglobin concentration in male puberty. *Acta Paediatr Scand., 75(5),* 793-6.

Thorne, A., & Wahren, J. (1989). Diet-induced thermogenesis in well-trained subjects. *Clin Physiol, 9,* 295-305.

Thorsen, K., Kristofferson, A., Hultdin, J., et al. (1997). Effects of moderate endurance exercise on calcium, parathyroid hormone and markers of bone metabolism in young women. *Calcif Tissue Int., 60(1),* 16-20.

Timmons, BW., Bar-Or, O., & Riddell, MC. (2003). Oxidation rate of exogenous carbohydrate during exercise is higher in boys than in men. *J Appl Physiol, 94(1),* 278-84.

Tipton, KD., Borsheim, E., Wolf, SE., et al. (2003). Acute response of net muscle protein balance reflects 24-h balance after exercise and amino acid ingestion. *American Journal of Physiology Endocrinology and Metabolism, 284,* E76-E89.

Tipton, KD., Ferrando, AA., Phillips, SM., et al. (1999). Postexercise net protein synthesis in human muscle from orally administered amino acids. *American Journal of Physiology, 276,* E628-E634.

Tipton, KD., Rasmussen, BB., Miller, SL., et al. (2001). Timing of amino acid-carbohydrate ingestion alters anabolic response of muscle to resistance exercise. *American Journal of Physiology Endocrinology and Metabolism, 281,* E197-E206.

Tolfrey, K. et al. (1998). Aerobic trainability of prepubertal boys and girls. *Pediatric Exer. Sci., 10,* 248-263.

Trinick, J., Knight, P., Whiting, A. (1984). Purification and properties of native titin. *Journal of molecular Biology., 180(2),* 331-356.

Tsolakis, C., Vagenas, G., & Dessypris, A. (2003). Growth and anabolic hormones, leptin, and neuromuscular performance in moderately trained prepubescent athletes and untrained boys. *J Strength Cond Res., 17(1),* 40-6, 2003.

Tsolakis, CK., Vagenas, GK., & Dessypris, AG. (2004). Strength adaptations and hormonal responses to resistance training and detraining in preadolescent males. *J Strength Cond Res., 18(3),* 625-9.

Tsuzuku, S, Ikegami, Y, Yabe, K. (1998). Effects of high-intensity resistance training on bone mineral density in young male powerlifters. *Calcif Tissue Int., 63(4),* 283-6.

Unnithan, V., & Eston, R. (1990). Stride frequency and submaximal running economy in adults and children. *Pediatric Exercise Science, 2,* 149-155.

Uusi-rasi, K, Haapasalo, H, Kannus, P, Pasanen, M, Sievanen, H, Oja, P, Vuori, I. (1997). Determinants of bone mineralization in 8 to 20 year old Finnish females. *Eur J Clin Nutr., 51(1),* 54-9.

Van Beurden, E., et al. (2003). Can we skill and activate children through primary school physical education lessons? "Move it Groove it" – a collaborative health promotion intervention. *Preventive Medicine, 36,* 493-501.

Van Loon, LJ., Greenhaff, PL., Constantin-Teodosiu, D., et al. (2001). The effects of increasing exercise intensity on muscle fuel utilisation in humans. *Journal of Physiology, 536,* 295-304.

Van Loon, LJ., Kruijshoop, M., Verhagen, H., et al. (2000). Ingestion of protein hydrolysate and amino acid-carbohydrate mixtures increases postexercise plasma insulin responses in men. *Journal of Nutrition, 130,* 2508-2513.

Van Loon, LJ., Saris, WH., Kruijshoop, M., et al. (2000). Maximizing postexercise muscle glycogen synthesis: carbohydrate supplementation and the application of amino acid or protein hydrolysate mixtures. *American Journal of Clinical Nutrition, 72,* 106-111.

Viidik, A. (1980). Interdependence between structure and function in collagenous tissues. *Biology of collagen.* London: Academic Press.

Villagra, F, Cooke, CB, McDonagh, MJ. (1993). Metabolic cost and efficiency in two forms of squatting exercise in children and adults. *Eur J Appl Physiol Occup Physiol., 67(6),* 549-53.

Viru, A., Laaneots, L., Karelson, K., Smirnova, T., & Viru, M. (1998). Exercise-induced hormone responses in girls at different stages of sexual maturation. *Eur J Appl Physiol., 77(5),* 401-8.

Virvidakis, K, Georgiou, E, Korkotsidis, A, Ntalles, K, Proukakis, C. (1990). Bone mineral content of junior competitive weightlifters. *Int J Sports Med., 11(3),* 244-6.

Viviani, F, Casagrande, G, Toniutto, F. (1993). The morphotype in a group of peri-pubertal soccer players. *J Sports Med Phys Fitness., 33(2),* 178-83.

Voet, D., & Voet J.G. (1995). *Biochemistry.* NewYork : Wiley.

Volek, JS. (2003). Strength nutrition. *Current Sports Medicine Reports, 2,* 189-193.

Von der Mark, K. (1981). Localization of collagen types in tissues. *Int Rev of Connective Tissue Res* 9: 265-305

Vujnovich, A.L., & Dawson, NJ. (1994). The effect of therapeutic muscle stretch on neural processing. *Journal of Othopaedic and Sports Physical Therapy, 20(3),* 145-153.

Waldo, BR. (1996). Grip Strength Testing. *Strength and Conditioning., 18(5),* 32-5.

Walshe, A.E., G.J. Wilson, & A.J. Murphy. (1996). The validity and reliability of a test of lower body musculotendinous stiffness. *European Journal of Applied Physiology, 73(3-4),* 332-339.

Wang, K, et al. (1993). Viscoelasticity of the sarcomere matrix of skeletal muscle: Titin-myosin composit filament is a dula-stage molecular spring. *Biophys J., 64,*1161-117.

Wang, K. & Ramirez-Mitchell, R. (1983). A network of transverse and longitudinal intermediate filaments is associated with sarcomeres of adult vertebrate skeletal muscle. *Journal of Cell Biology*, 96 (2), 562-570.

Wang, K., McCarter, R., Wright, J., Beverly, J., & Ramirez-Mitchell, R. (1991). Regulation of skeletal muscle stiffness and elasticity by titin isoforms: A test of the segmental extension model of resting tension. *Proceedings of the National Academy of Science, 88(6),* 7101-7105.

Wang, K., Rameriz-Mitchell, R., and Palter, D. (1984). Titin is an extraordinarily long, flexible, and slender myofibrillar protein. *Proceedings of the National Academy of Science, 81 (12),* 385-3689.

Webb, DR. (1990). Strength training in children and adolescents. *Pediatr Clin North Am., 37(5),* 1187-210.

Webster's Ninth New Collegiate Dictionary. (1990). Springfield: Merriam-Webster Inc.

Weise, M., Eisenhofer, G., & Merke, DP. (2002). Pubertal and gender-related changes in the sympathoadrenal system in healthy children. *J Clin Endocrinol Metab., 87(11),* 5038-43.

Welsh, L., et al. (2005). Effect of physical conditioning on children and adolescents with asthma. *Sports Med., 35(2),* 127-141

Welsman, J.R., et al. (1997). Responses of young girls to 2 modes of aerobic training. *Br. J Sports Med., 31 (2),*139-42.

Weltman, A., Janney, C., Rians, CB., Strand, K., Berg, B., Tippitt, S., Wise, J., Cahill, BR., & Katch, FI. (1986). The effects of hydraulic resistance strength training in pre-pubertal males. *Med Sci Sports Exerc., 18(6),* 629-38.

Werthner, P. (2001). Canadian journal for women in coaching. Communicating with clarity. *Coaches association of Canada, 1(3).*

Westman, EC., Mavropoulos, J., Yancy, WS., et al. A Review of Low-carbohydrate Ketogenic Diets. *Current Atherosclerosis Reports, 5,* 476-483.

Whitall, J., & Clark, J. E. (1994). The development of bipedal interlimb coordination. *Interlimb coordination: Neural, dynamical, and cognitive constraints.* New York: Academic Press.

Whitall, J., & Getchell, N. (1995) From walking to running: Applying a dynamical systems approach to the development of locomotor skills. *Child Development, 66,* 1541-1553.

Widmann, FK. (1978). *Pathobiology: how disease happens.* Boston: Little, Brown.

Wiegersma, P.H., Van der Velde, A. (1983). Motor development of deaf children, J. Child Psychol. *Psychiatry, 24(1),* 103-11, 1983.

Wiemann, K, Hahn, K. (1997). Influences of strength, stretching, and circulatory exercises on flexibility parameters of the human hamstrings. *Int J Sports Med., 18(5),* 340-6.

Wilk, B., & Bar-Or O. (1996). Effect of drink flavor and NaCl on voluntary drinking and rehydration in boys exercising in the heat. *J Appl Physiol, 80,* 1112-1117.

Wilk, B., Yuxiu, H., & Bar-Or, O. (2002). Effect of hypohydration on aerobic performance of boys who exercise in the heat. *Med Sci Sports Exerc., 34,* S48.

Willett, WC., & Leibel, RL. (2002). Dietary fat is not a major determinant of body fat. *American Journal of Medicine, 113,* Suppl 9B: 47S-59S.

Williams & Armstrong. (1991). The influence of age and sexual maturation on children's blood lactate response to exercise. *Pediatr Exerc., Sci. 3,* 111-120.

Williams C.A., et al. (2000). Aerobic responses of prepubertal boys to two modes of training, Br. J. *Sports Med., 34 (3),* 168-73.

Williams, H. (1983). *Perceptual and Motor Development.* Englewood Cliffs: Prentice Hall.

Williams, J.R. et al. (1992). Changes in peak oxygen uptake with age and sexual maturation: Physiologic fact or statistical anomaly? *Children and exercise.* Paris: Mason.

Williams, P.E., & G. Goldspink. (1976). The effect of denervation and dystrophy on the adaptation of sarcomere number to the functional length of the muscle in young and adult mice. *Journal of Anatomy, 122(2),* 455-465.

Williams, P.F. (1982). *Orthopedic Management in Childhood.* Blackwell Scientific Pub.

Williams, PL, et al. (1995). *Gray's Anatomy.* New York: Churchill Livingstone.

Williams, PL., Warwick, R., Dyson, M., & Mannister, LH. (1989). *Gray's Anatomy.* London: Churchill Livingstone.

Williford H.N., et al. (1996). Exercise training in black adolescents: changes in blood lipids and VO2 max. *Ethn. Dis., 6 (3-4),* 279-85.

Wilmore, J.H., Parr, R.B., Girandola, R.N., Ward, P., Vodak, P.A., Barstow, T.J., Pipes, T.V., Romero, G.T. & Leslie, P. (1978). Physiological alterations consequent to circuit weight training. *Med Sci Sports., 10(2),* 79-84.

Winter, D.A. (1990). *Biomechanics and Motor Control of Human Movement,* Second Edition. New York: John Wiley & Sons, New York.

Witzke, K.A. & Snow, C.M. (2000). Effects of plyometric jump training on bone mass in adolescent girls. *Med Sci Sports Exerc., 32(6),* 1051-7.

Witzmann, F.A., Kim, D. H. & Fitts, R. H. (1982) Hindlimb immobilization: length-tension and contractile properties of skeletal muscle. *J. Appl. Physiol., 53,* 335-345.

Wojtys, EM., Ashton-Miller, JA., Huston, LJ., Moga, PJ. (2004). The Association between athletic training time and the sagittal curvature of the immature spine. Retrieved from www.ncbi.hih.gov,, 2004.

Wolfe, BM. (1995). Potential role of raising dietary protein intake for reducing the risk of atherosclerosis. *Canadian Journal of Cardiology, 11(G),* 127G-135G.

Wolfe, BM., & Piche, LA. Replacement of carbohydrate by protein in a conventional fat diet reduces cholesterol and triglyceride concentrations in healthy noromolipidemic subjects. *Clinical Investigative Medicine, 22(4),* 140-148.

Wong, SH., & Williams, C. (2000). Influence of different amounts of carbohydrate on endurance running capacity following short term recovery. *International Journal of Sports Medicine, 21,* 444-452.

Wong, SH., Williams, C., & Adams, N. (2000). Effects of ingesting a large volume of carbohydrate-electrolyte solution on rehydration during recovery and subsequent exercise capacity. *International Journal of Sports Nutrition and Exercise Metabolism, 10,* 375-393.

Wong, SH., Williams, C., & Adams, N. (2000). Effects of ingesting a large volume of carbohydrate-electrolyte solution on rehydration during recovery and subsequent exercise capacity. International *Journal of Sport Nutrition and Exercise Metabolism, 10,* 375-393.

Woo, S., Matthews, JV., Akeson, WH., Amiel, D., & Convery, R. (1975). Connective tissue response to immobility: Connective study of biomechanical and biological measurements of normal and immobilized rabbit knees. *Arthritis Rheumatology, 18(3),* 257-264.

Yamauchi, K. (1988). Selective alterations of insulin actions by glucagon in isolated rat epididymal adipocytes. *Endocrinology, 123(6),* 2800-2804.

Yin, Z, & Moore, J. (2004). Re-examining the role of interscholastic sport participation in education. *Psychol Rep., 94,* 1447-1454.

Yoshizawa, S., et al. (1997). Effects of an 18-month endurance run training program on maximal aerobic power in 4- to 6-year-old girls. *Pediatric Exerc. Sci., 9,* 33-43.

Zachazewski, J.E. (1990). Flexibility for sports. *Sports physical therapy.* Norwalk: Appleton and Lange.

Zachwieja, JJ., Costill, DL., & Fink, WJ. (1993). Carbohydrate ingestion during exercise: effects on muscle glycogen resynthesis after exercise. *International Journal of Sports Nutrition,* 418-430.

Zariczny, B, Shattuck, LJM, Mast, TA, Robertson, RV, D'Elia, G. (1980). Sports-related injuries in school-aged children. *Am J Sports Med., 8,* 318-24.

Zatsiorsky, VM. (1995). *Science and Practice of Strength Training.* Champaign: Human Kinetics.

Ziegler, PJ., Khoo, CS., Kris-Etherton, PM., Jonnalagadda, SS., Sherr, B., & Nelson, JA. (1998). Nutritional status of nationally ranked junior US figure skaters. *J Am Diet Assoc., 98,* 809-811.

Brian J. Grasso

Brian Grasso is the Director of Athlete Development for The Sports Academy Northwest in South Barrington, Illinois and also serves as Executive Director of the International Youth Conditioning Association.

Brian has lectured at youth development and sport training conferences throughout the world and for many organizations including the National Alliance for Youth Sports, the National Coaching Education Program, the Illinois Olympic Development Program, the United States Figure Skating Association, Skate Canada, IHRSA, the Canadian Athletic Therapists Association, Children's Memorial Hospital and the Korean Aerobic Association.

Brian was honored to receive an invitation from Zambia's Sport In Action Program as well as the Ministry of Education to travel to Africa in order to re-write and re-structure Zambia's elementary school's physical educational curriculum.

Brian also writes for many sport and fitness-based publications throughout the world including, Men's Fitness, Men's Health, Sporting Kid, American Track & Field, Personal Fitness Professional and the British publication, Successful Coaching.

Brian began his sport-training career as a Performance Coach to Olympic, professional and elite athletes. He has worked with several professional and Olympic athletes from a variety sports, and has traveled extensively throughout North America and Europe as a Conditioning Consultant for both the Canadian and United States National Team athletes.

Brian recently released his new book, 'Training Young Athletes – The Grasso Method'.

Lee Taft

Lee Taft gained his BS in Physical Education from Cortland State, New York in 1989. In 2004 Lee earned his MS in Sports Science from the United States Sports Academy in Daphne, Alabama. Lee has spent several years as a Physical Education teacher in the New York Public Schools System working with the youth population. He has also been a head coach of football, basketball, track and field, and cross-country. Training young athletes has been apart of his life for over 16 years.

In 1991, Lee went full time into the world of sports performance training at Bolletteris Tennis Academy, and a year later at Palmer Tennis Academy as a movement specialist and strength coach. A year later, Lee started his own business full time in sports performance. Lee is known as one of the top athletic movement specialists in the industry and his multi-directional speed techniques are becoming the used methods by many coaches throughout the world. He frequently lectures and performs clinics for athletes, coaches and trainers on the subject of speed and quickness technique in all directions.

Now located in Indiana with his wife and two daughters, Lee and his company, Sports Speed, Etc., LLC, travel around the country putting on clinics for coaches and teachers, speed camps for athletes, and as a lecturer at sports performance conferences. Lee serves as Executive Vice President of the International Youth Conditioning Association.

Dr. Cynthia LaBella

Cynthia LaBella, M.D. is the medical director for the Institute for Sports Medicine at Children's Memorial Hospital in Chicago, Illinois, and assistant professor of pediatrics at Northwestern University's Feinberg School of Medicine. Dr. LaBella earned her medical doctorate (1994) from Cornell University Medical College in New York, NY and is an alumni member of Alpha Omega Alpha. She completed her internship and residency training in pediatrics (1997) at Johns Hopkins Hospital in Baltimore, MD, and completed a fellowship in sports medicine (2001) at the University of North Carolina at Chapel Hill. Board-certified in both pediatrics and sports medicine, Dr. LaBella specializes in the diagnosis, treatment, and prevention of sports-related injuries and medical conditions unique to young athletes.

Dr. LaBella has served as team physician for several sports teams at the high school, college, and professional level, and has traveled internationally to provide medical coverage for US Soccer youth teams. She contributes her knowledge and expertise to several professional organizations, including the American College of Sports Medicine, and the American Medical Society for Sports Medicine. She is a fellow of the American Academy of Pediatrics (AAP) and serves on the AAP Council on Sports Medicine and Fitness. As a member of the Illinois State High School Association Sports Medicine Advisory Committee, Dr. LaBella has played an important role in formulating policies and guidelines for safety in high school sports.

Dr. LaBella has published several articles and given many presentations on topics in pediatric and adolescent sports medicine. Her original research entitled, "The effect of mouth-guards on dental injuries and concussions in college basketball" was published in the January 2002 issue of the peer-reviewed journal, *Medicine and Science in Sports and Exercise*, and highlighted in the New York Times and CNN News. Dr. LaBella's current research efforts focus on identification of risk factors for injury in youth sports and development of strategies for prevention. In 2004, she received grant support from the Children's Memorial Hospital Office of Child Advocacy to implement a neuromuscular training program aimed at reducing knee injuries in adolescent female athletes.

Dr. Kwame Brown

Dr. Kwame M. Brown is an Elite Trainer and Director of Youth Athletics / Conditioning at Shula's Athletic Club (Miami Lakes, FL), where he initiated several programs for youth athletes 8-17 years of age of all ability levels. He also works with children with motor difficulties. In addition, he serves as a Performance Coach at Chris Carter's FAST Program (Coral Springs, FL), where he has worked with many professional, college, and youth athletes.

Dr. Brown earned a Ph.D. (2003) from the Interdisciplinary Program in Neuroscience, Georgetown University (Washington, DC) with a concentration in spinal cord injury and sensorimotor development. He completed his postdoctoral work at The Miami Project to Cure Paralysis and was on his way to a promising career in Neuroscience research until he decided to work full time with children. He also holds a B.A. in Molecular Biology (1995) from Hampton University (Hampton, VA) and is a Certified Strength and Conditioning Specialist (CSCS) with the National Strength and Conditioning Association (NSCA).

Having been involved in neuroscience from the molecular level all the way up through human subjects, Dr. Brown has presented research at meetings for both the Society for Neuroscience and the National Neurotrauma Society, and has been published in Developmental Brain Research and the Journal of Neurotrauma. He has recently decided to leave the world of academic science to dedicate himself full-time to applying what he has learned (and continues to learn) about the central and peripheral systems during development.

Dr. Brown is a firm believer in the plasticity (adaptability) of the human nervous system, and is determined to educate those that work with children to ensure that these individuals are aware of the scientific principles governing development and apply these principles properly to provide for the safe and effective development of not only young athletes, but of children in general and those with special needs.

Dr. John Berardi

Dr. John Berardi earned a doctoral degree from the University of Western Ontario (2005) with a specialization in the area of exercise biology and nutrient biochemistry. Prior to his doctoral studies, Dr. Berardi studied Exercise Science at Eastern Michigan University (Masters program; 1999) as well as Health Science, Psychology, and Philosophy at Lock Haven University (Undergraduate program; 1997).

Throughout, Dr. Berardi's research has focused on the interaction between nutrition, sports supplementation, and exercise performance. This research has led to the publication of 8 scientific abstracts, 12 scientific papers and textbook chapters, and over a dozen presentations at scientific meetings. Further, Dr. Berardi has taught courses in Strength Training, Exercise Science, Laboratory Techniques in Exercise Science, Nutrient Metabolism, Fitness and Wellness, and Exercise Nutrition.

Currently, Dr. Berardi is an adjunct professor of Exercise Science at the University of Texas at Austin.

Dr. Berardi, through his company – Science Link, has worked in the exercise and nutrition arena for over a decade, having the opportunity to work with individuals from all walks of life, including athletes at the highest level of sport.

Currently, Dr. Berardi is the director of performance nutrition for the Canadian National Cross Country Ski Team and is a performance nutrition consultant to a number of elite level individual athletes, sports teams, and Olympic training centers including:

- The US Bobsled Team
- The Canadian National Alpine Ski Team
- The Canadian National Speed Skating Team
- The Calgary Sports Centre/Olympic Oval (Calgary, Alberta)
- The Manitoba Sports Centre (Winnipeg, Manitoba)
- The University of Texas Women's Track and Field Team
- Individual athletes in nearly every sport including professional football (NFL and CFL), professional hockey (NHL and AHL), professional baseball (MLB), professional basketball (NBA) and more.

Dr. Evan Osar

Evan Osar is a chiropractic physician, massage therapist and certified personal trainer. Dr. Osar earned a bachelor of science and chiropractic degrees from Palmer College of Chiropractic. He has also received a diploma in clinical massage therapy from the Soma Institute The National School of Clinical Massage Therapy and national certifications from the National Academy of Sports Medicine and the National Strength and Conditioning Association.

Dr. Osar has dedicated himself to learning by attending over one thousand hours of continuing education and through teaching others. He holds a faculty position at the Soma Institute The National School of Clinical Massage Therapy where he teaches Kinesiology and Clinical Integration. He has authored four manuals on functional training and conditioning including Complete Core Conditioning, Complete Hip and Lower Extremity Conditioning, Complete Shoulder and Upper Extremity Conditioning and Form and Function which is currently being used in both chiropractic and massage therapy schools.

Dr. Osar currently presents lectures for personal trainers, massage therapists and other health care practitioner. He is the co-developer of the Chain Activation Technique, a revolutionary soft tissue and rehabilitation technique designed to optimize athletic performance through a combination of specific soft tissue releases and muscle activation. Additionally, he is the developer of the Fast and Furious seminar series focusing on biomechanics and the proper execution and progressions of corrective exercise.

Currently, Dr. Osar currently operates O.S.A.R. Consulting, a consulting firm specializing in the treatment and rehabilitation of neuromusculoskeletal injuries. He serves as the chiropractic physician for the Joffrey Ballet of Chicago and Zephyr Dance companies and is consultant to athletes in the National Football League and Major League Baseball.

Craig Ballantyne

Craig Ballantyne, CSCS, M.Sc., is a sought after fitness expert and consultant to Men's Fitness and Maximum Fitness magazines – two of the most popular fitness publications in the world. Craig is on the Training Advisory Board for both of those magazines as well as Sylvester Stallone's new magazine – Sly. Craig also writes exercise columns for Men's Fitness and Muscle & Fitness Hers. In these columns, Craig shows readers how to improve their exercise selection so that readers get the most results in the least amount of time.

Craig's areas of expertise include helping busy executives lose fat and gain muscle and training young athletes to improve performance in all sports. Craig also has an extensive research background and keeps up to date on the latest scientific findings that will help improve your health and wellness and your physical and mental performance.

Craig has written extensively on sport conditioning and bodybuilding on his original website, www.cbathletics.com. He publishes a newsletter on cbathletics.com that is now over 140 issues strong. It features workout routines and interviews with the top names in the strength & conditioning world, including many of the IYCA experts. Craig is also the Training Director for the world's first female-specific, sport-specific website, www.grrlAthlete.com.

Craig trains young athletes in Toronto, Ontario, Canada. In addition to coaching and training youth athletes, Craig is a member of the Sport Science committee of the Canadian National Rugby Senior Men's Team. He also trains the men's rugby team at McMaster University.

Craig earned a Master's of Science Degree (2000) from McMaster University in Hamilton, Ontario, following an Undergraduate degree in Kinesiology from McMaster (1998). Craig is CSCS-certified (1998) and is a Level 1 Hockey Coach with the Canadian Minor Hockey Association.

Craig is a firm believer in treating young athletes with respect and providing them with education on improving their physical and mental performance capabilities. He believes there is a lot to be learned from both the Russian and North American methods of coaching, so that all coaches must keep an open mind to training methodologies. He looks forward to continuing his education in coaching and learning from everyone in the field of youth athletics.

Scott Colby

Scott Colby is the President of SC Fitness in Dallas, TX, and is the Texas Area Coordinator of Achieve Fitness USA as well as the Education Specialist for Fundamental Fitness Products. He holds a Master's degree from the University of Virginia in Biomedical Engineering specializing in Biomechanics where his graduate work included creating a database for comparing children who had pathological gait problems with healthy children of the same age.

From 1998-2004, Scott worked in the Movement Science Laboratory at Texas Scottish Rite Hospital for Children in Dallas, TX as a Bioengineer. He designed, executed, and analyzed research investigations involving human movement and performance of children and evaluated movement pathologies to guide clinicians in the treatment of various neuromuscular disorders

Previously, Mr. Colby worked in the Human Performance Laboratory at Duke University where his research interests included the mechanisms of ACL injuries during athletic competition and the higher rates of ACL injuries in female versus male athletes. He helped evaluate the fitness levels of the University of North Carolina's women's soccer players and participated in a research project examining the landing mechanisms of the Duke University men's basketball players. Mr. Colby did a sports medicine research internship in 1996 in Vail Colorado at the Steadman Hawkins Sports Medicine Foundation where he conducted a research project assessing functional tests for screening knee patients and for evaluating progress in rehabilitation

Mr. Colby has given presentations at the American College of Sports Medicine, the American Society of Biomechanics and the Clinical Gait and Movement Analysis conferences, and has published research articles in Spine, The Journal of Pediatric Orthopedics, Clinical Biomechanics, The American Journal of Sports Medicine, Journal of Orthopedic and Sports Physical Therapy, and Gait and Posture.

Bill Hartman

Bill Hartman is a physical therapist and strength & conditioning coach in Indianapolis, Indiana. A lifetime athlete, Bill was a 4-sport letter winner in high school and a top ten finisher in the National Junior Olympics in the javelin after only two months of specific training. Bill continued his athletic career in college in both football and in track and field as a javelin thrower. Bill also placed second at the Purdue Bodybuilding Championships; at the time was the largest, full-time student bodybuilding contest in the country.

Bill graduated with distinction from Purdue University in 1988 with a degree in Movement and Sports Science and completed 1 year of Masters degree-level coursework in Exercise Physiology before being accepted into the Indiana University Physical Therapy Program. As a graduate of the Indiana University Physical Therapy Program in 1991, Bill was chosen by the faculty to give the student representative address at the commencement ceremonies.

As a physical therapist, Bill has worked in a variety of setting including acute care, extended care, neurological rehabilitation, and orthopedics/sports medicine, which is his current specialty. Bill has received advanced training in treatment of spinal disorders to include spinal mobilization, treatment of lumbo-pelvic disorders, shoulder rehabilitation, knee rehabilitation, core conditioning, and treatment of soft-tissue disorders. Bill is also an Active Release Techniques Practitioner with credentials to treat upper extremity, lower extremity, and spinal disorders.

Bill holds certifications with the National Strength and Conditioning Association as a Certified Strength and Conditioning Specialist and with USA Weightlifting as a Sports Performance Coach. Bill also sits on the Board of Directors of the International Youth Conditioning Association.

Bill regularly works with athletes at the high school, collegiate, and amateur levels in a number of sports including football, basketball, martial arts, tennis, and racewalking. He is probably best known for his athletic approach to the physical preparation for golf and works with golfers on both amateur and professional levels. Bill is also in the process of developing fitness and sports training camps for athletes age 6 and up.

Tony Reynolds

Tony Reynolds is revered as one of brightest minds in the world of strength and conditioning. His unique methods of training have been implemented into thousands of athletic performance programs throughout the world. Prior to founding Progressive Sporting Systems, Tony served as Head Strength and Conditioning coach for Rose Hulman Institute of Technology where he worked with football, baseball, volleyball, soccer, softball, wrestling, and track and field. In addition to duties at Rose Hulman, Tony has worked extensively with Indiana State University and St. Mary of The Woods University providing sport performance enhancement for numerous teams.

In 2000, Tony served as the Head Strength and Conditioning Coach for the Cincinnati Reds Double A-team the Chattanooga Lookouts. Prior to his stint in Chattanooga, Tony completed an assistantship with the International Performance Institute in Bradenton Florida where he worked with professional football, baseball, soccer, tennis, and golf.

Tony received his Masters Degree in Biomechanics in Human Performance from Indiana State University (ISU) and currently serves as the Chief Operations Officer for the IYCA.